Longman

Foundation Science 2

for GCSE

Mark Levesley

Penny Johnson

Richard O'Regan

Sarah Pitt

Nicky Thomas

Bob Wakefield

Contents for Foundation Science

cabbage → snail → hedgehog → fox

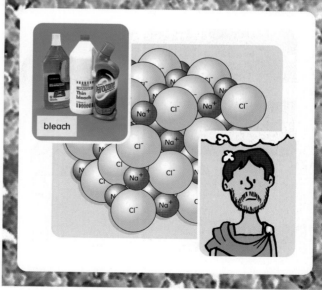

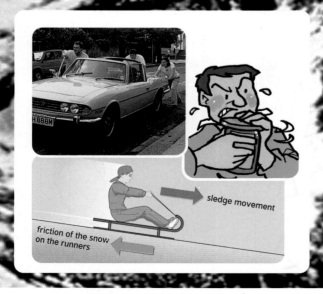

sledge movement

friction of the snow on the runners

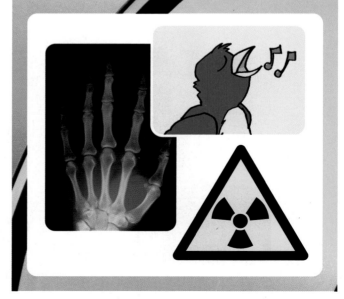

Somewhere to live

What are habitats, communities and populations?

Animals and plants live in many different places. Rabbits live in fields or woodland. Penguins live in the frozen Antarctic. Cactus plants live in the hot desert. The place where an animal or plant lives is called its **habitat**. A habitat must give an animal or plant all the things it needs to survive.

 1 What is a habitat?

An animal's habitat must give it:

- food
- somewhere to shelter and be safe from other animals
- a place to breed and bring up its young (**offspring**).

 2 a) Why do rabbits live underground in burrows?
b) Why do they dig their burrows in fields or woodland?

3 a) Why do birds build nests?
b) Why do they build their nests high up in trees?

4 Why do herons live near lakes, rivers or the sea?

A Rabbits eat grass and other plants. They live in burrows underground.

B Birds bring up their young in a nest.

C Herons live near lakes, rivers or the sea.

D Deserts are usually very hot and dry.

E It can be very dark in the middle of woods and forests.

A plant's habitat must give it:

- sunlight
- carbon dioxide
- water and nutrients.

5 a) Why are few plants found living in the desert?
b) Why do most plants live in the open?

Many animals and plants may share the same habitat. All the animals and plants which live together in a habitat make up a **community** of living things. The word community describes all the living things that are found there.

A Year 11 class looked at what animals and plants they could find living in a hawthorn hedge around a field. They found grass, dandelions, ferns and nettles. There was also an oak tree with moss and lichen growing on its bark. One group spotted a sparrow's nest in the branches. Another group found woodlice, beetles, ladybirds, ants, slugs and worms in the undergrowth. Wasps and butterflies were feeding from the wild flowers. Although no one saw any rabbits, they did find lots of rabbit droppings.

All the animals or plants of one kind make up a **population**. The community in the hedge had many different populations. All the woodlice living there made a population of woodlice. All the nettles growing there made a population of nettles.

7 Name five animals and five plants which are part of the community living in the hedge.

8 Copy out the sentences here. Fill in each space using the words *community* or *population*.

The _____ in the hedge was made up of many different living things. The pupils found different kinds of animals, including a _____ of sparrows living in a nest and a _____ of woodlice living under a dead branch. The _____ had many different plants too including a _____ of dandelions and a _____ of ferns.

9 Explain the difference between a community and a population.

P How could you investigate a hedgerow community?

G

6 What is a community?

F *A hedgerow is a habitat for a large community of animals and plants.*

Summary

The place where an animal or plant lives is called its _____. An animal's habitat must give it_____, somewhere to shelter and be safe from other animals and a place to breed and bring up its _____ (offspring). A plant's habitat must give it sunlight, carbon dioxide, _____ and nutrients. All the animals and plants which live together in a habitat make up a _____. All the animals or plants of one type make up a _____.

community   food   habitat   population   water   young

Adaptation

How can some animals and plants survive in difficult conditions?

Millions of different animals and plants live on the Earth. Most of them can only live in certain places. They are suited to the habitat that they live in. Scientists say that they are **adapted** to where they live. **Adaptation** means that animals and plants have things about them which help them to survive in their habitat.

 A

1 What is adaptation?

2 Look at photograph A. Why does a polar bear have:
a) a thick layer of blubber?
b) big feet?
c) white fur?

The bear has white fur. This helps to camouflage it so that it can creep up on other animals without being seen.

This bear has a thick layer of fat under its skin called blubber. This helps to keep it warm. The bear can also use the blubber for energy when food is hard to find.

The bear has a thick fur coat to help keep it warm.

The bear's sharp claws help it to grip on the ice when it is running.

The bear has big feet which spread its mass out over the ground. This stops it from sinking into the snow.

! Cod living in the Antarctic have a kind of antifreeze to stop their blood freezing.

3 Copy and complete the sentences here by choosing the right ending from the box.

a) The camel has a sandy colour . . .
b) The camel makes very little urine . . .
c) The camel can drink . . .
d) The camel does not have a layer of body fat . . .
e) The camel's big feet spread its mass out . . .
f) The camel stores fat . . .
g) The camel has long eyelashes to stop sand . . .

. . . so that it does not sink into the sand.
. . . up to 100 litres of water at once and store it in its stomach.
. . . in its hump which it can use for energy when there is not much food.
. . . or sweat so that it does not lose too much water.
. . . to camouflage it in the desert.
. . . blowing into its eyes.
. . . as this would keep heat in and stop it cooling down.

B

Animals that live in hot counties tend to have large surface areas compared with their volumes. This means they have as much skin as possible in contact with the air. As blood flows through the skin it loses heat to the air. This helps to cool the animal down. An African elephant makes its surface area bigger by having very big ears and lots of folds in its skin. Although a polar bear is a big animal, it is very compact and has a small surface area compared to its volume. This cuts down heat loss.

4 a) How does an African elephant increase its surface area?

b) Why do polar bears have very small ears?

C

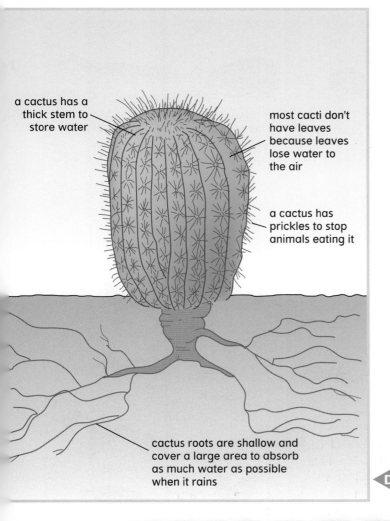

a cactus has a thick stem to store water

most cacti don't have leaves because leaves lose water to the air

a cactus has prickles to stop animals eating it

cactus roots are shallow and cover a large area to absorb as much water as possible when it rains

D

5 Look at diagram D. Why has the cactus got:
a) no leaves?
b) roots which cover a large area?
c) a thick stem?
d) sharp prickles?

6 How might the adaptations listed here help the animals or plants to survive?
a) Rabbits have very good hearing and eyesight.
b) A chameleon can change the colour of its skin.
c) Seaweed has air sacs which help it float (Hint: think how a plant gets its energy).

Summary

The _____ that animals and plants live in can be very different. Some habitats like the desert can be very hot and _____. Other habitats like the Arctic can be very _____. Animals are _____ to the habitat that they live in. This means that they have things about them which help them to _____. Polar bears have thick, white _____ and a layer of blubber to help keep them _____. Camels can store lots of _____ in their stomachs and produce very little _____ or urine. Animals which live in _____ countries usually have a _____ surface area compared to their size as this helps to cool them down.

adapted   big   cold   dry   fur   habitats   hot   survive   sweat   warm   water

Chains and pyramids

What are food chains and pyramids of numbers?

A **food chain** tells you what different animals eat. The food chain in picture A tells you that a fox eats hedgehogs, that hedgehogs eat snails and that snails eat cabbages. The arrows in a food chain always point from what is being eaten to the animal that is eating it.

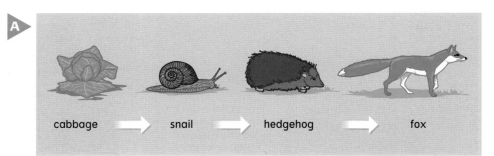

cabbage → snail → hedgehog → fox

1 What do food chains tell you?

2 Which way do the arrows in a food chain point?

Food chains always start with a plant. Plants are called **producers** because they can make or *produce* their own food by photosynthesis. All animals are called **consumers** because they eat or *consume* other living things. Consumers can be **herbivores** or **carnivores**. Herbivores are animals which eat plants. Carnivores are animals which eat other animals.

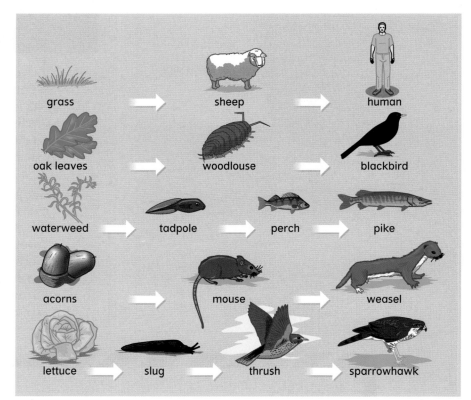

grass → sheep → human

oak leaves → woodlouse → blackbird

waterweed → tadpole → perch → pike

acorns → mouse → weasel

lettuce → slug → thrush → sparrowhawk

3 a) Why are plants called producers?
b) Why are animals called consumers?

4 Look at the food chains in picture B.
a) What do mice eat?
b) What eats grass?
c) What do pike eat?
d) What eats lettuce?
e) What do blackbirds eat?

5 Look at the food chains in picture B again.
a) Name five producers.
b) Name twelve consumers.
c) Name five herbivores.
d) Name seven carnivores.

6 Use the information here to write out two food chains.
a) Lions eat zebras. Zebras eat grass.
b) Herons eat fish. Water snails eat water weed. Fish eat water snails.

Pyramids of numbers

Look at the food chain in picture C and think about how many animals or plants are eaten at each step of the food chain in a week. Each big fish may eat four small fish. Each small fish may eat 10 tadpoles. This means that there must be at least 40 tadpoles to feed the small fish. Each tadpole may eat 100 cells of algae. This means there must be at least 4000 cells of algae to feed the tadpoles.

You can draw a food chain as a **pyramid of numbers**. The size of each box in the pyramid gives you an idea of how many plants or animals there are at that step of the food chain. They are called pyramids of numbers because they are usually shaped liked a pyramid.

! A robin can eat up to 50 worms in one day.

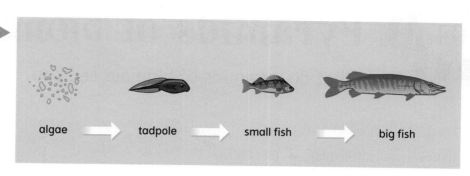

algae   →   tadpole   →   small fish   →   big fish

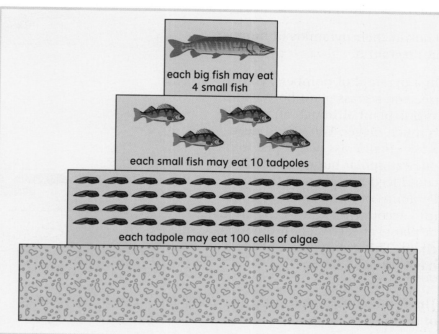

each big fish may eat 4 small fish

each small fish may eat 10 tadpoles

each tadpole may eat 100 cells of algae

D

Summary

Plants are called _____ because they make their own food. Animals are called _____ because they eat other living things. _____ are animals which eat plants. _____ are animals which eat other animals. Food _____ tell you what different animals eat. They always start with a _____. A pyramid of _____ tells you roughly how many animals or plants there are at each step of a food chain.

carnivores   chains   consumers
herbivores   numbers
plant   producers

7 Look at the pyramid of numbers in diagram D again. Copy and complete the sentences here by choosing the right word from the brackets.
  a) As you go up a pyramid of numbers there are usually (more/fewer) living things at each step.
  b) As you go up a pyramid of numbers the animals or plants at each step usually get (bigger/smaller).

8 Draw pyramids of numbers for these food chains.
  a) grass ⟶ grasshopper ⟶ frog
  b) dandelion ⟶ woodmouse ⟶ barn owl

9 Pyramids of numbers are usually pyramid shaped but not always. Use the information here to write out a food chain and then draw a pyramid of numbers to go with it.
  ● Lots of aphids feed on one rosebush.
  ● Sparrows feed on aphids.

Pyramids of biomass

What do pyramids of biomass tell you?

Look at the food chains here.

oak tree → caterpillar → blackbird

grass → caterpillar → blackbird

Look at their pyramids of numbers in diagram A.

In a pyramid of numbers, an oak tree and a grass plant both count as one plant although an oak tree is much bigger. You would need a few small grass plants just to feed one caterpillar but one big oak tree could feed hundreds of them. Pyramids of numbers do not take into account the size of the animals or plants at each step of the food chain. This is why some of them have strange shapes.

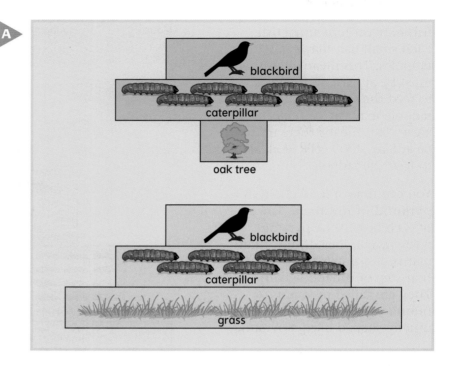

The word **biomass** means the mass of living material. A **pyramid of biomass** shows you the mass of living material at each step of the food chain. In other words it shows you how much mass all the animals or plants at each step would have if you put them all together.

1 a) What does biomass mean?
b) Which has a bigger biomass, an oak tree or a grass plant?

2 What does a pyramid of biomass tell you?

 A pyramid of biomass shows the mass of living material at each step of the food chain.

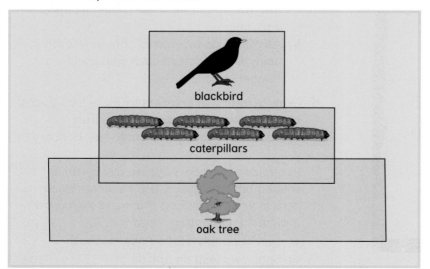

Look at the pyramid of biomass in diagram B. It looks very different from its pyramid of numbers in diagram A. This is because it takes into account the mass of the oak tree. There is still only one oak tree but it has a big biomass. This is why the box at the bottom of the pyramid is big. There may be 1000 caterpillars at step 2 but 1000 caterpillars do not have much mass when compared to an oak tree! This is why the box for caterpillars is smaller. Pyramids of biomass are nearly always shaped like a pyramid.

	Food chain	Pyramid of numbers	Pyramid of biomass
3 Copy and complete Table C by matching up each food chain from below with the correct pyramid of numbers. Then draw in a pyramid of biomass. 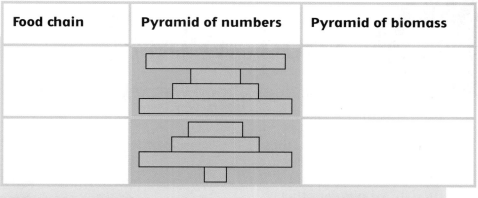			

dandelion → rabbit → fox → flea   apple tree → aphid → ladybird → thrush

As you go along a food chain, the total biomass at each step gets less. This is because biomass is wasted or used up for energy by each consumer. Look at the food chain here.

leaf → slug → hedgehog → fox

4 Look at diagram D.
  a) How much of the leaf is lost from the food chain as waste?
  b) How much of the leaf is used up by the slug for energy?
  c) How much of the leaf becomes new biomass in the slug?

5 Look at diagram E.
  a) How much of the slug is lost from the food chain as waste?
  b) How much of the slug is used up by the hedgehog for energy?
  c) How much of the slug becomes new biomass in the hedgehog?

6 Look back at diagrams D and E.
  a) If the slug ate 100 grams of leaves, how many grams of leaf would be turned into part of the slug's body?
  b) If the hedgehog ate 500 grams of slugs, how many grams of slug would be turned into part of the hedgehog's body?
  c) Why are pyramids of biomass nearly always pyramid shaped?

! It takes 1000 tonnes of plankton at the start of a food chain to make 1 tonne of shark at the end.

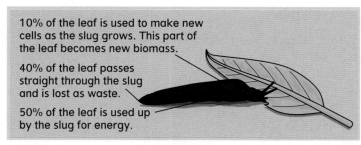

10% of the leaf is used to make new cells as the slug grows. This part of the leaf becomes new biomass.

40% of the leaf passes straight through the slug and is lost as waste.

50% of the leaf is used up by the slug for energy.

D

E

10% of the slug is used to make new cells as the hedgehog grows. This part of the slug becomes new biomass.

40% of the slug passes straight through the hedgehog and is lost as waste.

50% of the slug is used up by the hedgehog for energy.

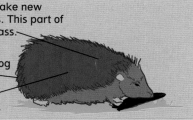

Summary

_____ means the mass of living material. Pyramids of biomass show the _____ of living material at each step of a _____ chain. As you go along a food chain the total biomass at each step gets _____ . This is because most of the biomass at one step does not get turned into biomass at the next step. Some of it will be lost from the food chain as _____ . Some of the biomass will be used up for _____ . Pyramids of biomass are nearly always shaped like a _____.

biomass   energy   food   less
mass   pyramid   waste

Food webs

What does a food web tell you?

Food chain A tells you that a rabbit eats grain and a fox eats rabbits. In the wild though, rabbits eat other things as well as grain, and foxes eat other animals as well as rabbits.

If you want to see everything that an animal eats in a habitat, you have to look at a **food web**.

grain ➡ rabbit ➡ fox

A

A food web. **B**

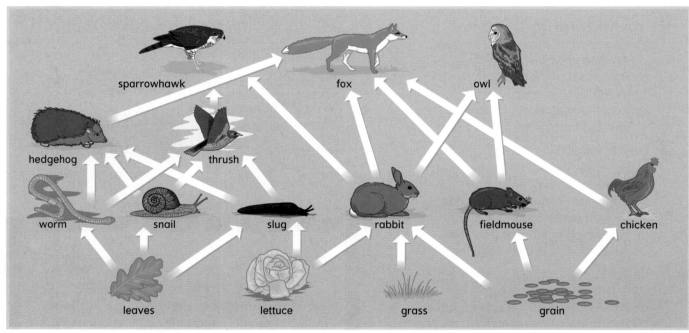

sparrowhawk   fox   owl

hedgehog   thrush

worm   snail   slug   rabbit   fieldmouse   chicken

leaves   lettuce   grass   grain

1 Look at food web B.
  a) What do slugs eat?
  b) Which two animals eat fieldmice?
  c) What do hedgehogs eat?
  d) Which three animals eat leaves?
  e) What does a thrush eat?
  f) Which three animals eat rabbits?

2 Look at food web B again.
  a) Name the four producers.
  b) How many consumers are there?
  c) Name six herbivores from the web.
  d) Name five carnivores from the web.

3 Food webs are made from different food chains linked together. Write out five food chains from food web B. One has been done to start you off.

grain ➡ chicken ➡ fox

4 Make your own food web using the information in the box.

> The two producers in a pond are water weeds and green algae. Snails feed on water weeds and water fleas feed on the green algae. The tadpoles eat either producer. Minnows are small fish which eat tadpoles and water fleas. Perch are bigger fish which eat minnows and tadpoles. The frogs in the pond eat snails. Herons which live nearby eat frogs and perch. Pike are very big fish which also eat perch.

Food chains and food webs always start with plants. Plants provide the food for the whole community. Herbivores feed on plants. Carnivores depend on plants too. If there were no plants for the herbivores to eat, then there would be no herbivores for the carnivores to eat!

Diagram D shows you how plants make food by photosynthesis. All living things depend on energy from the Sun. Plants could not make food to start food chains and food webs without sunlight. Plants transfer the light energy into chemical energy which is then locked up in their cells and tissues. This energy is passed along the food chain to herbivores and then to carnivores.

leaves ➞ worm ➞ shrew ➞ weasel

C

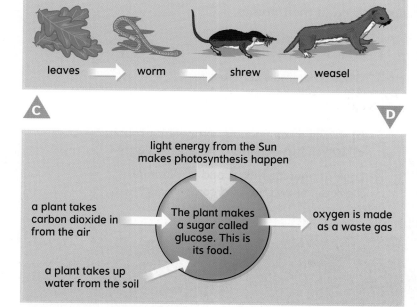

D

light energy from the Sun makes photosynthesis happen

a plant takes carbon dioxide in from the air

The plant makes a sugar called glucose. This is its food.

oxygen is made as a waste gas

a plant takes up water from the soil

Summary

Food _____ give you more information than food chains. They tell you all the things that animals eat in a _____. All the _____ in a food web depend on plants. Plants can make their own _____ to start the web off. Plants make their food by _____. Photosynthesis needs _____ energy to make it happen. If there was no sunlight then there would be no food for the community.

animals   food   habitat
photosynthesis   light   webs

5 Look at food chain C.
  a) What does the worm eat?
  b) Why would the shrew starve if there were no leaves?
  c) Why would the weasel starve if there were no leaves?

6 a) What gas do plants use up from the air?
  b) What do plants take up from the soil?
  c) What do plants make as their food?
  d) What waste gas do plants make?
  e) Plants need energy to photosynthesise. Where do they get this energy from?

7 Why do all living things depend on light energy for their food?

8 a) Look at food web B. What would happen to the number of thrushes if all the rabbits died of disease? Explain your answer.
  b) How might this affect the number of worms and slugs? Explain your answer.

G6 Competition

What is competition and what do living things compete for?

Many different animals may live in a habitat. Sometimes they may want to eat the same things. Sometimes they may want to breed or shelter in similar places. **Competition** is when different animals want the same things. Different animals may compete for the same food or for the same space to build their homes.

A

B

1 What is competition?

2 What do animals compete for?

3 Look at food web B on page 14.
   a) Which three animals compete for leaves?
   b) Which three animals compete for rabbits?
   c) Which two animals compete for slugs?

4 Look at photographs A and B. What do the squirrel and the bird compete for?

C *The gulls are competing for space as there are few nesting sites left.*

An anteater is adapted for catching ants. It can stick its tongue into the middle of an ant hill.

D

Competition does not matter when there is plenty of food and space for everyone. Competition does matter when there is not much food to go round or when space is scarce. When food is scarce, the animals which are best adapted to find or catch it will survive and the other animals may starve. If space is limited, then some animals may not find anywhere to breed or shelter.

5 Look at photograph C.
   a) What do you think the birds are competing for?
   b) What will happen to birds that cannot find a nesting site?

6 Look at photograph D. Many animals eat ants. What advantage would the anteater have over other competitors if ants were in short supply?

Plants compete for sunlight, water and nutrients. Some plants have big leaves to catch as much light as they can. Their leaves can put other plants in the shade. Other plants have long roots which go deep into the soil. Plants with shorter roots cannot compete when water and nutrients are in short supply.

A Year 11 class were looking at competition between two different plants, A and B. They planted 20 seedlings of plant A in one tray and 20 seedlings of plant B in another. Every 10 days they measured the average mass of each plant to see how quickly they were growing. Graph E shows how well the two plants grew.

The class then planted 20 seedlings of each plant altogether in one tray. Again, they measured the average mass of each plant every 10 days to see how quickly they were growing. Graph F shows how well the two plants grew when they were grown together.

7 **a)** What do plants compete for?
   b) Why do some plants have large leaves?
   c) Why do some plants have long roots?

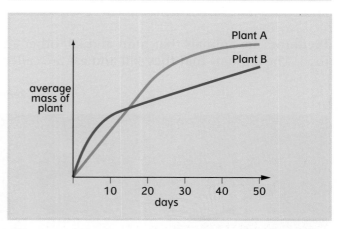

E   This graph shows how the plants grew when they were in separate trays.

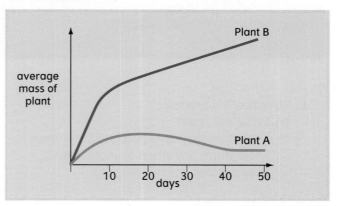

F   This graph shows how the plants grew when they were together in the same tray.

8 **a)** Which plant grew quicker to start with when they were grown separately?
   b) What happened when the two plants were grown together?

   Look at diagram G. It shows what the two plants looked like.

G

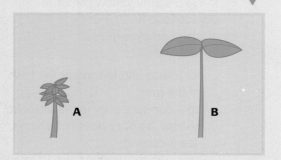

   c) What do you think the two plants were competing for when they were grown together?
   d) Why do you think plant B survived and not plant A?

9 Why do some woodland plants grow in the spring before all the trees get their leaves?

Summary

Sometimes different animals compete for _____ or a place to _____ and shelter.
Plants compete for _____ from the Sun, and water and _____ from the soil.
If resources in a _____ are in short supply then the animals and plants which are best _____ to living there will survive and their _____ may die out.

adapted   breed   competitors   food
habitat   light   nutrients

17

G7 · Predators and prey

What are predators and prey?

Predators are animals that hunt and kill other animals for food. The animals that they kill and eat are called **prey**.

Zebra and lion.

 Frog and insect. *Mouse and owl.*

1 a) What is a predator?
b) What are prey?
c) Look at photographs A, B and C. For each photograph, say which animal is the predator and which is the prey.

2 Copy and complete the sentences below to explain why the lion is a good predator. Finish off each sentence by choosing the right ending from the box.
a) The lion is a fast runner . . .
b) It has sharp claws and teeth . . .
c) It has a sandy yellow colour to camouflage it . . .
d) It has good eyesight . . .

> . . . for killing and tearing at the flesh of the prey.
> . . . so it can spot prey in the distance.
> . . . so that the prey does not always see it coming.
> . . . so it can chase and catch its prey.

Predators are adapted to their lifestyle. They have things about them which help them to hunt and kill their prey.

The number of predators in a community will depend on the numbers of prey. If there are lots of prey, the predators will have a lot to eat. If there is plenty of food, their young will survive and the population of predators will increase. If there are only a few prey, the predators will not have much food and some will die.

3 Why would a snail or a tortoise not be a very good predator?

4 What will happen to the population of predators if:
a) the numbers of prey increase?
b) the numbers of prey get less?

The lemming and the Arctic fox live in Alaska. The Arctic fox is a predator which feeds on the lemming. Graph G shows what happened to the number of lemmings and Arctic foxes in one habitat over a number of years.

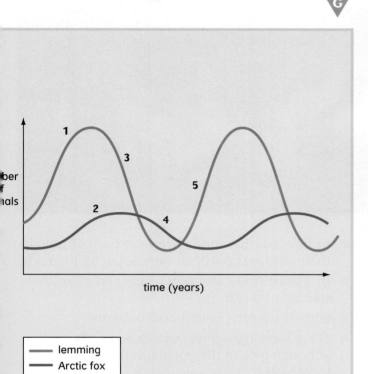

lemming
Arctic fox

E *An Arctic fox.*

A lemming. **F**

Summary

Predators _____ and kill other animals for their food. The animals which are hunted are called the _____. Predators are _____ to hunting and killing. They are usually fast and have sharp claws and _____. They also have good senses such as _____, smell and hearing. If the number of prey in a habitat increases then the number of predators will _____ too. If the number of prey decreases then the number of _____ will also decrease.

adapted   hunt   increase
predators   prey   sight   teeth

5 Which of the five labels here match up to each of the points 1 to 5 on graph G? Trace graph G and write each of the labels on in the right place.

a) The number of Arctic foxes increases as there are lots of prey for them to eat.

b) The number of lemmings starts to fall as there are now lots of Arctic foxes hunting and killing them.

c) There are now only a few Arctic foxes left. The number of lemmings increases as there are fewer predators. The whole cycle starts again.

d) There are not many lemmings left. As food is scarce, the number of Arctic foxes gets less.

e) In the beginning, the lemmings have plenty of food. They start to breed and have young. The number of lemmings increases.

6 Predators are adapted to hunting and killing their prey. What adaptations could the prey have that would help them escape?

19

Populations

What controls the size of a population?

A **population** of animals or plants in a habitat does not keep on getting bigger. The size of a population is usually controlled by a number of different things.

Scientists studied a population of mice living in a woodland habitat. The information here tells you what happened to the size of the population over a year.

- In January, 10 mice were found to be hibernating in the habitat.
- Very cold weather in February killed two of the mice but the rest of them survived.
- In March the mice started to breed.
- There were 12 mice born in April but four of them were eaten by owls.
- In May, seven of the mice were eaten by predators, including a badger and a fox, but another five mice were born.
- In June, a disease killed 10 of the mice but the ones that survived gave birth to six young.

- In July, another nine mice were born although three of the population were eaten by predators.
- In August, food was very scarce and 11 mice starved to death.
- Only three mice were born in August.
- There were eight mice born in September although four of the population were eaten by predators.
- In October, two of the mice died of disease.
- In November the remaining mice went into hibernation for the winter.
- All of the mice survived December.

1   Copy and complete table B to show what happened to the population of mice over the year.

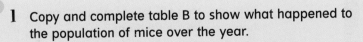

Month	January	February	March	April		December
Number of mice born	0	0				
Number of mice deaths	0	2				
Total number of mice in population	10	8				

2   During the year, how many mice:
   a) were born?
   b) died?

3   What was the size of the mouse population in:
   a) January?
   b) December?

4 Many things can affect a population of animals. Look at the list here. Copy out the ones which will limit the size of a population and stop it from getting too big.

- There is a shortage of food and water.
- The number of predators falls.
- Disease spreads through the population.
- Less competition from other animals.
- The population runs out of space.
- There is plenty of food available.
- More competition from other animals.
- The number of predators increases.

A population of plants will not keep on growing forever either.

- If the population gets too big, there may not be enough water or nutrients for all the plants, especially on a hot day.
- Overcrowding means bigger plants may put smaller ones in the shade. Plants that don't get enough light will die.
- Diseases spread quickly through an overcrowded population as the plants are a lot closer together.
- An increase in the number of herbivores feeding on the plants will keep the population down.

A swarm of locusts can eat a whole population of plants in minutes.

A large swarm of locusts can eat 20 000 tonnes of plant material in a day.

C

D

Summary

There are many things that will stop a _____ of living things from growing too big. A population of animals can be limited by a shortage of _____ or water, or more _____ from other animals in the habitat. If there are more _____, the population of the animals which are hunted will get less. A population of plants can be limited by a shortage of water or nutrients, or by competition for _____. _____ which feed on plants can keep the population down. _____ can spread through overcrowded populations of animals or plants very quickly.

| competition | diseases | food | herbivores | light |
| | population | predators | | |

5 a) Why is competition between plants for water more of a problem in the summer?
b) How can overcrowding affect smaller plants?
c) Why does disease spread quicker through an overcrowded population?
d) Look at photograph C. How will the swarm of locusts affect the plant population?

6 a) Some plants make sure that their seeds are spread a long way from the parent. Why does this give the seeds a better chance of surviving?
b) Find out about ways that plants spread or disperse their seeds.

G9 Estimating population sizes

How can you work out the size of a population?

Sometimes scientists want to work out how big a population of animals is. This is not very easy as animals move about and may be spread over a big habitat. Sometimes animals hide so they can't be seen. Some animals only come out at night.

You can estimate the size of animal populations by **mark**, **release** and **recapture**.

- Trap a sample of the population.
- **Mark** them in some way to show that they have already been caught once. Small animals such as insects can be marked by a small spot of paint. Birds often have a small ring put round one leg.
- **Release** the animals back into the habitat to mix with the rest of the population.
- Trap a sample of the population again.
- See how many of the sample have been **recaptured** by counting how many of them are already marked.

? 1 Why is it difficult to estimate the size of a population of animals?

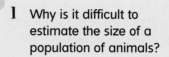

A

E Estimate the size of the population using this calculation.

$$\text{population} = \frac{\begin{array}{c}\text{number of animals} \\ \text{in first catch}\end{array} \times \begin{array}{c}\text{number of animals} \\ \text{in second catch}\end{array}}{\begin{array}{c}\text{number of animals that} \\ \text{were marked in second catch}\end{array}}$$

A group of pupils were investigating the size of different populations in a woodland habitat. Table C shows their results.

card lid

small stones

yoghurt pot

Animals	Number in first catch	Number in second catch	Number of marked animals in second catch
Woodlice	10	15	5
Snails	6	4	2
Beetles	12	10	6
Centipedes	8	6	2

C

B *Yoghurt pots or small plastic cups are often used as simple traps. Food is left in the bottom of the trap to attract small animals.*

Worked example

$$\frac{\text{Population}}{\text{of woodlice}} = \frac{10 \times 15}{5} = \frac{150}{5} = 30$$

? 2 What do scientists use mark, release and recapture for?

3 **a)** How are birds marked?
   b) How are small insects marked?

4 Why is food often left in the trap?

5 Look at table C.

a) Work out the population of each insect. The size of the woodlice population has already been worked out to start you off.

b) Draw a bar chart to show the population size of each insect.

Scientists estimate the size of a plant population using a quadrat. A quadrat is a metal or wooden frame. The quadrat is placed on the ground at random a number of times. You then simply look at what plants are found inside the frame at each different place.

A group of pupils were using a quadrat to estimate the number of buttercups in a garden. The garden was 100 m^2. The quadrat size was 1 m^2. They threw the quadrat 10 times. Each time the quadrat landed they counted the number of buttercups inside the frame. Their results are shown in table E.

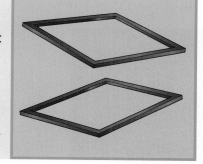

P How could you investigate a plant population?

F

Sample	1	2	3	4	5	6	7	8	9	10
No. Buttercups	0	0	10	5	0	3	3	0	4	0

6 What is a quadrat used for?

7 Look at table E.

a) How many m^2 of garden had the pupils sampled altogether?

b) How many buttercups did they find?

c) How big was the garden?

d) The pupils estimated that there would be 250 buttercups in the garden. How did they work out this answer?

8 Why is it important that quadrat samples are taken all over a habitat and not just in one small area?

9 A group of pupils were estimating the size of a bluebell population in a wood which was 500 m^2 big. They used a 1 m^2 quadrat and threw it 25 times. Altogether they counted 22 bluebells. Estimate how many bluebells were in the wood.

Summary

Scientists can work out the size of a population of animals by _____, release and recapture. First of all they _____ and mark a sample of the population. The animals are then _____ back into the _____. If they set a trap again they can estimate the size of the _____ by looking at how many of the second catch are marked already. Scientists use _____ to estimate the size of a plant population.

habitat   mark   population   quadrats   released   trap

Decomposition

What happens to animals and plants when they die?

A

Have you ever wondered where the dead leaves go when they fall off the trees in Autumn? Are they all swept up or do they just disappear? The answer is that they rot away or **decompose**. All living things decompose when they die. If they didn't, the Earth would be piled high with the bodies of dead animals and plants.

B

 1 What happens to dead leaves?

Dead animals and plants rot or decompose when they are being eaten by something else. Living things which eat dead animals and plants are called **decomposers**. Decomposers also feed on the waste materials that animals make when they are alive. This means they feed on animal droppings (faeces).

Decomposition happens in two stages. Firstly, small animals feed on the dead tissue or waste material. Secondly, decomposition is finished off by microorganisms such as **bacteria** and **fungi**.

2 What do decomposers feed on?

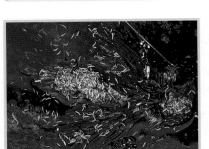

C

Small animals such as maggots, woodlice and earthworms start decomposition. They break down dead tissue and waste material into smaller pieces.

Microorganisms such as bacteria and fungi feed on these smaller pieces of tissue and waste.

D

3 a) Name three small animals that start decomposition.

b) Name two microorganisms that finish decomposition.

4 Look at diagram E.

a) What do microorganisms release to digest their food?

b) What is the dead tissue or waste material digested into?

c) What happens to these simple chemicals?

the microorganism absorbs some of these simple chemicals as its food

enzymes released by the microorganism digest dead tissue into simple chemicals

some of the chemicals pass into the surrounding soil

E *The fungi and bacteria release enzymes to digest the dead tissue and waste material.*

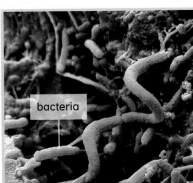

 bacteria

5 a) Why do living things respire?
  b) What gas do living things need for respiration?
  c) What waste gas do living things make in respiration?

Microorganisms like warmth, moisture and plenty of oxygen. Dead tissue will decompose quicker under these conditions as the microorganisms will be feeding and growing quickly.

P How could you investigate the effect of temperature on decomposition?

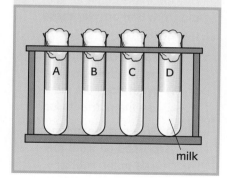

milk

6 Why does dead tissue decompose quickly when it is warm and damp?

7 Look at photograph F. Why did the dead body not decompose?

8 Look at photograph G. Why did the leaf not decompose properly?

9 The three main enzymes involved in digestion are proteases, carbohydrases and lipases. Find out what each enzyme does.

Decomposers get energy from their food using respiration just like we do. The simple chemicals that they take in will react with oxygen to give out energy, carbon dioxide and water. The decomposers will use the energy to stay alive. Living things respire to release energy from their food.

Respiration is a chemical reaction and can be written as a word equation.

oxygen + food ⟶ carbon dioxide + water (+ energy)

living things need oxygen gas for respiration

carbon dioxide gas is made as a waste product

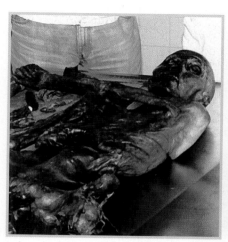

F This man's body was found frozen in ice.

G No air could get to this leaf as it was covered by sediment. The leaf has become a fossil.

Summary

_____ feed on dead animals and plants. They also feed on the _____ that animals make when they are alive. The most important decomposers are microorganisms like bacteria and _____. They release _____ which _____ or break down dead or waste material into simple chemicals. They use some of these chemicals for food, although many will pass into the surrounding _____. Things decompose quickly when it is _____ and damp and when there is plenty of _____ because these are the conditions that microorganisms like.

decomposers   digest   enzymes   fungi
oxygen   soil   warm   waste

More about decomposition

Why is decomposition important?

Nearly all of the living tissue which makes up an animal or plant is made from just six elements. These are carbon, hydrogen, oxygen, nitrogen, phosphorus and sulphur. When living things grow, they lock these elements up in their cells. The elements become part of their bodies. When they die, their bodies decompose and these important elements are put back into the environment for other living things to use again. If animals and plants did not decompose, we would soon run out of the elements to make new living things!

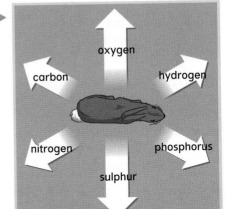

A

1   Name the six main elements which make up living tissue.

2   **a)** Why is decomposition important?
    b) What would happen if dead bodies did not decompose?

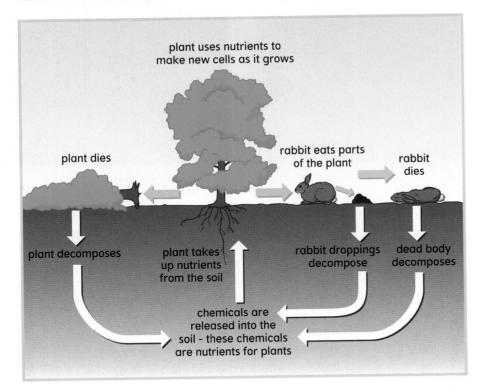

plant uses nutrients to make new cells as it grows

plant dies

rabbit eats parts of the plant

rabbit dies

plant decomposes

plant takes up nutrients from the soil

rabbit droppings decompose

dead body decomposes

chemicals are released into the soil - these chemicals are nutrients for plants

Use the information in diagram B to answer these questions.

3   **a)** Where does the plant get its nutrients from?
    b) What does the plant use the nutrients for?

4   **a)** How are the nutrients passed on from the tree to the rabbit?
    b) How would nutrients be passed on from a rabbit to a fox?

5   In what two ways are the nutrients released back into the soil?

Have you ever wondered why gardeners put horse manure on their roses or why farmers spread cow manure or slurry on their fields? Horse manure and cow muck are natural fertilisers! When the waste decomposes it releases chemicals into the soil which help the plants to grow.

B

C

6   Why do farmers spray cow manure on their fields?

Compost

Gardeners often dump dead plant material like grass cuttings in a big heap in the corner of the garden. Sometimes other plant material, like potato peelings or banana skins, is thrown on the heap too. This pile of dead plant material is called **compost**. Compost also acts like a natural fertiliser. As it decomposes it releases important nutrients. The gardener digs the compost into the soil so that it will help new plants to grow.

? 7 a) What things are thrown on a compost heap?
  b) Why do gardeners add compost to their soil?

Sewage

D

Sewage is human waste. Sewage works use microorganisms to decompose human waste and make it harmless. Some of the human waste is eaten or digested by microorganisms in sludge tanks. Some of the human waste is trickled out of big sprinklers onto a coke bed. (Coke is made from coal. A pile of coke just looks like a pile of stones.) Each piece of coke is covered by a layer of microorganisms. As the sewage trickles through the coke bed it is digested by the microorganisms.

E

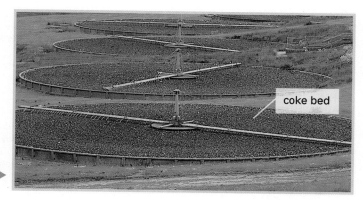

coke bed

F

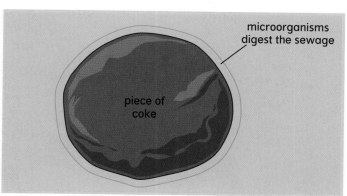

microorganisms digest the sewage

piece of coke

Summary

Animals and plants have important chemicals locked up in their _____. When they die their bodies _____ and these chemicals are released back into the _____ for other living things to use again. Microorganisms are used at _____ works to decompose human waste and make it harmless. Gardeners also use microorganisms to decompose dead plant material in _____ heaps. As the compost rots it releases _____ which help new plants grow.

cells   compost   decompose
environment   nutrients   sewage

? 8 a) What is sewage?
  b) What happens in sludge tanks?
  c) What happens to the waste as it trickles through the coke beds?

9 a) Look back at page 25. What conditions do microorganisms like best?
  b) Gardeners often 'turn' their compost heaps with a fork to allow air into the middle. Why do you think they do this?

The carbon cycle

What is the carbon cycle?

All living things need **carbon**. They need it to make carbohydrates, fats, proteins and other important chemicals. They use some of these chemicals to make new cells as they grow. They use some of the chemicals for respiration to give them energy.

Carbon is passed from one living thing to another in the **carbon cycle**.

> An average person contains enough carbon to make nearly 13 kg of coal.

> **1** What do living things use carbohydrates, fats and proteins for?

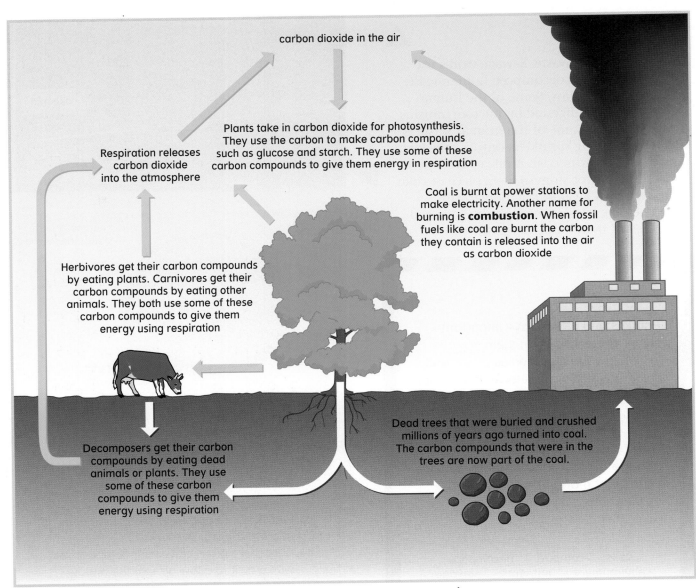

carbon dioxide in the air

Plants take in carbon dioxide for photosynthesis. They use the carbon to make carbon compounds such as glucose and starch. They use some of these carbon compounds to give them energy in respiration

Respiration releases carbon dioxide into the atmosphere

Coal is burnt at power stations to make electricity. Another name for burning is **combustion**. When fossil fuels like coal are burnt the carbon they contain is released into the air as carbon dioxide

Herbivores get their carbon compounds by eating plants. Carnivores get their carbon compounds by eating other animals. They both use some of these carbon compounds to give them energy using respiration

Decomposers get their carbon compounds by eating dead animals or plants. They use some of these carbon compounds to give them energy using respiration

Dead trees that were buried and crushed millions of years ago turned into coal. The carbon compounds that were in the trees are now part of the coal.

A The carbon cycle.

Living things respire to get energy from their food. **Respiration** is a chemical reaction and can be written as a word equation.

Plants photosynthesise to make their food. **Photosynthesis** is also a chemical reaction and can be written as a word equation.

oxygen + glucose $\longrightarrow$ carbon dioxide + water (+ energy)

| oxygen is taken in for respiration | carbon dioxide is given out as a waste product |

carbon dioxide + water (+ light energy) $\longrightarrow$ glucose + oxygen

| carbon dioxide is taken in for photosynthesis | oxygen is given out as a waste gas |

2 a) Why do plants photosynthesise?
b) What gas do plants use up from the air?
c) What waste gas is made?

3 How was coal formed?

4 a) What is combustion?
b) What gas is given out when fossil fuels are burnt?

5 a) How do herbivores get their carbon?
b) How do carnivores get their carbon?
c) How do decomposers get their carbon?

6 a) Why do all living things respire?
b) What gas do they use up in respiration?
c) What waste gas is given out?

7 Do each of these processes add carbon dioxide to the air or use it up?
a) respiration
b) photosynthesis
c) combustion.

8 How will the following affect the amount of carbon dioxide in the atmosphere?
a) cutting down the rain forests
b) burning more fossil fuels.

9 Living things use up oxygen all the time. How is the oxygen replaced so that we don't run out?

P How can you show that you are respiring?

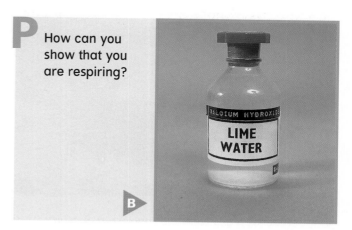

B

Summary

All living things need _____. They use carbon compounds for respiration and for making new cells when they _____. Carbon is passed from one living thing to another in the carbon _____. Plants get their carbon by taking in carbon dioxide for _____. Animals get their carbon compounds by feeding on _____ or other animals. All living things _____ and produce carbon dioxide as a _____ gas. Carbon dioxide is also released from the _____ of fossil fuels such as _____.

carbon	coal	combustion
cycle	grow	plants	photosynthesis
respire	waste

Population explosion

Will the Earth's resources last for ever?

The world's population is growing at a frightening speed. Over the last 100 years it has gone up from 2 billion to nearly 6 billion people. As the population increases we use up more and more of the Earth's **raw materials**.

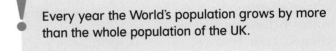

! Every year the World's population grows by more than the whole population of the UK.

A *Limestone is dug out of the Earth's crust at quarries.*

B *Iron ore is used to make steel.*

C *In the rainforests, trees like mahogany are cut down to make furniture and window frames.*

D *Scientists think we will soon run out of oil.*

Raw materials are natural materials which we get from the Earth. We use raw materials to make things. Limestone is a raw material which we use to make cement and glass. Limestone is dug out of the Earth's crust at quarries. Metal ores such as iron ore are also dug out of the Earth's crust. Iron ore is used to make steel. Wood is the raw material we use to make paper and furniture. The fossil fuels oil, coal and natural gas are all raw materials. Scientists think that we will run out of oil in about 30 years time if no new deposits are found.

? 1 What are raw materials?

2 **a)** Name six raw materials.
   b) What is made from limestone?
   c) What is made from iron ore?

3 Why are we cutting down trees from the rainforests?

4 When do scientists think we will run out of oil?

Many things we throw away can be **recycled** and used again. People now recycle bottles, cans and paper. Bottles are crushed and melted into new glass. Recycled paper is used to make newspapers. Aluminium cans are melted down so that we can use the aluminium again. Recycling saves scarce raw materials.

E

5 a) What happens to bottles that are recycled?

b) What is recycled paper used for?

c) Why are aluminium cans melted down?

d) Why is recycling a good idea?

F

As the population grows we are using up more and more land. We need more houses, roads, shops, factories, schools and hospitals. We also need to grow more food so large areas of land are being used for farming. As land is used up we are destroying many natural habitats. The animals and plants that lived there now face **extinction**. This means there will be none of them left.

G

Summary

As the human _____ grows, we use up more _____ for new buildings and for growing _____. We are also using up more of the Earth's _____ materials. Some raw materials such as _____ have nearly run out. We are now starting to _____ such things as bottles, _____ and paper. This saves us using up more raw materials.

cans   crops   land
oil   population   raw   recycle

6 a) Give two reasons why we are using up so much land.

b) What new building work is taking place near your home or school?

7 a) What does it mean if an animal or plant becomes extinct?

b) Why are many animals and plants facing extinction?

8 Think of as many reasons as you can why the Earth's population has increased so much over the last hundred years.

Land pollution

How are we polluting our land?

As our population grows we make more and more waste. A lot of this waste is just dumped into big holes in the ground. These rubbish tips are called **landfill sites**. Sometimes dangerous chemicals are dumped on rubbish tips. If they leak out into the soil they can poison the wildlife.

As towns keep on growing, local councils have to find more landfill sites to get rid of our rubbish. This can be quite difficult as most people do not want a rubbish tip near their house. Tips can be very smelly and they are not very nice to look at!

 In Britain alone we produce over 100 million tonnes of rubbish every year.

Many farmers spray **herbicides** and **pesticides** on their land. Herbicides are chemicals which kill weeds. Weeds compete with the farmer's crop for water, nutrients and light. Pesticides are chemicals which kill pests such as insects that feed on the crop.

Sometimes herbicides and pesticides can poison other animals too. Diagram C shows what happened when a pesticide called dieldrin was used in the 1950s.

4 a) What are herbicides?
   b) Why do farmers want to kill weeds?

5 Why do farmers use pesticides?

A *A landfill site.*

1 What is a landfill site?

2 Why should poisonous chemicals not be dumped on rubbish tips?

3 Why don't people want rubbish tips near their homes?

B **C**

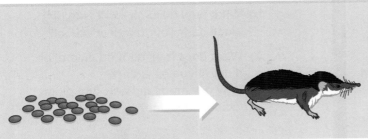 

Seeds were soaked in dieldrin to poison small animals that might eat them.

The poison was passed along the food chain.

Birds of prey such as falcons and sparrow hawks were also poisoned. The dieldrin also made the shells of their eggs very thin. Many eggs broke and the young did not survive.

D *A spoil tip.*

6 Look at diagram C.
Why were seeds soaked in dieldrin?

7 a) How were the sparrow hawks and falcons poisoned?

b) Why were fewer young born?

Mining produces lots of waste. Mining waste is called **spoil**. The spoil is just dumped on the Earth's surface. Eventually some spoil tips become so big that they look like hills. Spoil contains large amounts of poisonous metals like lead, copper and zinc. Compounds of these metals dissolve and leak into the soil.

Spoil tips look very ugly. People tried to grow grass and other plants on the tips to make them look nicer. Unfortunately the plants were poisoned by the metals and died. Scientists have now found some types of grass which are **tolerant** to the waste. This means that the plants are not affected by the poisonous metals. These grasses grow well on spoil tips, even though their cells and tissues contain a lot of the metal waste.

8 a) What is spoil?

b) What does spoil contain?

9 Why wouldn't most plants grow on the spoil tips?

10 What does it mean if a plant is tolerant to metals?

11 Look at food chain F. Why can't farmers graze their sheep or cows on the metal-tolerant grass?

P How can you investigate the effect of metals on plants?

E

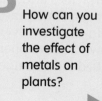

F

The cells and tissues of the tolerant grasses contain a lot of the metal waste.

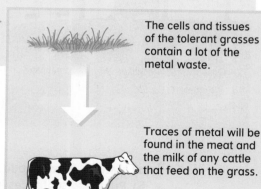

Traces of metal will be found in the meat and the milk of any cattle that feed on the grass.

Summary

Most of the waste we make is dumped in _____ sites. If dangerous chemicals are dumped they can leak out into the _____ . Herbicides and _____ are used to help crops grow by killing _____ and pests such as insects. These chemicals can get into _____ chains and poison other animals too. Mining waste, called _____, can contain poisonous _____ which can kill wildlife.

food   landfill   metals   pesticides   soil   spoil   weeds

12 Many governments are now using biological control to limit the population of pests which damage crops. In Holland, lice were damaging trees so the Government imported specially bred ladybirds which fed on lice.

a) Why did the Government introduce ladybirds into the community?

b) What is biological control?

c) Name one advantage of using biological control.

Water pollution
How do we pollute our lakes and rivers?

Sewage is human waste. Sometimes sewage is poured into rivers. Bacteria feed on the sewage and reproduce very quickly. Soon there are billions of them. The bacteria use up the oxygen in the water. Eventually there is no oxygen left and the fish die.

A

1 a) What is sewage?
   b) What happens to the sewage that is poured into rivers?
   c) What happens to the number of bacteria in the river?
   d) How does this kill the fish?

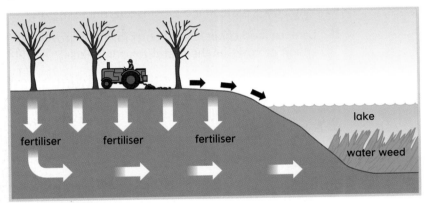

fertiliser   fertiliser   fertiliser

lake

water weed

B

Farmers add **fertilisers** to the soil to help their crops grow. Sometimes the fertilisers are washed out of the soil into rivers. The fertiliser helps water weed to grow and the river soon becomes full of plants. When the plants die they are eaten by bacteria. The bacteria reproduce very quickly and once again the oxygen in the water gets used up.

Farmers also add herbicides and pesticides to their crops. Sometimes these chemicals drain into the rivers too. Diagram C shows what happened when a pesticide called DDT drained into a lake.

2 a) Why do farmers add fertilisers to their crops?
   b) Put these sentences in order to explain how fertilisers can harm our rivers.
   • Bacteria reproduce quickly.
   • Fertiliser drains into the river.
   • The water weed dies.
   • Bacteria use up the oxygen.
   • It helps the water weed to grow.
   • Bacteria eat the dead water weed.

3 How did the DDT kill the grebes?

P How can you investigate water pollution?

C

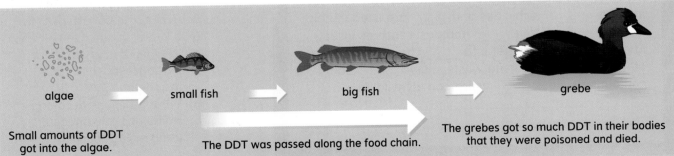

algae   →   small fish   →   big fish   →   grebe

Small amounts of DDT got into the algae.

The DDT was passed along the food chain.

The grebes got so much DDT in their bodies that they were poisoned and died.

Many factories tip poisonous chemicals into the water. There was a fishing town in Japan where a plastics factory was tipping waste mercury into the sea. The factory opened in 1952. People started dying from a mystery illness in 1953. Table D shows how many people died between 1952 and 1962.

4 a) What happened when fishing was banned in 1957?
b) What happened when fishing was allowed again in 1959?
c) What happened when fishing was banned in 1960?
d) How was the waste mercury poisoning people?

Year	Number of deaths
1952	0
1953	1
1954	12
1955	18
1956	53
1957 (fishing banned)	7
1958	5
1959 (fishing allowed again)	20
1960 (fishing banned)	4
1961	2
1962	1

D

Oil is carried around the world in huge tankers. Sometimes tankers run into rocks along the coastline and crude oil pours into the sea and onto the beaches. Oil kills the wildlife that lives there. It sticks to the feathers of birds such as gulls. It sticks to the fur of animals such as seals. The animals try to clean themselves and swallow the poisonous oil.

In 1989, the Exxon Valdez spilt 11 million gallons of crude oil into the sea around Alaska.

E

The Exxon Valdez oil disaster. **F**

Summary

Sewage is _____ waste. Any sewage poured into rivers is eaten by _____. The bacteria reproduce very quickly and use up the oxygen from the water. Soon there is none left for the fish. _____ which drains into rivers helps water weed to grow and the river is soon full of plants. When the plants die they are eaten by the bacteria. The bacteria reproduce and the _____ in the water gets used up. _____ chemicals that are tipped into rivers and lakes can get into _____ chains. Animals can be killed as the chemicals are passed down the food chain from one _____ to the next.

bacteria   consumer   fertiliser   food   human
oxygen   poisonous

5 a) Name two animals which are harmed by oil pollution.
b) How are the animals harmed by the oil?

6 Look back at table D. Draw a bar graph to show the number of people who died from mercury poisoning between 1952 and 1962. Label your graph to show the dates where fishing was banned and allowed again.

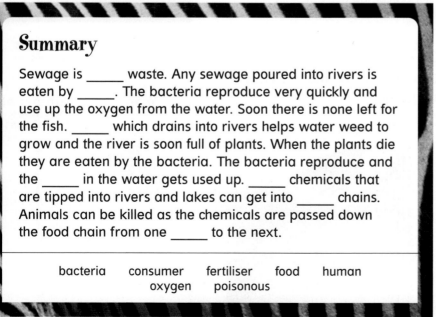

35

Air pollution

How are we polluting our air?

When fossil fuels burn they make **smoke** and harmful gases such as **sulphur dioxide** and **carbon dioxide**. Smoke is made of solid fuel particles which don't burn and float off into the air instead. You can see the effects of smoke if you look at the blackened buildings in many towns and cities.

1 a) What is smoke?

b) Name two gases that are made when fossil fuels are burnt.

A The Houses of Parliament before they were cleaned . . .

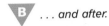
B . . . and after.

Sometimes smoke mixes with fog to make **smog**. In 1952 there was very bad smog in London. It was so thick that street lamps had to be kept on in the day. The tiny particles in smoke can damage your lungs and cause bronchitis. The London smog killed nearly 4000 people.

C

2 How can breathing in smoke harm you?

3 a) What is smog?

b) How many people died in the London smog of 1952?

The main causes of air pollution are cars and lorries. Their exhaust fumes contain many poisonous gases. Before unleaded petrol was available, exhaust fumes also contained lead. If too much lead is breathed in, it can damage the brain and nervous system.

Photochemical smog is common in cities such as Los Angeles, Tokyo and Mexico City. It is caused by the effect of sunlight on exhaust fumes. In Tokyo, many drivers now wear masks and there are special 'clean air' booths where people can get fresh air to breathe when the smog is really bad.

D

E The table shows the increase in the number of vehicles on Britain's roads.

Year	Number of vehicles (millions)
1930	2
1940	3
1950	4
1960	9
1970	15
1980	25
1990	38
2000	53

4 Why has unleaded petrol been introduced?

5 a) What causes photochemical smog?
b) Name three cities which suffer from this kind of smog.

 75% of all air pollution is caused by motor exhaust fumes.

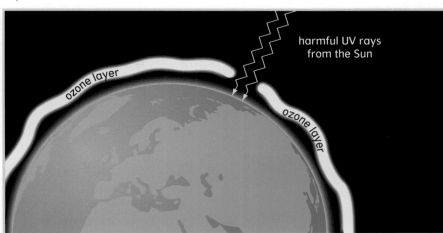

harmful UV rays from the Sun

ozone layer

ozone layer

CFCs (chlorofluorocarbons) are gases which used to be in spray cans and refrigerators. When these gases are released into the atmosphere they react with the ozone and break it up. This makes a hole in the ozone layer which allows UV rays through. As a result it is dangerous to go out in the Sun without sunscreen in some parts of the world as there is an increased chance of skin cancers. We no longer use CFCs.

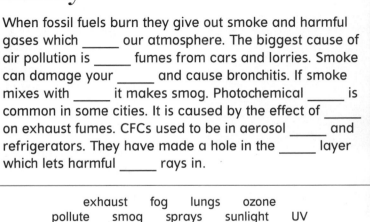

Summary

When fossil fuels burn they give out smoke and harmful gases which _____ our atmosphere. The biggest cause of air pollution is _____ fumes from cars and lorries. Smoke can damage your _____ and cause bronchitis. If smoke mixes with _____ it makes smog. Photochemical _____ is common in some cities. It is caused by the effect of _____ on exhaust fumes. CFCs used to be in aerosol _____ and refrigerators. They have made a hole in the _____ layer which lets harmful _____ rays in.

exhaust   fog   lungs   ozone
pollute   smog   sprays   sunlight   UV

P How can you investigate air pollution?

The Sun gives out harmful **ultraviolet rays** (UV rays) which can cause skin cancer. We are protected from them by a layer of **ozone** high up in the Earth's atmosphere. The ozone absorbs the UV rays and stops them reaching the Earth's surface.

6 a) How can UV rays harm animals?
b) How does the ozone layer protect us?

H

CFC FREE

7 a) What are chlorofluorocarbons better known as?
b) Why do aerosol cans no longer use CFCs?

8 Use table D to draw a graph showing how the numbers of cars and lorries have increased over the last 70 years.

Acid rain

What is acid rain and what problems does it cause?

A

Coal and oil contain sulphur. When they burn, the sulphur reacts with oxygen to form **sulphur dioxide**. The high temperatures produced when fuels are burnt in power stations and car engines also make nitrogen react with oxygen to form **nitrogen oxides**. Sulphur dioxide and nitrogen oxides are **acidic gases** which cause **acid rain**.

1 **a)** Name two acidic gases.
   b) How is sulphur dioxide made?
   c) How are nitrogen oxides made?

B

Sulphur dioxide dissolves in rain water to make sulphuric acid.
Nitrogen oxides dissolve in rain water to make nitric acid.

2 **a)** What acid is made when sulphur dioxide dissolves in rainwater?
   b) What acid is made when nitrogen oxides dissolve in rainwater?

3 **a)** What does acid rain do to soil?
   b) How does this affect plant life?

Acid rain makes soil more acidic. Many plants cannot live or grow in acidic soil. Sometimes trees can be killed and forests destroyed. Tree roots hold the soil together on hills and mountain sides. If the trees are killed then the soil is washed away and new plants cannot grow there. Acid rain can make water too acidic for animals to live in. Many lakes and rivers no longer have fish.

C

4 **a)** How is the soil held together on hills and mountain sides?
   b) What happens to the soil if the trees are killed by acid rain?

5 Why do many lakes and rivers no longer have fish?

6 Why are acid gas scrubbers fitted at power stations?

7 Why do modern cars have catalytic converters?

Many power stations now have **acid gas scrubbers** fitted to their chimneys. These remove the harmful gases before the fumes are released into the atmosphere. Modern cars have **catalytic converters** fitted which clean up their exhaust fumes. The only real way to stop acid rain though is by burning fewer fossil fuels.

Lichens are very useful organisms because they can tell us how polluted the atmosphere is. They are sensitive to the amount of sulphur dioxide in the air. Scientists can work out how polluted the air is by looking at how many kinds of lichen they can find. If there are not many types of lichen, then there must be a lot of sulphur dioxide in the air. If there are lots of different lichens then the air must be quite clean.

? 8 Why are lichens useful to scientists?

E *Lichens from an unpolluted area.*

Graph G shows how many different lichens were found in and around a city. It also shows how much sulphur dioxide there was in the air.

P How can you investigate the effect of acid rain on plants?
D

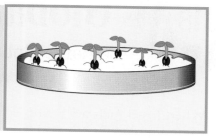

F *Lichens from a polluted area.*

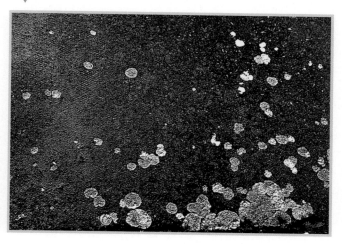

G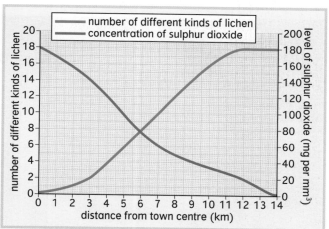

Summary

_____ dioxide and nitrogen oxides are _____ gases released when _____ fuels are burnt. When they _____ in rainwater they make weak acids. Sulphur dioxide forms _____ acid and nitrogen oxides form _____ acid. Acid rain can make _____ too acidic for plants to grow. It can also make _____ and lakes too acidic for _____ to live in.

acidic	dissolve	fish	fossil	nitric
rivers	soil	sulphur	sulphuric	

? 9 How many lichens were found:
  a) in the city centre?   **c)** 7 km out?
  b) 3 km out?   **d)** 12 km out?

10 What was the concentration of sulphur dioxide:
  a) in the city centre?   **c)** 7 km out?
  b) 3 km out?   **d)** 12 km out?

11 How will the following reduce acid rain?
  a) More use of wind and solar power.
  b) Cheap and efficient public transport.

Global warming

What is global warming?

When fossil fuels are burnt, carbon dioxide is released into the atmosphere. Scientists say that carbon dioxide is a **greenhouse gas** because it traps the Sun's heat in our atmosphere and makes the Earth warmer. This increase in the Earth's temperature is called **global warming**.

1 a) Why is carbon dioxide called a greenhouse gas?
b) What is global warming?

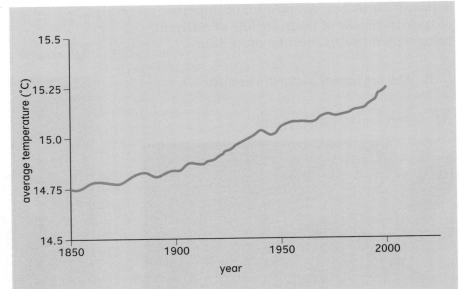

A

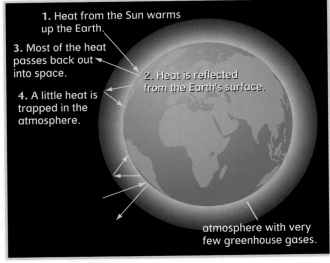

1. Heat from the Sun warms up the Earth.

3. Most of the heat passes back out into space.

4. A little heat is trapped in the atmosphere.

2. Heat is reflected from the Earth's surface.

atmosphere with very few greenhouse gases.

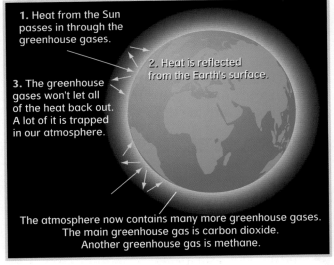

1. Heat from the Sun passes in through the greenhouse gases.

2. Heat is reflected from the Earth's surface.

3. The greenhouse gases won't let all of the heat back out. A lot of it is trapped in our atmosphere.

The atmosphere now contains many more greenhouse gases. The main greenhouse gas is carbon dioxide. Another greenhouse gas is methane.

B *Before global warming.*

C *Since global warming.*

2 Look at diagram B (before global warming).
a) Where does the Earth get its heat from?
b) What happens to most of the heat that is reflected from the Earth's surface?

3 Look at diagram C (since global warming).
a) Name two greenhouse gases.
b) Do greenhouse gases allow the Sun's heat into the Earth's atmosphere?
c) How are greenhouse gases making the atmosphere warmer?

Carbon dioxide and methane are called greenhouse gases because they act a bit like the glass in a greenhouse. The glass will let the Sun's heat in but it will not let it all back out again. This is why it is usually warmer inside a greenhouse than it is outside.

? 4 Why is it usually warm inside a greenhouse?

Scientists predict that the Earth's temperature will continue to rise as we make more and more greenhouse gases. They are worried that the polar ice caps will melt and the sea level around the world will start to rise. This will cause serious flooding in many countries. Changes to the Earth's climate may make other parts of the world too dry to grow crops. This could lead to food shortages and famine.

D

E

F

? 5 Why could global warming cause flooding?

6 How could global warming lead to famine?

7 Look at graph A.
  a) Scientists have recorded the average temperature every year since 1850. How can they use this information to work out the average temperature for the last 150 years?
  b) By how many degrees has the temperature gone up since 1850?

8 A lot of carbon dioxide is made when fossil fuels are burnt at power stations to make electricity. Think of all the things you could do at home which would help to reduce global warming.

Summary

Carbon dioxide and _____ are _____ gases. Carbon dioxide is the main greenhouse gas and it is made when we burn _____ fuels such as coal, _____ and natural gas. Greenhouse gases trap the Sun's _____ inside our atmosphere instead of letting it back out into space. This means that the Earth gets _____. This is called _____ warming. Scientists think that global warming may cause _____ and famine.

flooding   fossil   global   greenhouse   heat
       methane   oil   warmer

More about global warming

Why is global warming getting worse?

For many millions of years the amount of carbon dioxide in the air stayed about the same. Animals and plants added carbon dioxide to the air through **respiration**. Plants then used the carbon dioxide up for **photosynthesis**. The amount of carbon dioxide used up in photosynthesis balanced with the amount of carbon dioxide given out in respiration.

1 a) How do living things add carbon dioxide to the air?
b) How do plants remove carbon dioxide from the air?

A
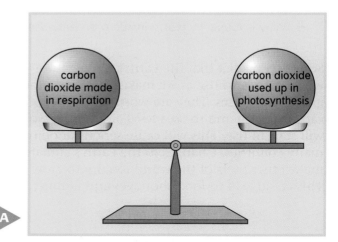

The amount of carbon dioxide in the atmosphere started to increase around about 1850. This was when we first started to burn fossil fuels to power engines and machinery.

B

C

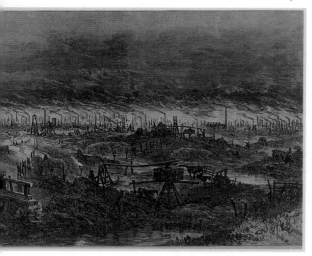

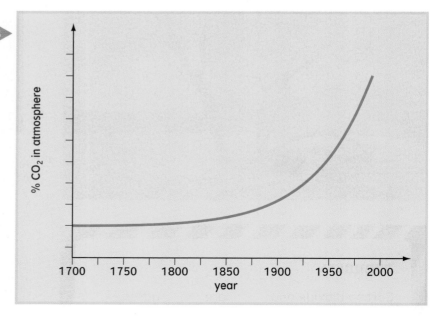

2 Why did carbon dioxide levels start to go up in about 1850?

Since 1850, we have continued to burn more and more fossil fuels. Coal, oil and natural gas are burnt at power stations to make electricity. Petrol, diesel oil and kerosene all come from oil and are used to power our cars, lorries, ships and aircraft. We burn so much fossil fuel that we add 20 000 million tonnes of carbon dioxide to the atmosphere every year.

A cruise liner has to burn 6500 gallons of diesel to travel 1 km.

3 a) What are the main reasons for burning fossil fuels?
b) How much carbon dioxide do we add to the air every year?

Not only are we producing more carbon dioxide, but we are also cutting down more and more trees. Every day, hundreds of hectares of tropical rainforest are cut down. This is called **deforestation**. All of these trees would be using up carbon dioxide for us if they were still living.

4 a) What is deforestation?
b) How is this affecting global warming?

To make matters worse, a lot of the land that is cleared of rainforest is now used to graze cattle. We need more cows to make more burgers! Cows produce huge amounts of methane when they fart. Methane is another greenhouse gas. It traps heat in the atmosphere like carbon dioxide does.

As the population grows we need more food. Rice is the main crop grown in many parts of the world. Rice also produces methane. As more rice is grown, more methane is added to the air.

Every year we produce millions of tonnes of rubbish. A lot of this is dumped in landfill sites. As the rubbish rots it also gives off methane gas.

 Rice fields in China.

Summary

For millions of years the amount of carbon dioxide in the _____ stayed about the same. The amount of carbon dioxide made by respiration balanced with the carbon dioxide used up by plants for _____. Carbon dioxide levels began to increase rapidly when we started burning _____ fuels for industry and transport. The problem is being made worse by _____, where we are cutting down trees that would have used the carbon dioxide up. _____ is another greenhouse gas. It is produced by cattle, _____ crops and rubbish tips. As the population increases we are rearing more cattle, growing more rice and making more _____.

| atmosphere | deforestation | fossil |
| methane | photosynthesis | rice | waste |

5 a) What gas do cattle produce when they fart?
b) What gas do rice plants produce?
c) What gas is given out by rotting rubbish?
d) How does methane make the problem of global warming worse?

6 Find out what you can about the world climate conference and what it is trying to do.

Further questions

1 Copy and complete the sentences here by choosing the right word from the box.

| community   population   habitat |

a) The place where an animal or plant lives is called its ____ (1)

b) All the animals and plants which live together in one place make up a ____. (1)

c) Any group of animals or plants of the same species make up a ____. (1)

2 Read this information about some of the animals and plants in a woodland community.

A vole may eat 100 caterpillars in a day. The caterpillars feed on the leaves of oak trees. One oak tree has enough leaves to feed many thousands of caterpillars. Owls eat voles. An owl may eat three voles each day.

Use this information to draw out:

a) a food chain. (1)

b) a pyramid of numbers. (1)

c) a pyramid of biomass. (1)

3 Match up each of the words in the box with the right description.

| decomposer   herbivore |
| producer   carnivore |

a) A plant which makes its own food using photosynthesis. (1)

b) An animal that feeds on other animals. (1)

c) An animal that feeds on plants. (1)

d) An animal that feeds on dead tissue or waste. (1)

4 Look at the food web.

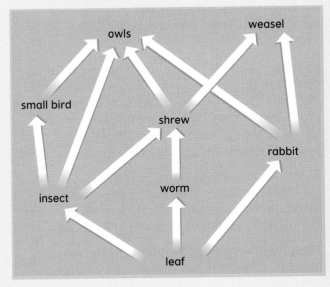

a) What do owls eat? (1)

b) What might happen to the number of weasels if all the rabbits died of disease? Explain your answer. (2)

c) What might happen to the number of shrews if all the rabbits died of disease? Explain your answer. (2)

d) Which animals compete for insects? (1)

e) Name one other thing that animals compete for apart from food. (1)

f) Name two things that plants compete for. (2)

5 How might the following adaptations help a camel to survive in the desert?

a) A camel can store up to 100 litres of water in its stomach. (1)

b) It stores its fat in its hump rather than as a layer under its skin. (1)

c) It produces very little urine or sweat. (1)

d) It is a sandy colour. (1)

e) It has big feet. (1)

6 Look at the food chain.

> plant ⟶ moth ⟶ toad ⟶ owl

a) Why would the owls and the toads starve if there were no plants? (1)

b) Why do all the animals and plants in the food chain depend on light energy for their food? (1)

c) For every 10 grams of moths that a toad eats, only 1 gram will be used to make new biomass. What happens to the other 9 grams that the toad has eaten? (2)

7 Lynx look a little like cats. They live in cold climates near the Arctic Circle. They hunt and kill hares for their food.

a) What name is given to animals like lynx which hunt and kill other animals for food? (1)

b) What name is given to the animals that are killed and eaten? (1)

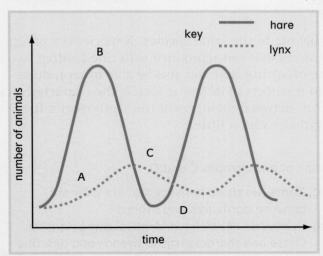

c) The graph shows what happened to the numbers of lynx and hares over a period of time.

  i) Why did the number of lynx start to increase at point A? (1)

  ii) Why did the number of hares start to decrease at point B? (1)

  iii) Why did the number of lynx start to decrease at point C? (1)

  iv) Why did the number of hares start to increase at point D? (1)

d) Name two other factors which could cause a population of animals to decrease. (2)

8 Look at the list of gases.

> sulphur dioxide   methane   carbon dioxide

a) Which two gases are the main causes of the greenhouse effect? (1)

b) Which gas is the main cause of acid rain? (1)

c) How is deforestation affecting global warming. Explain your answer. (2)

d) Name one thing we could do to reduce the amount of acid rain. (1)

9 The graph shows how adding sewage to a river affected the amount of oxygen in the water.

a) What happened to the oxygen concentration when the sewage was added? (1)

b) Explain why this happened. (1)

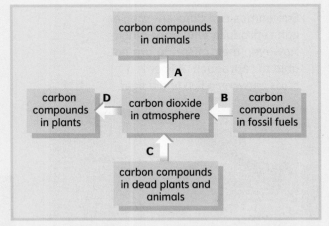

c) Why did the oxygen concentration go back to normal further down the river? (2)

10 The diagram shows part of the carbon cycle.

a) Match up each of the words below with the correct letter A to D on the diagram.

  i) decomposition   **iii)** combustion

  ii) respiration   **iv)** photosynthesis. (4)

b) Why is it very important that plants and animals decompose once they have died? (1)

Differences

Why are we all different?

All of us are different from each other. The most obvious differences are in what we look like but there are many other examples. For instance, different people enjoy doing different things and believe in different things. Despite these differences, we are all human beings.

 1 List three ways in which each of us is different.

What we look like and what we do are called our **characteristics**. Differences in characteristics are known as **variations**. Human characteristics vary from person to person.

 2 a) Write down a characteristic that is the same in all humans.
b) How does this characteristic vary from person to person?

Sometimes two different species can reproduce with each other. However, their offspring are not able to reproduce. A liger is a cross between a lion and a tiger. **B**

A *Despite our differences we all belong to the same species Homo sapiens.*

We all belong to the same **species**. A species is a group of organisms that can reproduce with one another to produce **offspring** that will also be able to reproduce. Between members of different species the characteristics vary a lot. Between members of the same species the characteristics vary a little.

3 Look at photographs C and D.

a) Name two characteristics that are different between aardvarks and hyenas.
b) Hyenas do not all have identical characteristics. Chose one characteristic of hyenas and describe how it varies from hyena to hyena.

An aardvark. **C**

D *Hyenas.*

4 What is a species?

Inherited variation

Offspring have similar characteristics to their **parents**. We all have charcteristics like hair on our heads because we are all human. However, any variation in these characteristics (e.g. hair colour) comes from our parents. We all get some characteristics from our mothers and some from our fathers. We say that we **inherit** these characteristics. Since we inherit a mixture of characteristics we look slightly different to our parents. This is called **inherited variation**.

Environmental variation

Variation can also be caused by the surroundings (environment). For example, a plant may not grow as tall as another plant of the same species if it gets less light. The environment causes many differences between humans. These include things like having a broken leg, having a cold, and even the clothes we decide to wear. Differences caused by the surroundings are known as **environmental variation**.

5 a) Young plants and animals have similar characteristics to their parents. What will the organisms in photographs E and F grow into?

E

F

b) Why do young plants and animals look similar to their parents?
c) What variation is there between the animals in picture E?

6 List two of your characteristics caused by:

a) what you inherited.
b) your surroundings.

7 How tall you grow is caused by characteristics that you inherited and the food that you eat (your environment). Name one other characteristic caused by a mixture of what you inherited and your surroundings.

8 Look at the picture of the liger.

a) Name one characteristic it has inherited from the lion.
b) Name one characteristic it has inherited from the tiger.
c) How can we be sure that lions and tigers are different species?

Summary

A _____ is a set of organisms that can produce _____ that can also reproduce. The features of an organism are called its _____. The differences in these features are known as _____. The differences may be caused by the _____ of an organism or the characteristics it _____ from its _____.

characteristics   environment   inherits
offspring   parents   species   variation

47

Genes

Where is the information for inherited variation found?

Forensic scientists are people who examine crime scenes. If they find some blood or skin they can get a substance called DNA out of it. Most of the cells in our bodies contain DNA and everybody's DNA is slightly different. DNA from a crime scene can be compared with DNA from the suspects and the scientists can work out if any of the suspects had been there.

P It is quite easy to get DNA out of some fruits. You need to grind up the fruit. Then add a solution containing 100 cm³ of water, 10 cm³ of washing-up liquid and 3 g of salt. Warm up the mixture for 15 minutes and then get rid of all the solid bits of the fruit. Next you need to pour a layer of ice cold ethanol on top of the juice. DNA should form between the two layers. Write out a more detailed plan of how you would do this and what equipment you would use.

A *Forensic scientists at work trying to solve a mystery.*

1 Skin cells fall off our bodies the whole time. Forensic scientists wear white body suits and gloves. Explain why.

There are three main parts of an animal cell: the cell membrane, the cytoplasm and the nucleus. Inside the nucleus there are long strands of DNA. These are called **chromosomes**.

2 a) Draw an animal cell. Label the cell membrane, cytoplasm and nucleus.
b) In which part of the cell are chromosomes found?
c) What are chromosomes made from?

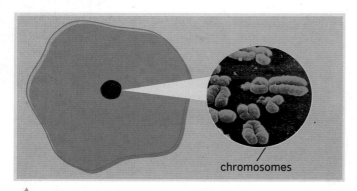

chromosomes

B *The chromosomes in this picture are magnified × 100 000.*

The nucleus of almost every human cell contains 23 different sorts of chromosomes and there are usually two copies of each sort. These are shown in photograph C.

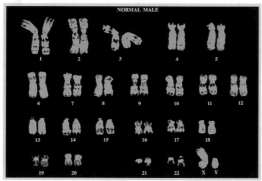

NORMAL MALE

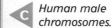

C *Human male chromosomes.*

3 How many chromosomes *in total* are usually found in the nucleus of a human cell?

Chromosomes are made up of many smaller sections called **genes**. Each chromosome carries a large number of genes and each gene does a particular job. Many genes control what we look like (our characteristics) and these include everything from how tall we grow, to the colour of our eyes and the shapes of our faces. Genes are what cause inherited variation.

! There are about 31 000 different sorts of genes in humans.

You can think of chromosomes as a set of books. Each book (chromosome) contains chapters of instructions (genes). All the books together contain all the instructions needed to produce a human being. Each of us inherits a slightly different set of instructions (different genes) and so we all look slightly different.

4 a) Where are genes found?
b) What do genes do?

We can't really see genes but, using special dyes, we can stain them to make them show up. Photograph F shows some chromosomes which have been stained to show two sorts of genes.

D Part of a chromosome showing its sections (genes).

This book contains the instructions for eye colour, height and nose shape

E

F

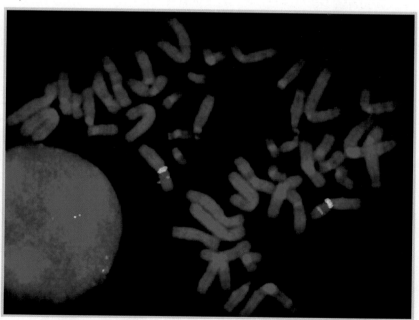

Summary

The nucleus of most cells contains strands called _____. These are made from a substance called _____. Each chromosome is made up of many _____ and these control our _____. Genes cause _____ _____.

characteristics
chromosomes   DNA
genes   inherited variation

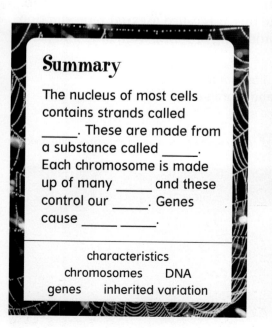

5 How do genes allow us to inherit characteristics which vary?

6 Look at photograph F. Why do you think that a total of four genes have been stained with the dye?

Reproduction in animals

What are sexual and asexual reproduction?

In the film 'Multiplicity', Doug Kinney finds that he has too much to do. He decides to get copies of himself to help him out. All of the copies have exactly the same chromosomes carrying the same genes and so have the same inherited characteristics. Exact copies like this are called **clones**.

?

1 What is a clone?

2 If you could make a clone of yourself, what colour eyes would the clone have?

3 Look at photograph A. Write down one example of *environmental* variation you can see between the four clones.

A *The four clones of Doug Kinney (all played by Michael Keaton).*

Human adults are difficult to clone, but many of the cells in your body often make exact copies of themselves – that is how you grow and replace damaged cells. A cell in your body makes a copy of all the chromosomes it contains and then **divides** into two. This is called **cell division**.

?

4 How many chromosomes does a human body cell need to copy before it can divide?

Single-celled organisms, like bacteria and amoebas, reproduce in the same way. When a whole organism reproduces like this, it is called **asexual reproduction**. This means 'producing offspring from only one parent'.

?

5 Draw a diagram to show how an amoeba reproduces.

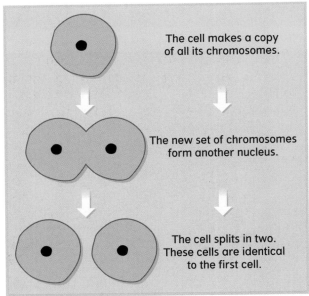

The cell makes a copy of all its chromosomes.

The new set of chromosomes form another nucleus.

The cell splits in two. These cells are identical to the first cell.

B

A bacterium dividing. **C**

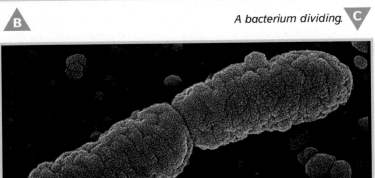

D *An amoeba (pronounced 'am-**mee**-ba') dividing.*

Some insects can also reproduce asexually. In the spring, aphids reproduce asexually. The eggs of a female aphid simply grow into new aphids – there is no need for a male aphid!

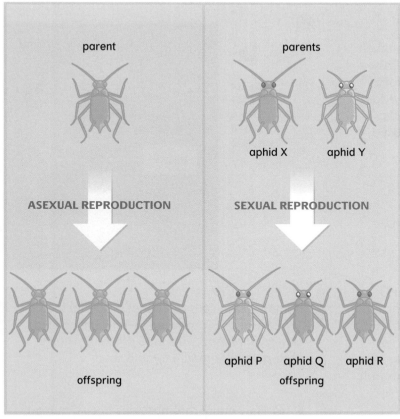

 E *Aphids can reproduce asexually.*

Aphids can also reproduce sexually. **F**

? **6** When aphids reproduce asexually, what do the offspring look like compared to the parent?

! A type of fly, called the cecidomyian gall midge, can also reproduce asexually. However, the offspring grow inside the mother and eat her alive!

In the autumn, aphids reproduce using **sexual reproduction**. A male and a female mate. The fertilised eggs produced have a mixture of chromosomes, some from each parent. Since they have a mixture of chromosomes, the offspring will also get a mixture of genes and so have a set of characteristics that is different from each parent.

? **7** When aphids reproduce *sexually*, what do the offspring look like compared to the parents?

Asexual reproduction is faster than sexual reproduction because the organisms do not need to find a mate. However, asexual reproduction does not produce variation, whereas sexual reproduction does.

? **8** Copy and complete this table to compare sexual and asexual reproduction.

Type of reproduction	Speed	Number of parents	Variation produced
Sexual			
Asexual			

9 Look at Picture F.

a) Name one characteristic that each aphid (P, Q and R) has inherited from aphid X.

b) Name one characteristic that each aphid (P, Q and R) has inherited from aphid Y.

Summary

Body cells _____ in two so that you can grow and replace worn out _____. Single-celled organisms can make copies of themselves like this. When a whole organism makes an exact copy of itself, the copy is called a _____. This method of reproduction is called _____ reproduction. _____ reproduction needs two _____. Asexual reproduction is _____ than sexual reproduction but sexual reproduction produces _____.

asexual   cells   clone   divide   faster   parents   sexual   variation

Sexual reproduction in animals

How do gametes join to make baby boys and girls?

In most species, after sexual reproduction has taken place, the females give birth to the offspring. In sea-horses, the males give birth! The female sea-horse places **egg cells** into a pouch in the male. He adds **sperm cells** which **fuse** (join) with the egg cells. This process is called **fertilisation**. Each **fertilised egg cell** develops into a baby sea-horse.

 A

Each of these baby sea-horses is about 1 cm long.

pouch

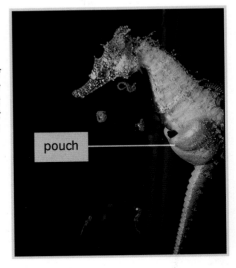

1 Copy and complete these sentences.

   a) When a sperm cell and an _____ _____ join they are said to _____.

   b) This joining is called _____.

Sperm cells and egg cells are known as **gametes** and carry chromosomes from parents to offspring. Unlike other **body cells**, gametes only have half the normal number of chromosomes. This is so that when they fuse, the fertilised egg cell contains the right number of chromosomes (and not double the number).

Human sperm cells are about 0.06 mm long. The sperm cells produced by a fruit fly called *Drosophila bifurca* are 6.35 cm long. The fly itself is smaller than a tomato seed!

2 a) How many chromosomes does a human gamete contain?

   b) How many chromosomes *in total* does a *fertilised* egg cell contain?

In humans, fertilisation occurs inside the woman. The fertilised egg cell contains a mixture of chromosomes (23 from each gamete). It will therefore have a mixture of genes and so it will grow into a baby with a set of characteristics that is different to each parent.

D *This child has inherited a set of characteristics that makes her different to each of her parents.*

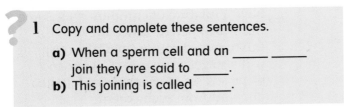

the sperm cell contains 1 set of chromosomes (23)

the egg cells contains 1 set of chromosomes (23)

the gametes fuse in fertilisation

the fertilised egg cell contains the normal number of chromosomes (2 sets. 23 pairs)

B

A sperm cell fusing with an egg cell. **C**

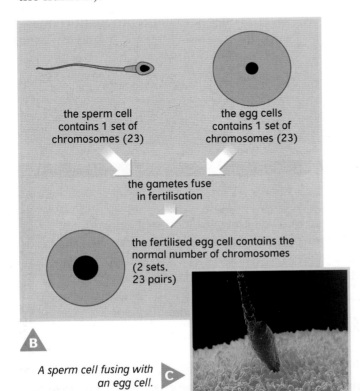

3 Look at photograph D.
  a) Which parent has the child inherited her eye colour from?
  b) Write down one other inherited variation of the child.
  c) Which parent has this inherited variation come from?

4 a) Look at photograph E. Are these chromosomes from a man or a woman?
  b) Look back at photograph C on Page 48. Are these chromosomes from a man or a woman?

One pair of chromosomes in the fertilised egg cell controls whether it will grow into a boy or a girl. These are called **sex chromosomes**. There are two types. One type looks like an X and the other looks like a Y. Women have two X sex chromosomes and men have one X and one Y. Women are described as being XX and men as XY.

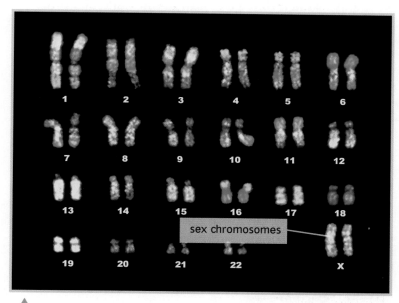

E Chromosome pairs found in a female body cell.

Half of a man's sperm cells contain an X sex chromosome, and the other half contain a Y sex chromosome. All egg cells contain an X sex chromosome. So, whether a baby is a boy or a girl depends only on the sperm cell.

5 Are your sex chromosomes XX or XY?

6 Look at diagram F. Draw a similar diagram to show how the gametes could produce a baby boy.

F

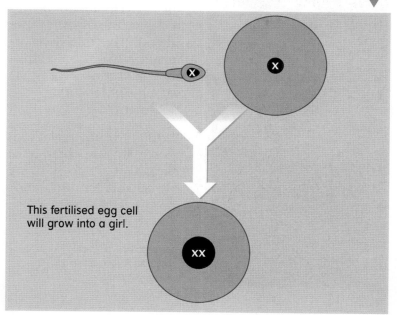

This fertilised egg cell will grow into a girl.

Summary

Sperm cells and egg cells are called _____. They only contain one _____ of chromosomes. In fertilisation, a sperm cell and an _____ cell _____ (join) together and form a _____ egg cell, which grows into a baby. The sex of the baby is controlled by the _____ _____. Men have _____ sex chromosomes and women have _____.

| egg | fertilised | fuse | gametes |
| set | sex chromosomes | XX | XY |

7 Name one way in which an egg cell is different from a normal body cell.

8 Explain why roughly 50% of children born are girls.

Fertility

How can a woman control her fertility?

Normally, women only give birth to one child at a time. Only once have eight *living* babies (octuplets) ever been born together. One died a week later, but the others are still alive. Their mother, Nkem Chukwu, became pregnant with so many babies as a result of **fertility treatment**.

 1 Why did Nkem Chukwu have so many children?

Each month a woman releases an egg cell from an **ovary**. This process is controlled by **hormones**. These are substances which act like 'chemical messengers', travelling in the blood and 'telling' certain cells to do something.

 2 What are hormones?

 An egg cell being released from an ovary. Magnification × 2130.

A

The hormones that control the release of egg cells are produced by the **pituitary gland**. If a woman is finding it difficult to become pregnant it may be because the egg cells are not being released. To help this process she can have injections of **fertility drugs** containing these hormones. This is an example of **fertility treatment**.

Fertility treatment can cause more than one egg to be released at a time, so many egg cells are fertilised, and many babies start to grow.

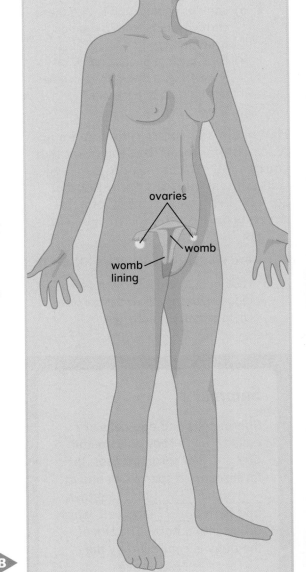

B

 3 What is injected during fertility treatment?

4 Where is the pituitary gland?

Nearly 10 000 sets of twins are born naturally in the UK each year. Non-identical twins are the result of two egg cells being released at the same time. Identical twins are the result of a fertilised egg cell dividing, and the two new cells separating. Each cell grows into a baby.

While an egg cell is getting ready to be released, the lining of the womb gets thicker. The thick womb lining contains many blood vessels to supply a growing baby with food and oxygen. The hormones that cause this thickening are produced by the ovaries. If an egg cell is not fertilised, the hormones stop being produced and the womb lining breaks apart. This is called a **period**. The cycle starts again with another egg cell getting ready to be released.

5 **a)** What do the hormones released by the pituitary gland do?
b) What do the hormones released by the ovaries do?

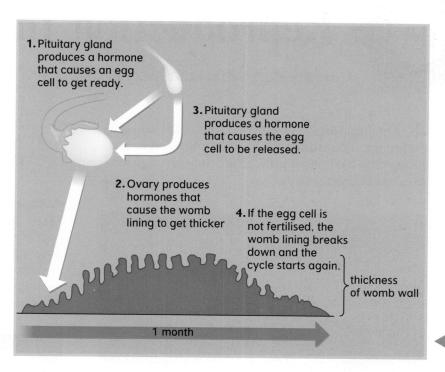

1. Pituitary gland produces a hormone that causes an egg cell to get ready.

3. Pituitary gland produces a hormone that causes the egg cell to be released.

2. Ovary produces hormones that cause the womb lining to get thicker

4. If the egg cell is not fertilised, the womb lining breaks down and the cycle starts again.

thickness of womb wall

1 month

C

Contraception is used to prevent pregnancies. Some contraceptives come as pills which a woman can swallow. The pills contain hormones which stop egg cells being released. This is called **oral** (by mouth) **contraception**.

Oral contraception works about 99% of the time. However, there can sometimes be problems. The pills:

- can cause headaches or sickness
- can (very rarely) cause heart problems
- will not work if a woman forgets to take them – most types need to be taken at the same time every day.

6 What do oral contraceptives do?

7 What might happen if a woman forgets to take them?

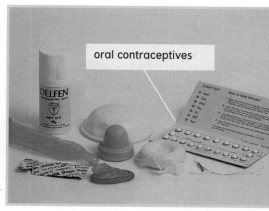

oral contraceptives

Different methods of contraception. D

8 Copy and complete this table.

Use of hormones	Benefits	Problems
Fertility treatment		
Oral contraception		

9 Identical twins always look very similar but non-identical twins often look very different. Explain why.

Summary

Substances called _____ act like 'chemical messengers'. A hormone from the _____ _____ causes an egg cell to be released from an _____. Hormones from the _____ cause the _____ lining to get thicker. _____ drugs contain hormones and cause more egg cells to be released. _____ _____ contain other hormones and stop egg cells being released.

fertility   hormones   oral contraceptives
ovary   pituitary gland   womb

Reproduction in plants

How can we make clones of plants?

The Quaking Aspen trees in picture A are all really one plant. The trunks are joined by underground roots. One tree has produced all the others using **asexual reproduction**.

A

1 A leaf is cut off a plant.

2 Rooting powder contains a plant hormone which helps new roots to grow.

3 The plastic bag helps to keep the conditions around the leaf damp, otherwise it might dry up.

4 After a few weeks, new roots have grown. The leaf can now get water from the soil and the plastic bag is not needed any more. After a couple of months a new plant has grown.

 1 What is asexual reproduction?
(*Hint: You may need to look back to page 50.*)

Asexual reproduction in plants

Many plants use asexual reproduction to make copies of themselves so that they can spread over a large area very quickly. Strawberry plants are another example. A stem called a 'runner' grows out of the parent plant. New plants grow at points along the runner.

runner

B *A strawberry plant can reproduce asexually using runners.*

The new strawberry plants contain exactly the same genes as the parent plant. They are **clones**. Since clones of any organism contain identical genes, they are said to be **genetically identical**.

 2 What are clones?

3 Write a short piece for a magazine explaining how to grow African violets from cuttings. Your article should contain:

a) step by step instructions
b) an explanation of why each step is necessary.

Gardeners can make clones of plants by cutting off parts of a plant and growing new plants from them. This is called taking **cuttings**. Picture C shows how new plants are grown from African violet plants.

C

! Parts of water hyacinth plants break off and grow into new plants. In a single summer, up to 60 000 clones can be produced from one plant. It is a serious pest because it blocks up rivers.

D

E Growing plants from cuttings.

P How would you find out if it is only leaves that can be used for cuttings or whether other parts of plants will work just as well?

Plant growers often grow plants from cuttings rather than seeds because it is cheaper and quicker.

? **4 a)** Why do plant growers grow new plants from cuttings?

b) If a plant grower grows hundreds of plants from cuttings it is too fiddly to put plastic bags over each pot. How do you think a plant grower would keep the atmosphere damp.

Sexual reproduction in plants

Many plants have flowers. These produce male gametes (pollen grains) and female gametes (egg cells). Pollen grains are carried from one flower to another by insects or the wind. The pollen grains can then fuse with the egg cells and seeds are produced. The seeds grow into new plants.

Summary

New plants can be grown from parts of plants. This is called taking _____. This is an example of _____ reproduction since all the new plants will be _____ _____ to the parent plant. The new plants are _____. Taking cuttings is _____ and _____ but the cuttings need to be grown in a _____ atmosphere until the new roots have grown.

asexual   cheap   clones
    cuttings   damp
genetically identical   quick

? **5 a)** Which plants will have inherited variation, those grown from seeds or those grown from cuttings?
b) Explain your answer to part **a**.

6 Why do you think strawberry plants reproduce both sexually and asexually?

7 Find out about another method of asexual reproduction in plants. State where you get your information from.

The discovery of genes

How was the idea of genes developed?

The *idea* of genes was first put forward by an Austrian Monk in 1865. His name was Gregor Mendel and he came up with his theory by looking at pea plants. Between 1856 and 1863 he grew nearly 30 000 pea plants in the monastery garden!

Mendel looked at different characteristics of the pea plants, one of which was their height. Some pea plants were naturally tall and some were naturally short.

He bred (crossed) these plants together, grew the seeds and looked at the characteristics of the new plants.

A *Gregor Mendel (1822–1884).*

1 a) Who first put forward the idea of genes?
b) What plant did he use in his investigations?

C *One of Mendel's crossing experiments.*

B *Some pea plants are naturally tall and others naturally short.*

2 a) What is meant by 'crossing' plants?
b) Does crossing involve sexual or asexual reproduction?

At the time, scientists thought that offspring got a 'blend' of characteristics from the parents. If this theory was right, then Mendel should have got medium height pea plants by crossing a tall plant with a short one. He didn't. He only got tall plants.

Mendel wondered where the 'shortness' characteristic had gone and whether he could get it back. So he crossed two of the new tall plants.

Mendel's next crossing experiment. **D**

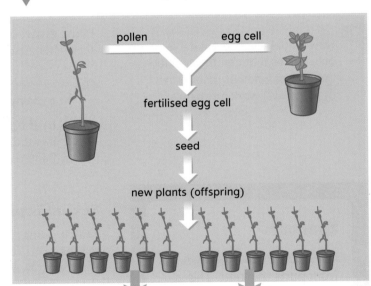

pollen   egg cell

fertilised egg cell

seed

new plants (offspring)

3 Look at diagram D.

    a) Did Mendel manage to get the short characteristic back again?

    b) What percentage of the pea plants were short?

Mendel decided that 'factors', each carrying the information for a certain characteristic, were passed from parents to offspring. He said that these 'factors' could not be changed and so the pea plants could either be tall or short depending on the 'factor' that they inherited. Pea plants could not have medium heights.

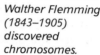

Walther Flemming (1843–1905) discovered chromosomes. **E**

4 **a)** What did Mendel's 'factors' do?

    b) What do we call his 'factors' today?

F *Wilhelm Johanssen (1857–1927) developed Mendel's ideas and invented the word 'gene'.*

In Mendel's day, chromosomes had not been discovered and his work was ignored. Scientists could not understand how 'factors' could explain the large variation of some characteristics (like height in humans). Nor could they see how to use Mendel's theory to explain Darwin's theory of evolution (see page 78). They argued that if the factors could not change, then a species could not change (evolve) into other species over thousands of years.

Chromosomes were discovered in the 1880s and once they had been studied in more detail, scientists began to see how Mendel's 'factors' could work. By the early 1900s scientists were beginning to accept Mendel's ideas and the word **gene** was invented in 1909.

G *James Watson (1928–) and Francis Crick (1916–) discovered the structure of DNA in 1953.*

Summary

Scientists used to think that characteristics _____ together in offspring. Gregor _____ did not agree and suggested that the offspring _____ either one characteristic or another. His _____ was not believed because scientists could not see how Mendel's _____ could cause so much variation. Nor could they see how different species could _____. Today we know that Mendel was right and his 'factors' are called _____.

    blended   evolve   factors   genes
        Mendel   inherited   theory

5 Write down one reason why Mendel's theory was ignored.

6 What was Mendel's evidence that characteristics did not 'blend'?

7 There is a lot of variation in human height. What else, apart from genes, controls how tall you grow?

8 **a)** List the names of the scientists mentioned on these two pages and write down a brief sentence about what each one did.

    b) Find out about one other scientist and his or her work on the discovery of genes.

Alleles

What are dominant and recessive alleles?

As a result of all his experiments, Mendel thought that the 'factors' controlling characteristics came in pairs. We now know that chromosomes come in pairs. Since each chromosome in a pair contains the same genes, there must be two genes for each characteristic.

 1 Explain why normal body cells in organisms contain two genes for each characteristic.

Another characteristic of pea plants that has been used in the study of genes is the colour of the flowers. Pea plants have either red or white flowers. If red-flowered plants are bred with white-flowered plants all the offspring have red flowers; no white or pink or anything else. This is explained by the idea that some genes for the same characteristic (e.g. flower colour) contain slightly different instructions (e.g. white and red). Different versions of the same gene are called **alleles** (pronounced '*a-leels*').

 B *Genes for the same characteristic contain slightly different instructions.*

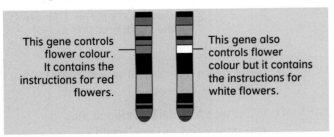

This gene controls flower colour. It contains the instructions for red flowers.

This gene also controls flower colour but it contains the instructions for white flowers.

Gametes contain only one of each type of chromosome. So each gamete will contain only one allele for flower colour.

 2 What are alleles?

3 **a)** What are the gametes produced by humans called?

b) What are the gametes produced by plants called?

c) Explain why pea plant gametes only have one type of allele for flower colour.

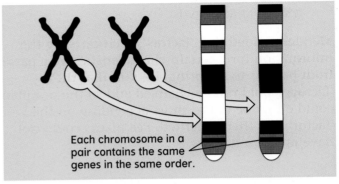

Each chromosome in a pair contains the same genes in the same order.

A *Most cells have two chromosomes of the same type, so there are two copies of each gene.* C

The flower colour alleles are both the same. They contain the instructions for red flowers.

The flower colour alleles are both the same. They contain the instructions for white flowers.

All the pollen grains (male gametes) will get one copy of the red flower colour allele.

All the egg cells (female gametes) will get one copy of the white flower colour allele.

All the offspring have both alleles. However, all the flowers are red. This is because red is the dominant allele.

When the gametes fuse, the fertilised egg cell gets two alleles for flower colour. Every cell in the new plant will therefore have both alleles. In diagram C, the offspring has one allele for white flowers and one for red flowers. The red flower allele is said to be **dominant**. It does not allow the white flower allele to work and so all the plants have red flowers. The white flower allele is said to be **recessive**.

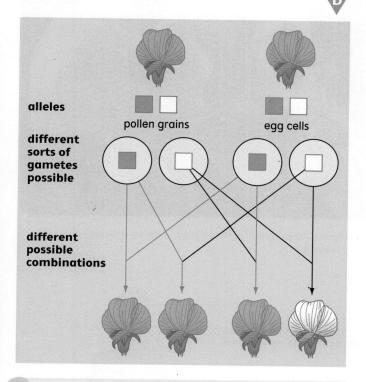

D

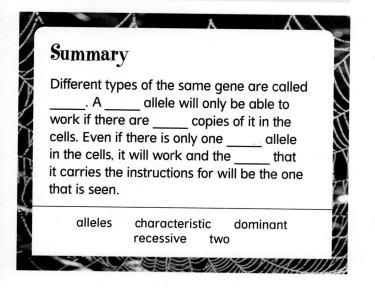

5 In what circumstances will the characteristics of a recessive allele be seen?

Summary

Different types of the same gene are called _____. A _____ allele will only be able to work if there are _____ copies of it in the cells. Even if there is only one _____ allele in the cells, it will work and the _____ that it carries the instructions for will be the one that is seen.

alleles	characteristic	dominant
	recessive two	

4 Look back at page 58. There are two alleles for pea plant height. One is for tall plants and the other is for short plants.

a) Which allele is dominant?
b) Which allele is recessive?

Look at diagram D. If we take two of the plants which contain the two different alleles and cross them, we will get some plants with white flowers again.

The characteristics from recessive alleles are only seen if there are two copies of the recessive allele. The characteristics from dominant alleles are seen even if there is only one copy.

The photographs show a leopard and a black panther. They are in fact the same species. The black panther has two recessive alleles that make its fur black rather than spotted.

E

F

6 Look at the photographs of the leopard and panther. There are two alleles, one for spotted fur and one for black fur.

a) Which is the dominant allele?
b) What possible combinations of alleles could the leopard have?

7 Draw a diagram, like diagram D, to show how Mendel got some short plants by crossing two tall ones. You may need to look back at page 58.

Inherited diseases

What are inherited diseases?

Some diseases that affect nerves cause the body to shake or jerk. From ancient times, until about 250 years ago, it was thought that people with these diseases were possessed by a demon. To try to cure the disease, holes were often cut into people's skulls, to try to release the demon!

 1 Name one symptom that might be caused by a nerve disease.

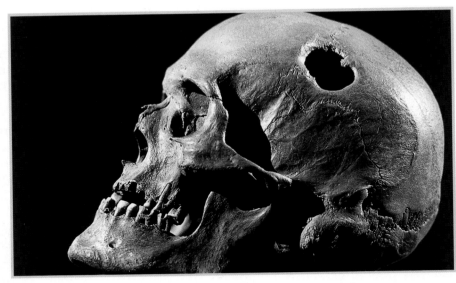

A The skull of someone who probably suffered from a nerve disease. This skull is 2500 years old.

Huntington's disease

We now know much more about what causes diseases. **Huntington's disease** is caused by genes and is an example of a **genetic** or **inherited disease**. You can only get inherited diseases if your cells contain the alleles that cause them. You can't catch them.

 2 What is an allele?

3 a) What is an inherited disease?
b) Give one example.

Huntington's disease only affects people when they are about 40 years old. At this time nerves begin to be destroyed and the person's body starts to jerk uncontrollably.

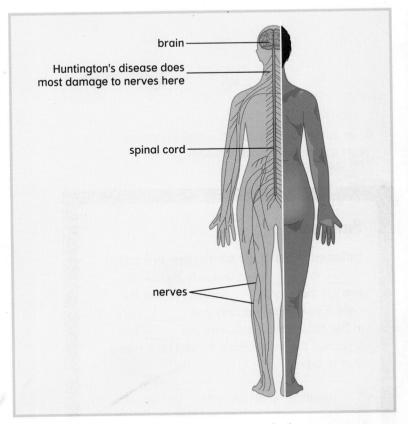

brain

Huntington's disease does most damage to nerves here

spinal cord

nerves

B The parts of the nervous system. The nerves in the nervous system are damaged by Huntington's disease.

4 a) What is meant by the 'nervous system'?
b) Where are most nerves damaged by Huntington's disease?

A parent with Huntington's disease may pass it onto his or her children. It is a dominant allele and so even if a child only gets one copy of the allele, they will still get the disease. There is no cure for Huntington's disease.

5 What is a dominant allele?

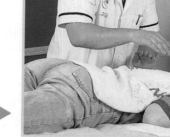

Treatment for cystic fibrosis. The person is hit gently on the back to help get rid of the mucus.

C ▷

Cystic fibrosis

This is an inherited disease that causes faulty cell membranes. Cells in the lungs produce too much of a sticky substance called mucus. This collects in the lungs and needs to be removed by special treatment (photograph C). There is no cure.

6 People with cystic fibrosis often have trouble breathing. Why do you think this is?

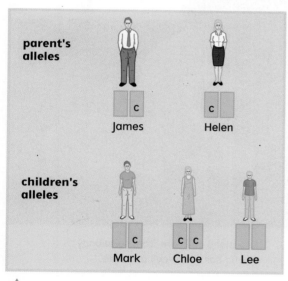

parent's alleles

James · Helen

children's alleles

Mark · Chloe · Lee

D

Cystic fibrosis is caused by a recessive allele. People who have one copy of this allele are called **carriers**. They do not have the disease but they can pass the allele on to their children. If both parents have this recessive allele there is a chance that some of their children may get two copies of the allele. If this happens, a child will have cystic fibrosis.

7 Diagram D shows some pairs of alleles in a family. The small letter 'c' in a box shows the allele which causes cystic fibrosis. A blank box shows a normal allele.

a) Explain why neither parent has cystic fibrosis.
b) Which of their children have cystic fibrosis?
c) Which of their children are carriers of the disease?

8 Why can Huntington's disease be passed on by only one parent?

9 Draw diagrams, like the one in diagram D on page 61, to show why:

a) about 50% of children born to someone suffering from Huntington's disease get the disease.

b) about 25% of children born to a couple who are both carriers of cystic fibrosis get the disease.

Summary

Huntington's disease affects the _____ _____. It is caused by a _____ allele and so only needs one _____ to pass it on. _____ _____ is a disease that affects the cell _____. As it is caused by a recessive _____ it needs two parents who have the allele to pass it on to their children. Diseases caused by alleles are called _____ diseases.

| allele | cystic fibrosis | dominant | inherited |
| membranes | nervous system | parent | |

Sickle-cell anaemia

Why are sickle-cell anaemia alleles sometimes useful?

Some alleles that cause inherited diseases can actually help people. An example is the allele that causes **sickle-cell anaemia**. This disease causes faulty haemoglobin to be made. Haemoglobin is the substance found in red blood cells that allows them to carry oxygen. The faulty haemoglobin has two effects on red blood cells:

- it makes them less able to carry oxygen
- it makes them 'sickle-shaped'.

A

A sickle.

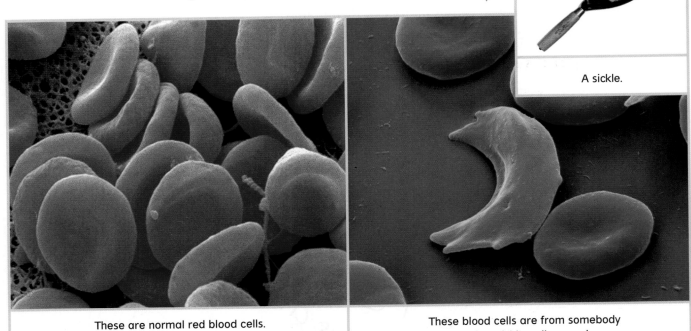

These are normal red blood cells.

These blood cells are from somebody who has sickle-cell anaemia.

1 a) What does haemoglobin do?
  b) What is the name of the disease that causes faulty haemoglobin?
  c) How do you think the disease got the first part of its name?

A person needs two copies of the sickle-cell anaemia allele to get the disease. People with the disease suffer from **anaemia**. This is a condition when someone is always tired and short of breath. Sickle-cell anaemia is a very serious form of anaemia and often kills people. It is also very painful since the red blood cells stick together and get stuck in the blood vessels.

2 Look at diagram B. The boxes show the alleles of three different people. The small letter 's' in a box shows an allele that causes sickle-cell anaemia. The blank box shows a normal allele.

  a) Who has sickle-cell anaemia?
  b) Who is a carrier for sickle-cell anaemia?
  c) Who could not pass the sickle-cell anaemia allele onto his/her children?
  d) Who would always pass one copy of the sickle-cell allele onto his/her children?

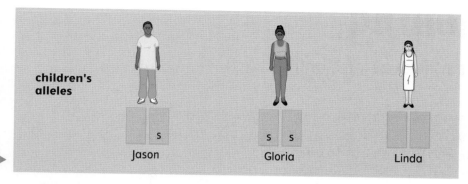

children's alleles

Jason   Gloria   Linda

People who have one copy of the sickle-cell anaemia allele are carriers. Carriers only get a mild form of sickle-cell anaemia. However, carriers are less likely to get **malaria**, a very serious disease caused by a microbe which attacks red blood cells. Malaria often kills people. Being a carrier for sickle-cell anaemia can be an advantage if you live in an area where there is malaria.

Scientists can stop babies being born with some genetic diseases. Eggs are taken from a woman, fertilised with sperm, and allowed to develop into balls of eight cells (embryos). One cell is removed from each embryo and its genes are examined. Embryos that are found to be clear of alleles that cause genetic diseases are placed into the womb of the mother to develop into babies.

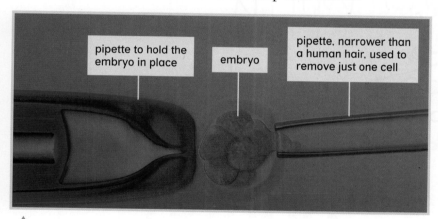

pipette to hold the embryo in place

embryo

pipette, narrower than a human hair, used to remove just one cell

D One cell from each embryo is removed and its genes are examined.

C Areas where malaria is found are coloured pink.

! Malaria kills between 1.5 and 2.7 million people every year.

? **3** Look at map C.

   a) Name one area of the world where malaria is common.

   b) Imagine you live in this part of the world. Why might it be an advantage to be a carrier of sickle-cell anaemia?

4 Why do you think that people with sickle-cell anaemia feel short of breath?

5 Name one disease (other than sickle-cell anaemia) that kills many young people in Central Africa.

6 a) Explain how scientists can find out if an embryo contains alleles for a genetic disease.

   b) Write down three disease alleles that they might look for.

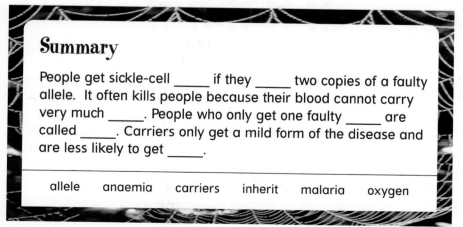

Summary

People get sickle-cell _____ if they _____ two copies of a faulty allele. It often kills people because their blood cannot carry very much _____. People who only get one faulty _____ are called _____. Carriers only get a mild form of the disease and are less likely to get _____.

allele   anaemia   carriers   inherit   malaria   oxygen

More cloning

How do farmers make use of cloning?

An individual cell can be removed from an embryo so that doctors can find out what alleles it carries. The rest of the embryo will grow and develop normally. This technique can also be used to make clones (exact copies) of animals. The cells in an animal embryo are split apart and each one is allowed to develop into a new embryo. The new embryos will all be identical and are put into the wombs of 'foster' animals. This technique is called **embryo transplanting** or **embryo splitting**.

?
1 Embryos are often split when they contain eight cells. How many new cloned embryos could be made from an embryo like this?

2 Explain why all the new embryos made by embryo transplanting are identical.

!
A British doctor, Paul Rainsbury, has proposed that human embryos should be split to create clones. One embryo would be frozen and used as a backup in case the first child dies.

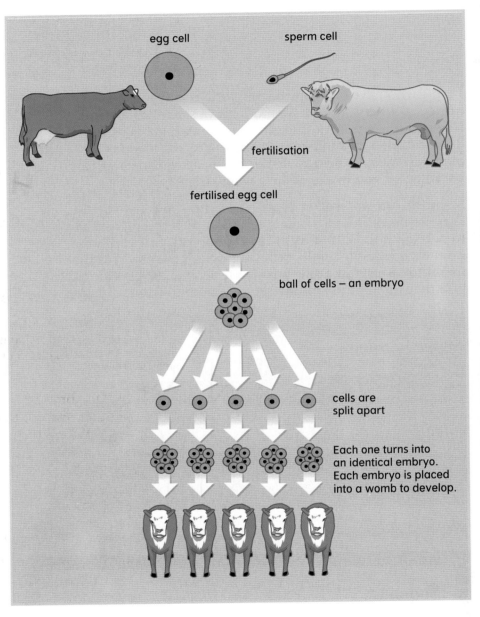

egg cell   sperm cell

fertilisation

fertilised egg cell

ball of cells – an embryo

cells are split apart

Each one turns into an identical embryo. Each embryo is placed into a womb to develop.

Embryo transplanting is used in farming since a large number of animals can be produced quickly. A farmer may want to breed from a cow that produces a lot of milk, in order to get more cows that also produce a lot of milk. Many more good milk-producing cows can be produced using embryo transplanting.

? 3 Why do farmers use embryo transplanting?

Farmers also use cloned plants. Producing cloned plants by taking cuttings does not work very well on some plants and the small cuttings are at risk from diseases. **Tissue culture** is a way of producing thousands of cloned plants quickly, without them getting diseases.

A small piece of a plant (even a single cell) is taken and placed in a special solution or a jelly. The cells grow into an embryo which grows into a new plant. Everything is kept very clean (**sterile**) so that the plants do not get diseases.

B *These plants were grown from single cells using tissue culture.*

C *In Malaysia, one oil palm which produced a lot of oil was used to make thousands of clones.*

?

6 What characteristic do all the cloned oil palms have?

7 Using cloned plants may cause problems. Explain why.

8 **a)** A farmer wants to breed from a good meat producing pig. Why will the farmer not necessarily get good meat producing pigs by embryo transplanting.
   b) Find out about 'nuclear transfer'.

P Small pieces of cauliflower can be cloned using tissue culture. How do you think this could be done using this equipment?

D

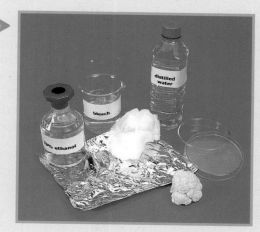

● How would you stop microbes growing in the jelly and ruining the experiment?

?

4 List two disadvantages of taking cuttings.

5 Which method do you think will produce the most clones, tissue culture or taking cuttings? Explain your reasoning.

One problem of using so many clones is that a disease might kill them all. If they were all grown from seed, there would be more variety of characteristics and so some of them might not get the disease.

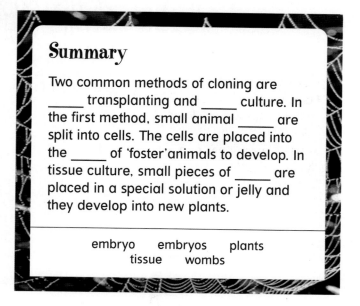

Summary

Two common methods of cloning are _____ transplanting and _____ culture. In the first method, small animal _____ are split into cells. The cells are placed into the _____ of 'foster' animals to develop. In tissue culture, small pieces of _____ are placed in a special solution or jelly and they develop into new plants.

embryo   embryos   plants
tissue   wombs

67

Genetic engineering

How is genetic engineering done?

The film Gattaca is set in 'the not too distant future'. In the film, scientists use **genetic engineering** to allow parents to choose what characteristics they want their children to have. At the moment, this cannot be done on humans, although genetic engineering is widely used on many organisms.

The organisms that are most commonly used for genetic engineering are bacteria. Genetically engineered bacteria produce a wide range of different products that humans use.

A *The tomatoes used in this puree have been genetically engineered to improve their flavour and shelf-life.*

B *Products from genetically engineered bacteria*

Product	Example of a use
Enzymes	Used in biological washing powders
Antibiotics	Used to treat diseases caused by other bacteria
Insulin	Used to treat people with diabetes
Human growth hormone	Used to treat people who lack this hormone and so do not grow very tall

? 1 What are the most common genetically engineered organisms?

2 List three products made using genetically engineered organisms.

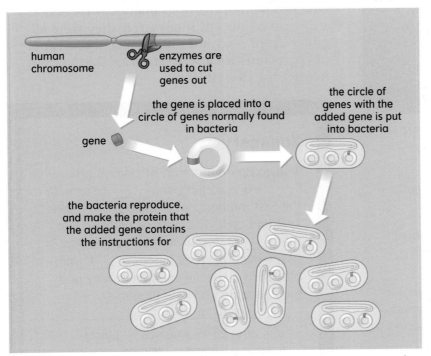

human chromosome

enzymes are used to cut genes out

the gene is placed into a circle of genes normally found in bacteria

gene

the circle of genes with the added gene is put into bacteria

the bacteria reproduce, and make the protein that the added gene contains the instructions for

Bacteria are quite easy to genetically engineer. C

A gene from an organism can be cut out of a chromosome using enzymes. The enzymes act a bit like tiny pairs of scissors. Bacteria naturally have small circles of DNA which contain genes and the new gene can be put into one of these circles. The new circle of genes is then put into bacteria which reproduce and copy the circle of DNA. The bacteria have now been genetically engineered (sometimes said to be 'genetically modified').

Genes contain instructions on how to make a protein. The genetically engineered bacteria will make the protein that the new gene carries the instructions for. The bacteria are grown in huge tanks and the useful protein is extracted. All the substances in table B are proteins made in this way.

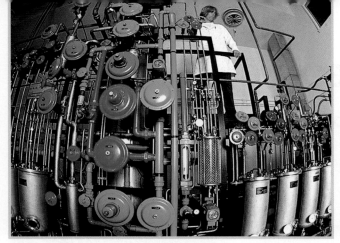

D These tanks contain genetically engineered bacteria that produce the human hormone insulin.

E This mouse has been genetically engineered with genes from a jellyfish which make it glow.

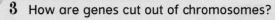

3 How are genes cut out of chromosomes?

4 What are the cut out genes put into before they are put into bacteria?

Genes can also be put into plants and animals when they are embryos. This is more difficult to do and is often done using a virus. The virus is able to put genes into chromosomes. The virus itself has to be genetically engineered to stop it causing any diseases.

Genetic engineering can be used to modify crops so that they are not attacked by pests. Salmon have been genetically engineered to make them grow faster than normal salmon. Genetic engineering can also be used to help humans. There is a genetic disease, called ADA deficiency, that stops immune systems working. People with this disease can be treated by a form of genetic engineering called gene therapy. Their white blood cells have normal alleles added to them to allow them to work properly. Photographs E and F show some other things that have been genetically engineered.

Carnations are usually pink, white or red. These ones have been genetically engineered to be purple. F

P All of the examples of genetic engineering on this page seem to be either interesting or good. However, many people are worried about genetically engineered things. Organise a debate in your class about genetic engineering. It might be about one particular example on this page or just genetic engineering as a whole. Are you for or against it?

5 What substance do genes make?
   Choose the correct answer from the box.

   | carbohydrates | fats | proteins |
   | fibre | DNA | |

6 What sort of substance is the hormone insulin? Explain your reasoning.

7 Find out why the film title 'Gattaca' only contains the letters G, A, T and C.

Summary

Putting genes from one organism into another is called _____ _____. This is most often done with _____. A gene can be 'cut out' of a chromosome using _____ and put into a circle of _____ which is then put into bacteria. Genetically modified bacteria can produce useful things like medicines and _____.

bacteria   enzymes   genes
genetic engineering   hormones

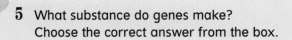

Selective breeding

How are new varieties produced without using genetic engineering?

Photograph A shows a quagga. Herds of these animals used to roam the plains of South Africa but were hunted to extinction in the 19th century. The last one died in Amsterdam Zoo on 12th August 1883.

It used to be thought that the quagga was a species. However, scientists took samples from the stuffed quagga in photograph A and looked at the genes of the animal. They discovered that it was not a species but a breed of plains zebra (photograph B).

A **breed** (or **variety**) is a group of animals or plants that look slightly different to other members of the species. For example, all dogs are the same species but there are nearly 150 different breeds.

A *A quagga.*

A plains zebra. B

?
1 Why did quaggas become extinct?
2 What is a breed?

Scientists in South Africa are now trying to recreate quaggas using **selective breeding** (sometimes called **artificial selection**). They took plains zebras from the wild that had the most characteristics in common with quaggas. They then mated these animals with each other. From the offspring, they took (or 'selected') only those which looked most like quaggas and mated them together. They hope that by doing this over and over again they will end up with animals that look like quaggas.

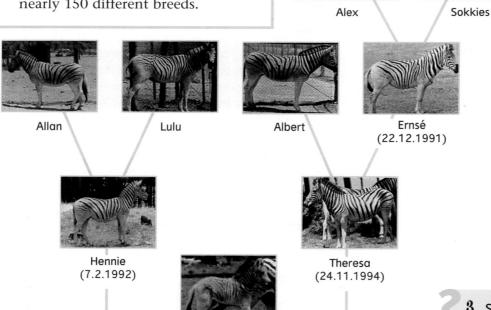

Alex Sokkies

Allan Lulu Albert Ernsé (22.12.1991)

Hennie (7.2.1992) Theresa (24.11.1994)

Etienne (14.10.1998)

C

Scientists are trying to recreate quaggas using selective breeding.

?
3 Scientists are trying to recreate the quagga. Name one characteristic that they are selecting for.

4 What is selective breeding sometimes called?

In the second century AD, the Chinese selectively bred the Pekinese dog to look like a small lion – the lion spirit of Buddha.

D

E *A mouflon sheep.*

Modern day sheep. **F**

G

People have selectively bred plants and animals for thousands of years. Photograph E shows a mouflon sheep. It has been farmed for thousands of years but it has fatty meat and is more hairy than woolly. Over a long time, farmers have 'selected' for sheep which have leaner (less fatty) meat and which have woolly fleeces, like the ones in photograph F.

5 Look at photographs E and F. Name one other characteristic that has been selected for in modern sheep.

Plants have also been selectively bred. Diagram G shows which characteristics have been selected from wild mustard plants. Plants are also selected for their flavour, how well they cope with diseases (**disease resistance**) and how much food they produce for us (the yield).

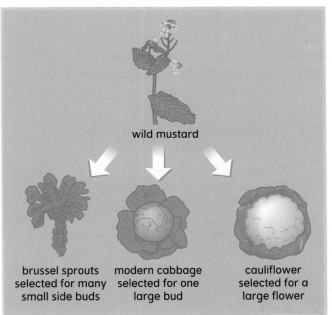

wild mustard

brussel sprouts selected for many small side buds

modern cabbage selected for one large bud

cauliflower selected for a large flower

Summary

People often choose animals or _____ with useful variations in _____ and breed from them. This is called _____ breeding (or _____ selection). Farm animals are often bred to give better _____. Plants are often bred to be less likely to get diseases (have better _____ resistance) and to produce more food for us (give a higher _____).

artificial   characteristics   disease
meat   plants   selective   yield

6 Which feature of wild cabbages has been selected for in cauliflowers?

7 Suggest two things you would selectively breed for in:

a) chickens   **b)** roses   **c)** cows.

8 Doberman Pinscher dogs have part of their tails removed at a young age. This is called 'docking'. How would you selectively breed Dobermans that have naturally short tails?

9 Imagine quaggas were still alive today. Without looking at their genes, how could you show that they were a breed of plains zebra and not a separate species? (Hint: You may need to look back to the beginning of this module.)

Agricultural problems

What are the problems of selective breeding and cloning?

In 1970, in the United States, 1 billion dollars worth of maize plants were destroyed by a fungus disease called corn leaf blight. Eighty-five per cent of all the maize plants were **clones**, which produced a good yield but were not resistant to the fungus.

 1 What sort of organism causes corn leaf blight?

Since all clones are identical, one disease will kill all of them. Planting different varieties of plants often means that some varieties will survive a disease.

 2 Copy and complete this sentence using one of the phrases in the box.

Clones are organisms that . . .

> . . . look quite like each other.
> . . . have identical genes.
> . . . are very different from each other.
> . . . are easily killed by fungus diseases.

 A *Decimation of maize plants by corn leaf blight.*

Different varieties contain different alleles. Planting only one variety every year means that other varieties are not used and can become extinct. Their alleles will be lost and some of these alleles may be useful in the future.

Selective breeding also reduces the numbers of alleles available, since only certain characteristics are chosen. If conditions change, the lost alleles are no longer available to use for future selective breeding.

 B *A Gloucester Old Spot pig.*

 3 **a)** Name two ways in which alleles can be lost from a species.
b) Why does it matter if alleles are lost from a species?

 C *A Large White pig.*

Conditions can change because of a new disease, a change in the weather or a change in what people want. Until the Second World War, many people preferred pigs that produced a lot of fat. Pig fat (lard) was used a lot for cooking and the fatty meat did not go off very quickly. Pig breeds like the Gloucester Old Spot were very popular.

Today, people use vegetable oil for cooking because it is healthier, and almost everyone has a fridge. The most common breed of pig today is the Large White, since it grows very big rapidly and has lean (non-fatty) meat.

4 a) Why were Gloucester Old Spot pigs popular in the 1930s?
  b) Why is it a rare breed now?

5 What is the most common breed of pig today?

Rare breeds of farm animals are kept on 'rare breeds farms' to stop them becoming extinct. Rare varieties of plants are stored in 'gene banks' or 'seed banks'. This preserves alleles and means that we can use old breeds again if conditions change.

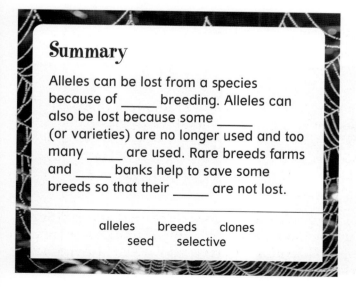

D Rare breeds of animals are kept on rare breeds farms. The photographs show a Long-horn cow and a Soay sheep.

E Plant seeds or parts of plants are stored in seed or gene banks.

Summary

Alleles can be lost from a species because of _____ breeding. Alleles can also be lost because some _____ (or varieties) are no longer used and too many _____ are used. Rare breeds farms and _____ banks help to save some breeds so that their _____ are not lost.

alleles   breeds   clones
seed   selective

! During the Second World War, Leningrad (now St Petersburg) was under siege for 900 days. Many scientists died of starvation even though their laboratories were full of seeds and potatoes that they had collected for one of the world's first seed banks.

6 a) Where are rare breeds of farm animals kept?
  b) How are different varieties of plants kept?
  c) Why is it important to keep rare breeds of animals and plants?

7 At the beginning of the 1970s, 99% of all wheat plants grown in Canada were identical. Suggest why they now grow about 10 different varieties.

Natural selection

What do we mean by 'survival of the fittest'?

Photograph A shows a peppered moth. Like all organisms, peppered moths show **variation**. This is because different peppered moths have different alleles.

Many peppered moths are speckled and some are black. In Manchester in 1850, the black variety was very rare but by 1895, 98% of peppered moths were black.

A

1 What do we mean by the word 'variation'?

2 What percentage of peppered moths were speckled in 1895 in Manchester?

During the last part of the 19th century many factories were built around cities. These churned out huge amounts of soot which made the buildings go black.

Buildings were often turned black due to soot from factory chimneys. B

Photograph C shows a speckled moth on a tree. You can hardly see it. However, birds could easily spot these moths on the blackened buildings and most of them were eaten. The black moths were much harder to spot and so more of them survived. They went on to reproduce and so their numbers increased.

3 a) In cities at the end of the 19th century, speckled moths were more likely to be eaten by birds. Why was this?

   b) Why did the numbers of black moths in cities increase so much?

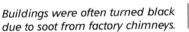

C *A speckled peppered moth on a tree.*

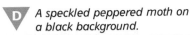

D *A speckled peppered moth on a black background.*

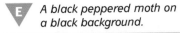

E *A black peppered moth on a black background.*

There are black squirrels around London. They were more common at the end of the 19th century.

F

This increased survival of organisms with certain characteristics in nature is called **natural selection** or 'survival of the fittest'. Only the organisms that are most suited (**adapted**) to their surroundings will survive and reproduce. Their alleles will then be passed on to their offspring (the next generation).

P Design a game to demonstrate natural selection to young children. The children will represent birds. Different colours of pasta will represent caterpillars. The 'birds' have to hunt for caterpillars.

● Write a list of rules for your game.
● Write down what you would expect to happen and why.

G

Disease can cause natural selection

Some members of a species will be killed off by a disease and others will have alleles that allow them to survive. Those that are resistant to the disease will survive and produce resistant offspring.

Competition can cause natural selection

Organisms are in **competition** with each other for things that they need. Organisms that are better at getting hold of these things are more likely to survive. For example, in a year when there are few rabbits, only fast foxes will catch enough rabbits to survive. Slower foxes will not have enough food and may die. The faster foxes will have more offspring and so there will be more of the faster foxes in the next generation.

 5 **a)** List two things that plants might compete for.
b) List two things that animals might compete for.

6 Explain what natural selection is?

7 Suggest why there were more black squirrels in London at the end of the 19th century than there are today.

Summary

Varieties of organisms that are best _____ to their environments are more likely to survive than _____ less well suited. This is called _____ selection. Organisms are more likely to survive and _____ if:

● they are less likely to be _____
● they are resistant to _____
● they can _____ better for the things they need.

adapted   compete
disease   eaten   natural
organisms   reproduce

Mutations

How are new alleles produced?

The African clawed frog in Photograph A was born with three back legs. This was caused by a **mutation**.

Organisms in the same species vary because they have different alleles. New alleles can be produced from existing ones by mutations. Mutations are sudden changes in an allele. A change may be very small but it can be enough to completely change the instructions carried on the allele. If we think of a gene as a sentence, even a small change can completely alter the meaning of the sentence:

A

 B *'Nits' are the eggs laid in human hair by animals called head lice.*

 C *'Nits' are the eggs laid in human hair by animals called head **m**ice.*

?
1 Why do different members of the same species vary?

2 **a)** What is a mutation?
  b) What did the mutation in the African clawed frog cause?

! Some people are born with an extra finger caused by a mutation. Anne Boleyn, one of Henry VIII's wives, had an extra finger on her left hand. **D**

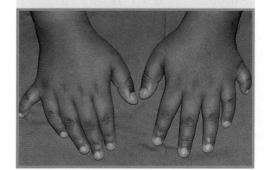

Mutations happen naturally, but the chance of one occurring is increased by:

● ionising radiation
● certain chemicals.

Ionising radiation

Radiation from radioactive substances, ultraviolet light and X-rays are all types of **ionising radiation**. They can produce reactive particles inside cells called ions. The ions damage the DNA that make up your alleles.

?
3 List two things that can cause mutations.

4 **a)** List three types of ionising radiation.
  b) What sort of particles does ionising radiation produce?

Scientists sometimes use radiation from radioactive substances to cause mutations. The fly on the left of photograph E was produced using this method.

Ultraviolet light can cause mutations in the genes which control how quickly cells grow and divide. The cells start to divide very quickly. This is cancer. People who sunbathe without sunscreen are at risk from developing skin cancer.

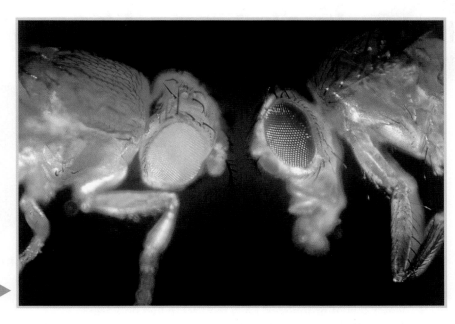

The white eyes of the fly on the left are caused by a mutation. **E**

F *This type of skin cancer is called a melanoma.*

Summary

A sudden change in an allele is called a _____. The chance of a mutation occurring is increased by _____ radiation (including radiation from _____ substances, _____ light and _____-rays). Certain _____ can also cause mutations. Mutations produce new _____ from existing ones.

| alleles | chemicals | ionising | mutation |
| radioactive | ultraviolet | X |

? 5 Look at photograph E. What is the effect of the mutation?

6 Why are people advised to put on sunscreen at the beach?

X-rays were discovered in 1895. At the beginning of the 20th century it became fashionable to have X-ray pictures taken – including family portraits! It was then discovered that people who had had a lot of X-rays taken developed cancer. Today, the X-rays used in hospitals are much safer.

Chemicals

Certain chemicals can cause mutations. For instance, some of the chemicals in cigarette smoke cause lung cancer.

? 7 Mutated alleles in humans can be inherited. For each of these alleles, write down whether you think the mutation is inherited or has occurred during the person's life.

a) someone with blue eyes
b) someone with skin cancer
c) someone with cystic fibrosis.

8 Smoking can cause lung cancer. Explain, in as much detail as you can, how this happens.

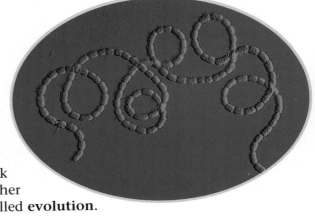

Evolution: Theory

What is the theory of evolution?

Most scientists think that all life on Earth developed originally from bacteria living in the sea, like those shown in photograph A.

The first simple bacteria appeared on Earth about 3.8 billion years ago. Since that time many different species of animals and plants have existed. Scientists think that organisms gradually change from one species into other species over thousands of years. This gradual change is called **evolution**.

A *These are very primitive bacteria called cyanobacteria.*

1 What sort of organisms were the first to live on Earth?

2 What is the gradual changing of one species into another called?

Darwin's rather long-winded title for his book published in 1859.

B

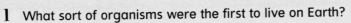

THE ORIGIN OF SPECIES

BY MEANS OF NATURAL SELECTION

OR THE

PRESERVATION OF FAVOURED RACES IN THE STRUGGLE FOR LIFE

By CHARLES DARWIN, M.A.,

LONDON :
JOHN MURRAY, ALBEMARLE STREET
1859

Charles Darwin and Alfred Russel Wallace were the first scientists to work out *how* it happens. They said that over long periods of time, **natural selection** happens over and over again to produce new species.

3 What process causes evolution?

Elephants evolved from an animal the size of a pig, called *Moeritherium* (pronounced '*meer-uh-theer-ee-um*'), which lived about 55 million years ago.

Moeritherium was **prey** for other animals. Like all animals, *Moeritherium* varied and the taller animals could more easily spot their **predators** and run away.

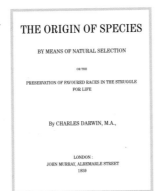

C *Moeritherium was the ancestor of elephants.*

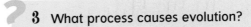

D *An African elephant.*

More of the taller animals survived and reproduced. Over thousands of years, the tallest animals became the most common. However, getting taller meant that the animals had to crouch down to drink and so were less likely to spot predators. Animals that happened to have a longer 'nose' and could use it to drink were at an advantage. So, over millions of years the tallest animals with the longest 'noses' (trunks) became the most common.

4   What animal did elephants evolve from?

5   Picture E shows a woolly mammoth. These animals also evolved from *Moeritherium*. Suggest why it was an advantage for them to evolve thick hair.

E ▶

! There are two species of elephant, the African and the Asian. Photograph F shows Asian elephants taking part in a race in Bangladesh!

F ▼

Evolution is still occurring today and in very small organisms, like bacteria, it can happen very quickly. Antibiotics are medicines that kill bacteria. However, all bacteria vary and some of them, just by chance, will contain alleles which mean that they are not killed by a certain antibiotic. These **resistant** bacteria will then reproduce. This is a problem, since diseases like tuberculosis, which used to be easily treated using antibiotics, are now much more difficult to treat.

6   Look at pictures D and F. Name one thing which varies between these two species.

7   Why did elephants evolve trunks?

8   Explain why tuberculosis is getting more difficult to treat.

9   Suggest another way, not mentioned on the page, that elephants have evolved so that they are not easy prey.

10 Look at picture B. Suggest what Darwin means by "The preservation of Favoured Races in the Struggle for Life".

Summary

The first living things appeared on Earth over 3 _____ years ago. The theory of _____ states that all the _____ on Earth have evolved from these simple life forms. Evolution occurs by _____ selection happening over and over again. It is usually very _____ but simple organisms, like _____, can evolve quickly and become _____ to antibiotics.

bacteria   billion   evolution   natural
resistant   slow   organisms

Evolution: Evidence

How do fossils provide evidence for evolution?

In 1644, the Vice Chancellor of Cambridge University, Dr. John Lightfoot, claimed to have worked out when the world was created: Sunday September 12th, 3928 BC. According to him, humans were created at 9:00 am the following Friday.

Dr. John Lightfoot (1602–1675). **A**

When Darwin first suggested his theory of evolution, most people did not believe it because:

- many people believed that God created the world and all its species in six days
- they did not believe the Earth was old enough to allow such a slow process
- there were not many good collections of fossils.

It took many years before people started to accept the theory of evolution. Today, one of the best pieces of evidence for evolution is from fossils (the remains of dead plants and animals found in rocks). Since Darwin's time, scientists have found many more fossils.

?
1 Give two reasons why people did not believe Darwin's theory when he suggested it.

2 What can we use as evidence to support the theory today?

Scientists can work out how old rocks are. If fossils are found in a rock they can then work out how old the fossils are. The evolution of the horse is now well known thanks to fossils (see diagram C).

Hyracotherium was an animal about the size of a dog. It was well adapted to its marshy surroundings because it walked on four toes that were spread out, so it did not sink into the ground. It hid from predators in bushes growing in the marshes.

?
3 Look at diagram C. How tall was *Hyracotherium*?

4 How many toes did *Hyracotherium* walk on?

!
The oldest rock is 4.4 billion years old.
The oldest fossil is 3.5 billion years old.

B *These fossil hunters work carefully to uncover dinosaur bones..*

Over millions of years, the marshy ground was replaced by drier grassland and there were fewer bushes to hide behind. Natural selection favoured animals that could run faster and get away from predators. Running on fewer toes is faster. Over millions of years natural selection favoured animals which had less toes touching the ground.

Organisms need to survive changes in their surroundings, new types of predators, new diseases or new competitors. Unless they change (evolve) to become better adapted to a new situation, the species may die out altogether (become **extinct**).

▼ C

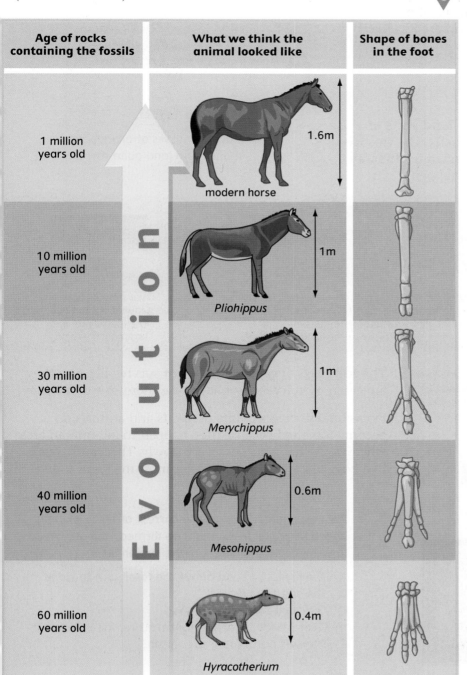

Age of rocks containing the fossils	What we think the animal looked like	Shape of bones in the foot
1 million years old	modern horse 1.6m	
10 million years old	*Pliohippus* 1m	
30 million years old	*Merychippus* 1m	
40 million years old	*Mesohippus* 0.6m	
60 million years old	*Hyracotherium* 0.4m	

Evolution

5 a) How did the area where horse-like animals lived change over millions of years?

b) How did the horse-like animals evolve to cope with this change?

6 Some people think that dinosaurs became extinct because new competitors evolved. What might these animals have competed for?

7 Modern horses are taller than their ancient ancestors. Suggest why.

! Scientists think that 99% of all the species that have ever lived are now extinct.

Summary

Good evidence for evolution comes from _____. We can use information about the ages of rocks to work out roughly how old a fossil is. Organisms must _____ to become better _____ to changes in their environment, otherwise they may become _____.

adapted   evolve
extinct   fossils

Fossils

How are fossils formed?

The logs in photograph A are made out of stone! They are a type of fossil and are millions of years old.

Fossils are the remains of ancient plants and animals, and are normally found in rock. Most fossils are of sea creatures because to make a fossil a dead organism needs to be covered quickly in something like mud or sand. Animals and plants which die on land are less likely to get covered up quickly in this way.

Fossils are formed in four main ways.

Turned to stone

 This normally happens to the hard parts of an organism like bones and shells. The tree fossils in photograph A were also formed in this way. Diagram B shows how it can happen.

A These logs are actually made of stone. Wood like this is said to be 'petrified'.

?
1 What is a fossil?
2 Why are fossils of organisms that live on land quite rare?

Dead sea snail 300 million years ago.

Soft parts of the body eaten by other organisms.

Shell covered in layers of sand. The shell starts to slowly crumble and minerals replace it, turning it into a stone-like substance with the same shape as the shell. This takes millions of years.

Over millions of years more layers of sand build up. The layers turn into sedimentary rocks.

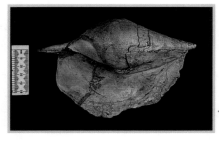

This fossilised sea snail is millions of years old.

C

The soft parts of organisms do not survive because they are eaten by microbes which cause them to rot or **decay**.

Occasionally, the soft parts of plants and animals do become fossilised because they happen to fall into an area where decay happens very, very slowly. This can happen in a bog, where it is too acidic for most microbes to live.

These leaves became fossilised because they fell into a bog.

D

?
3 Put these sentences into the correct order to explain how a sea snail fossil might be formed. You only need to write down the letters of the sentences.

A The layers of sand above the fossil turn to stone.
B The sea snail dies.
C The shell is covered in sand.
D Over millions of years, minerals replace the shell.
E The soft parts rot or are eaten.

Hard parts of animals are preserved

Shells and bones can sometimes remain as they are. This often happens to shells if they are covered in other bits of shell.

Dead ammonite 200 million years ago.

Soft parts of the body are eaten or decay.

Shell covered in bits of other shells.

Over millions of years the ammonite shell stays the same as the layers of broken shells above it turn into a sedimentary rock (limestone).

 F *These ammonites are 200 million years old.*

This man was buried under ice for 5000 years. G

4 Why are ammonites commonly found in limestone?

Whole organisms are preserved

Microbes need oxygen, warmth and water to survive. If one of these is missing, no decay will happen and so a whole organism might be preserved.

 A dinosaur footprint.

Traces of animals or plants

Sometimes fossilised footprints or other traces of plants and animals are found. Look at photograph H. A dinosaur left this footprint in soft mud millions of years ago. The mud baked hard in the Sun and was then covered by more mud which also baked hard. Over millions of years the layers of baked mud turned into mudstone. Peeling off the other layers of rock has revealed the footprints.

5 Look at photograph G. Why did this man's body not decay?

6 Explain how an animal burrow could be fossilised.

7 Suggest why plant fossils are much rarer than animal fossils.

Summary

Fossils are normally found in _____. They can be formed by _____ replacing the _____ parts of animals or plants. Sometimes the hard parts of animals (like _____) stay as they are if they are surrounded by the same substance from which the hard part is made. Whole organisms can be fossilised if _____ are unable to cause decay. Traces of animals or plants can sometimes be fossilised, for example _____.

footprints   hard   microbes   minerals
rocks   shells

Further questions

1 a) Write out these sentences in the correct order to explain how cells make copies of themselves.

- The cell splits into two.
- Exact copies are made of all 46 chromosomes.
- There are now two cells, each with a nucleus containing a full set of chromosomes.
- The nucleus splits into two. (3)

b) What is this process called? (1)

c) Name one organism that has 46 chromosomes in the nucleus of each cell. (1)

2 The diagram shows a strawberry plant. It can reproduce by sexual and asexual reproduction.

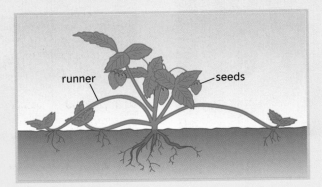

runner   seeds

a) Which part of the plant allows it to reproduce asexually? (1)

b) Which part of the plant has been formed using sexual reproduction? (1)

c) The new plants grow. Which plants will be identical to the parent plant, those produced sexually or those produced asexually? (1)

d) Explain your answer to part **c**. (1)

3 A gardener bred a sweet pea plant which had purple flowers with a sweet pea plant with white flowers. All the new plants had purple flowers.

a) Before Mendel suggested his theory, people thought that offspring inherited a 'blend' of characteristics from their parents. How do the results of the gardener's crossing suggest that 'blending' does not happen? (1)

b) Which of the alleles for flower colour was dominant? (1)

c) Each plant will have two alleles of each gene in the nucleus of each cell. Which two alleles will the plant with white flowers have? (1)

d) Which alleles will the plant with purple flowers have? (1)

e) Which alleles will the offspring plants have? (1)

f) A company called Florigene has recently produced a purple carnation. Carnations are normally red, pink or white. How do you think they have produced the purple carnation? Choose from the following list:

i) selective breeding   ii) artificial selection
iii) artificial insemination
iv) genetic engineering
v) natural selection   vi) evolution (1)

4 The diagram shows a modern horse and an animal that it evolved from called *Hyracotherium*.
The diagram also shows some of the bones from the right front leg.

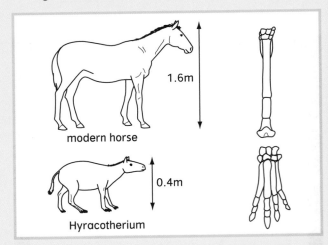

1.6m

modern horse

0.4m

Hyracotherium

a) *Hyracotherium* lived in marshes. How was it adapted to live in this environment? (1)

b) Why would a modern horse not be well adapted to living in marshes? (1)

c) Apart from the bones in the leg, describe one other way in which the modern horse is different from *Hyracotherium*. (1)

d) What is the advantage for the modern horse of the change you described in part c? (1)

e) Evolution occurs by 'natural selection'. Explain what natural selection is. (2)

5 Look at the three family trees below. There is an inherited disease in each of the families.

a) What is an inherited disease? (1)

b) One of the family trees shows a disease that only affects one sex. Which one? (1)

c) Which family tree shows a disease which is caused by a dominant allele? (1)

d) In family tree B, only one person has an inherited disease. Explain how this person could get the disease if neither of her parents had the disease. (2)

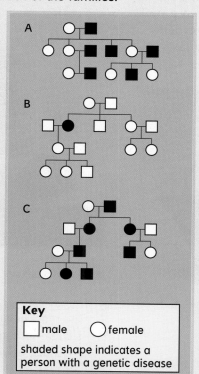

Key

☐ male   ○ female

shaded shape indicates a person with a genetic disease

6 Some people can roll their tongues. Other people cannot. The allele that allows tongue rolling is called '**R**'. It is dominant over the allele that does not allow tongue rolling – '**r**'.

a) Copy the diagram and add in the letters '**R**' or '**r**' to show the different alleles that the gametes of these two people will contain. (2)

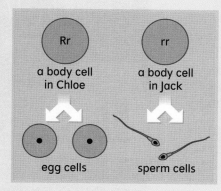

b) Continue your diagram to show what alleles a fertilised egg would contain if each of the egg cells joined with each of the sperm cells. (2)

c) What percentage of their children would you expect to be unable to roll their tongues? (1)

7 The diagram shows the female reproductive system.

a) Which letter on the diagram shows the part that egg cells are released from? (1)

b) How can a woman increase the number of egg cells that are released?

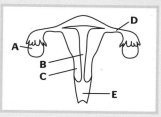

Choose from these answers:

i) eating more cheese

ii) having fertility treatment

iii) taking oral contraceptives

iv) having gene therapy. (1)

c) Egg cells are the female gametes. What are the male gametes called? (1)

d) What happens during 'fertilisation'? (1)

e) The part labelled C gets thicker and thinner in a monthly cycle. What is the name of this cycle? (1)

f) This cycle is controlled by chemicals. What are these chemicals called? (1)

g) Choose *two* places from the list below where these chemicals are made in a woman. (2)

liver	stomach	pituitary gland	testis
	ovary	vagina	

h) Which letter on the diagram shows the part where the baby develops? (1)

8 Put the following into size order, starting with the smallest. (4)

chromosome	embryo	gamete	gene
	nucleus	organism	

9 In embryo transplanting, a fertilised egg cell is allowed to develop into a ball of cells (an embryo). The embryo is then split apart and each cell is allowed to grow into a new embryo. These embryos are placed into the wombs of 'foster' animals to develop.

a) Each of the offspring produced using embryo transplanting is a 'clone'. What is a clone? (1)

b) Name one advantage of this process for a farmer. (1)

c) Name one disadvantage of this process. (1)

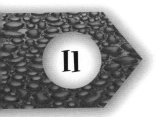

11

Rates of reaction

What do we mean by the 'rate of reaction'?

Chemical reactions happen at different speeds. Some are very slow, like rusting, which can take years. When a nail rusts, the iron (or steel) reacts very slowly with oxygen (from the air) and water. Other reactions are very fast, like explosions. They are over very quickly.

B *Explosions are very fast reactions*

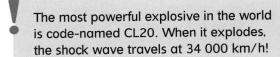

The most powerful explosive in the world is code-named CL20. When it explodes, the shock wave travels at 34 000 km/h!

A *Rusting is a very slow reaction.*

  1 Write down an example of a slow chemical reaction.

2 Write down an example of a fast chemical reaction.

Measuring the rate of a reaction

Timing how long a reaction takes is a bit like timing a 100-metre sprinter. It is easy to time the sprinter from start to finish. However, it is difficult to know how fast the sprinter is going at different stages in the race. The sprinter is going slower at the start as he or she picks up speed. The sprinter may run very fast in the middle of the race and may slow down or speed up near the end.

A chemical reaction also goes at different speeds until it has finished. Unlike a sprinter, a reaction usually starts off quicker and then slows down. The speed of a reaction is called the **rate of reaction**. There are different ways of measuring the rate of reaction. If the reaction gives off a gas, then you can trap it in a measuring cylinder.

3 What does 'rate of reaction' mean?

C *A sprinter runs at different speeds during a race.*

Measuring a rate of reaction

Calcium carbonate is the chemical name for marble. It will react with hydrochloric acid. Carbon dioxide gas is one of the **products**.

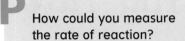
How could you measure the rate of reaction?

- How will you measure the volume of gas given off?
- How often will you take measurements?
- How will you know when the reaction has finished?

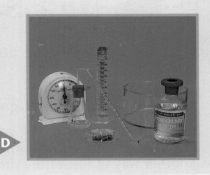

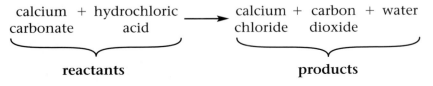

$$\underbrace{\text{calcium carbonate} + \text{hydrochloric acid}}_{\textbf{reactants}} \longrightarrow \underbrace{\text{calcium chloride} + \text{carbon dioxide} + \text{water}}_{\textbf{products}}$$

The gas is collected in a measuring cylinder filled with water. It pushes the water out so it is easy to measure the volume of gas. The volume of gas in the measuring cylinder is measured every 10 seconds until the reaction is over.

Table F shows the results. A graph of the results would look like this:

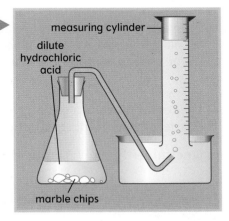

measuring cylinder
dilute hydrochloric acid
marble chips

 F

Time (seconds)	Volume of gas (cm³)
0	0
10	35
20	53
30	65
40	73
50	73
60	73

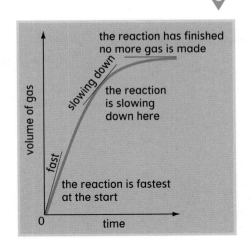

the reaction has finished no more gas is made
slowing down
the reaction is slowing down here
fast
the reaction is fastest at the start
volume of gas
time

The graph is steepest at the beginning. This means that the rate of reaction is fastest at the beginning of the reaction. When the slope goes horizontal (flat), the reaction is over. One, or both of the reactants has been used up.

4 Why does the reaction stop?

5 How can you tell from the graph that the reaction has finished?

6 Look at the results in table F.

    a) Plot a graph of the results.
    b) What was the volume of gas made at the end of the reaction?
    c) How long did the reaction take to finish?

7 Use your graph to find the volume of gas made:
    a) after 15 seconds.
    b) after 35 seconds.

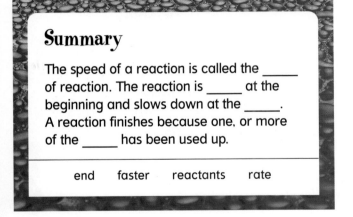

Summary

The speed of a reaction is called the _____ of reaction. The reaction is _____ at the beginning and slows down at the _____. A reaction finishes because one, or more of the _____ has been used up.

end   faster   reactants   rate

12

Measuring rate of reaction - 1

How else can the rate of reaction be measured?

Method 1 – Volume of gas given off

You have already seen how gas can be trapped by pushing water out of a measuring cylinder. Another way of measuring the volume of a gas is to use a syringe.

P How can you measure the rate of reaction using a gas syringe?

- How often will you take measurements?
- How will you know when the reaction has finished?

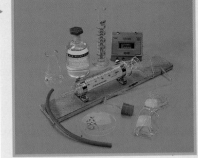

A

 1 Name two pieces of equipment that can be used to measure the volume of a gas.

In the reaction below a gas is given off and pushes the syringe out. The faster the gas is given off, the faster the syringe is pushed out.

magnesium + hydrochloric acid $\longrightarrow$ magnesium chloride + hydrogen

 B

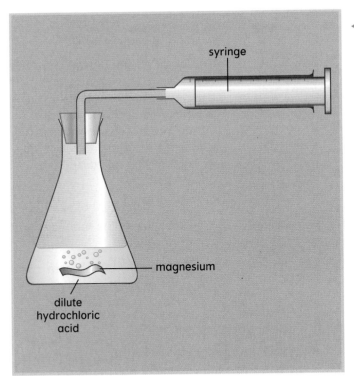

syringe

magnesium

dilute
hydrochloric
acid

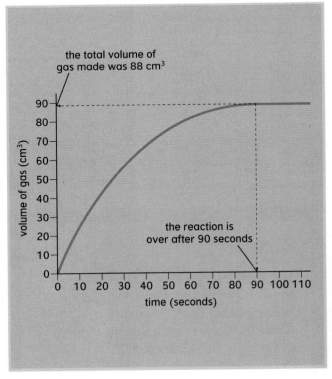

the total volume of
gas made was 88 cm³

the reaction is
over after 90 seconds

volume of gas (cm³)

time (seconds)

The reaction finishes because one of the reactants has been used up. The graph is very steep at the beginning. This means that the reaction is going fastest at the start.

 2 How can you tell when the reaction has finished?

Here is a graph of the results from the experiment.

 C

Method 2 – Mass of gas given off

We can measure the rate of reaction in a different way by measuring the mass of gas given off.

We don't actually measure the mass of gas given off, but we can work it out. The gas escapes from the flask and so the flask loses mass (gets lighter). If the flask loses 1.5 g in mass, then 1.5 g of gas must have been given off. If the flask loses 3.7 g in mass, then 3.7 g of gas must have been given off. The faster the gas is given off, the faster the flask loses mass. The faster the flask loses mass, the faster the rate of reaction. This method of measuring the rate of reaction is sometimes called the 'loss in mass' method.

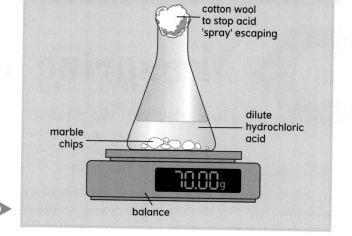

cotton wool to stop acid 'spray' escaping

marble chips

dilute hydrochloric acid

70.00 g

balance

D

P Calcium carbonate reacts with hydrochloric acid. How could you measure the rate of this reaction using the 'loss in mass' method?

- What measurements will you take?
- What will you need cotton wool for?

3 Why does the flask lose mass? Choose the correct answer from the box below.

> the flask gets lighter   gas is added to the flask
> gas escapes from the flask

4 Imagine you were doing an experiment to measure the rate of a reaction. How would you know when the reaction was over using:

a) the 'volume of gas given off' method?
b) the 'loss in mass' method?

5 A student added some marble chips to acid and measured the mass every minute.
Here are the results from the experiment:

Time (min)	0	1	2	3	4	5
Mass (g)	130.13	129.98	129.95	129.91	129.85	129.74
Loss in mass (g)						

Time (min)	6	7	8	9	10	11
Mass (g)	129.69	129.66	129.63	129.61	129.60	129.60
Loss in mass (g)						

a) Copy the table.
b) Complete the table by working out the figures for 'loss in mass'.
c) Plot the results on a graph, with time on the horizontal axis (x-axis) and loss in mass on the vertical (y-axis).
d) Why did the mass get less?
e) Does the reaction slow down or speed up as time goes by?

Summary

There are different ways to measure the rate of a reaction. One way is to measure the _____ of gas given off. This means measuring the volume of gas in a _____ . The other is to measure the _____ (sometimes called the 'loss in mass' method). This means that you have to measure the mass of a flask and its contents on a _____ . The mass of the flask drops because a _____ is made in the reaction and it leaves the flask.

> balance   gas   mass
> syringe   volume

13

Measuring rate of reaction - 2

How else can we measure the rate of reaction?

The 'disappearing cross' method

You have already seen how to measure the rate of reaction by how quickly a gas is given off. Some reactions make a solid. You can also measure how quickly a solid is made. For example, in diagram A, the two chemicals react together to make sulphur, which is a solid. The sulphur makes the solution go cloudy. The more sulphur that is made, the cloudier the solution goes. Eventually, the solution gets so cloudy that it is difficult to see through.

? 1 What makes the solution turn cloudy?

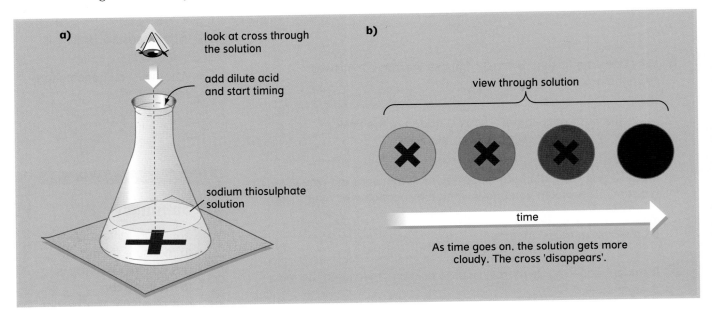

a) look at cross through the solution

add dilute acid and start timing

sodium thiosulphate solution

b) view through solution

time

As time goes on, the solution gets more cloudy. The cross 'disappears'.

A

sodium thiosulphate + hydrochloric acid → sodium chloride + sulphur + sulphur dioxide + water

? 2 Why is the method shown in diagram A called the 'disappearing cross' method?

This experiment is sometimes called the 'disappearing cross' experiment. Timing how long it takes the cross to disappear can be used to measure the rate of reaction. The faster the cross disappears, the faster the reaction.

P How could you measure how quickly a solid is formed in a reaction?

● How will you decide when the reaction has finished?

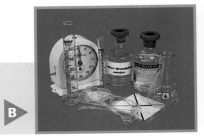

B

Hazard symbols

In many experiments, the chemicals that you use can be harmful and dangerous. There are special symbols on the bottles to warn you of the dangers. You must take great care when handling chemicals because they can do real harm to you or someone else. You may have seen some of these hazard symbols on the sides of bottles at school or on cleaning products used at home.

D *Toxic* chemicals can cause death if swallowed, breathed in, or allowed to absorb through the skin.

C *Highly flammable.* The petrol in this tanker will catch fire easily.

E *Harmful* substances are like toxic substances but less dangerous. Substances which are *irritants* are not corrosive but can cause skin to go red or blister.

F *Oxidising* substances, like hydrogen peroxide, provide a source of oxygen which allows other things to burn fiercely.

G *Corrosive* substances, like battery acid, attack and destroy living tissues like eyes and skin.

---

3 What problems can irritants cause?

4 a) What can happen to chemicals that are highly flammable?

b) Name any chemical that is flammable.

5 A new chemical, 'dramicon' can be used to clean car engines. It has these properties:

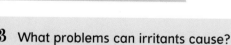

- it burns easily
- it helps other chemicals to burn
- if you spill it on your skin, it causes an itchy rash all over your body.

a) Draw and name the hazard symbols that should be on a bottle of 'dramicon'.

b) Write down a list of safety instructions for people who are going to use the chemical.

Summary

The reaction between _____ acid and sodium thiosulphate makes _____. The rate of reaction can be measured by timing how long it takes a cross on a piece of paper to _____ from view. The faster the cross disappears, the _____ the rate of reaction. _____ symbols tell us the problems a chemical can cause.

---

disappear   faster   hazard
hydrochloric   sulphur

Effect of concentration

How does changing the concentration affect the rate of reaction?

Lots of solids, like salt and sugar, dissolve in water. Copper sulphate is a **salt**. If it is dissolved in water, a solution is made. The more copper sulphate you add to the water, the more **concentrated** the solution. There are more particles of copper sulphate in the same volume of water.

Look at diagram A.

The volume of water in each beaker is the same. If more and more copper sulphate is added to the same volume of water, the **concentration** of the solution increases. This means that the solution with the highest concentration is beaker 3.

A

copper sulphate

water

Add solid | Stir | Copper sulphate solution. All the solid has dissolved.

1 1 spatula of copper sulphate added

2 2 spatulas of copper sulphate added

3 3 spatulas of copper sulphate added

? **1** How do you make a more concentrated solution of copper sulphate?

Changing the concentration

Look at this experiment. The concentration of acid is changed each time.

The *total* volume of acid and water is kept the same each time (50 cm³) to make it a **fair test**. Also, the same mass of marble chips is used and the chips are similar sizes. For example, it would not be a fair test if in one experiment you used large chips, and then in another you used smaller chips. Remember, you are only changing one thing – the concentration of acid. Everything else must be kept the same.

? **2** Look at diagram B. What two things must be kept the same to make it a fair test?

B

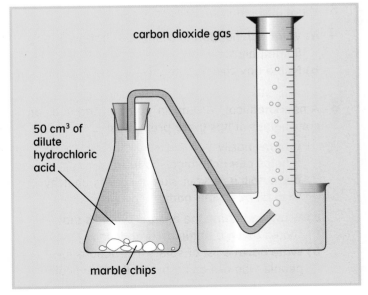

carbon dioxide gas

50 cm³ of dilute hydrochloric acid

marble chips

Here are the results from the experiment:

Solution	Volume of acid (cm³)	Volume of water (cm³)	Time to collect 20 cm³ of gas (s)
V	10	40	255
W	20	30	132
X	30	20	70
Y	40	10	51
Z	50	0	42

Solution V is the least concentrated (most **dilute**). Moving from V to Z, the solutions get more concentrated. Solution Z is the most concentrated and gives the fastest reaction. As the concentration increases, the rate of reaction increases.

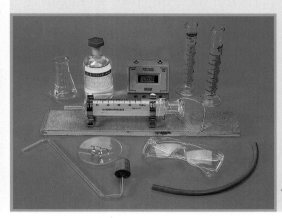

P How could you investigate the effect of concentration on the rate of reaction?

● How will you change the concentration of the acid?

● How will you make it a fair test?

D

3 Look at table C

a) Which solution is the most concentrated?

b) Which solution is the least concentrated?

c) Which solution gave the fastest reaction?

d) Which solution gave the slowest reaction?

4 Look at the results in table C.

a) Plot a graph of the results using axes like these:

b) Use your graph to find the time to collect 20 cm³ of gas using these volumes of acid:

  i) 15 cm³

  ii) 35 cm³

  iii) 25 cm³.

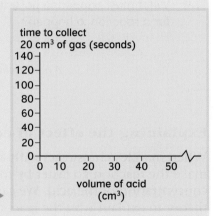

E

Summary

When a solid is dissolved in a liquid like water, a _____ is made. If only a small amount of solid is dissolved, the solution will be _____ . If more and more of the solid is dissolved, the solution will be _____ . As the concentration of a chemical in a reaction _____, the rate of reaction increases.

concentrated   dilute
increases   solution

5 A student made five solutions of copper sulphate that had different concentrations. She made them by dissolving different amounts of copper sulphate in different volumes of water.

Solution M = 2 g dissolved in 500 cm³ of water.

Solution N = 2 g dissolved in 5000 cm³ of water.

Solution P = 4 g dissolved in 1000 cm³ of water.

Solution Q = 3 g dissolved in 250 cm³ of water.

Solution R = 4 g dissolved in 1500 cm³ of water.

a) Which two are actually the same concentration?

b) Put the solutions in order, with the most concentrated first.

15

Collision theory

Why does increasing the concentration speed up a reaction?

All substances are made up of tiny **particles**. These tiny particles might be **atoms** or **molecules**. Molecules are made up of atoms that are joined together. For a chemical reaction to take place, the reactant particles must bang into each other. They must **collide**. If they bang into each other hard enough, they will react.

This idea about colliding particles is called **collision theory**. The more collisions there are in a certain time, the faster the reaction.

1 What must happen to particles for a reaction to happen?

A hard collision!

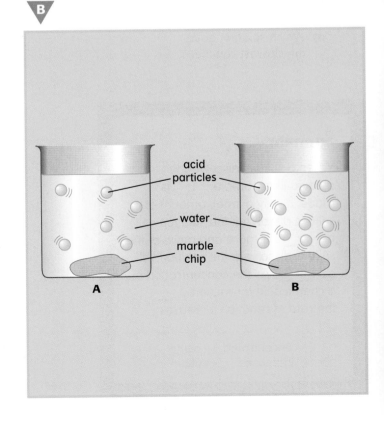

Explaining the effect of concentration

When marbles chips react with acid, you can make the reaction go faster by increasing the concentration of the acid. We can use collision theory to explain why the reaction is faster when the concentration is increased.

In beaker B there are more acid particles in the same volume of liquid. It is more concentrated. The acid particles are more crowded. This means that there is a greater chance of acid particles colliding with particles on the surface of the marble. There are more collisions in a certain time and so the rate of reaction increases.

2 Why does increasing the concentration increase the rate of reaction?

3 Copy out the beakers A and B. Draw another beaker to show an even higher concentration of acid. Label your diagram.

acid particles

water

marble chip

A   B

It's a bit like dancers on a dance floor. When a good track is played, more people get up to dance and the dance floor becomes crowded. The concentration of people on the dance floor increases and there is more chance of bumping into someone! There are more collisions.

C

Increasing the concentration increases the rate of reaction.

 4 Look at beaker B. What would happen to the rate of reaction if there were even more particles in the same volume?

Gas reactions

Look at the syringe in diagram D. There are two gases inside reacting with each other. If the end is sealed you can increase the pressure inside the syringe by pushing the plunger. By pushing the plunger down, the particles of gas get squashed together and are now in a smaller volume. This means the concentration has increased and so the rate of reaction increases.

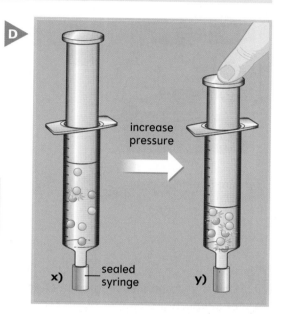

D

increase pressure

x) — sealed syringe   y)

Increasing the pressure of gases increases the rate of reaction.

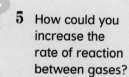 **5** How could you increase the rate of reaction between gases?

6 Two students are studying the effect of concentration on the rate of reaction. They use magnesium reacting with hydrochloric acid. Hydrogen gas is made in the reaction and all the magnesium is used up. Three different concentrations of acid were used: A, B and C.

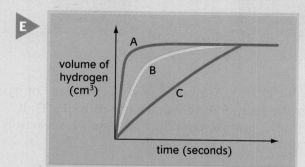

E

volume of hydrogen (cm³)

A
B
C

time (seconds)

a) What would the students have to do to make it a fair test? Write down two things.
b) Which concentration of acid gives the fastest reaction?
c) Explain your answer to part b.

7 a) Sketch the graphs from question 6 into your book.
b) Draw on your graph a line for acid with a concentration less than A, but higher than B. Label your line 'D'.

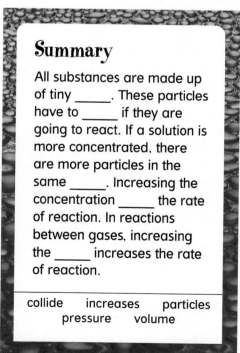

Summary

All substances are made up of tiny _____. These particles have to _____ if they are going to react. If a solution is more concentrated, there are more particles in the same _____. Increasing the concentration _____ the rate of reaction. In reactions between gases, increasing the _____ increases the rate of reaction.

collide	increases	particles
	pressure	volume

16

Effect of temperature

What effect does temperature have on the rate of reaction?

We keep food in a fridge to stop it 'going off'. Some substances in food react with oxygen in the air to make the food go off or turn 'rancid'. Microbes also make food go off. Even food kept in a fridge will eventually go off, but the low temperature slows down the reactions that turn the food rancid.

 1 **Why does food take longer to go off in a fridge?**

If lowering the temperature slows down the rate of reaction, then increasing the temperature should increase the rate of reaction.

Look at the experiment below. A student was timing how long it took to collect 20 cm³ of gas.

A

B

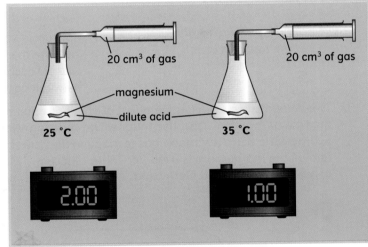

20 cm³ of gas

20 cm³ of gas

magnesium

dilute acid

25 °C

35 °C

2.00

1.00

P How could you investigate the effect of temperature on the rate of reaction?

● How many different temperatures will you choose?

● What will be the lowest and highest temperatures you will choose?

● How will you know when the reaction has finished?

C

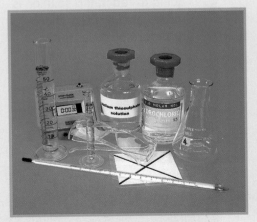

At 25 °C, it took 2 minutes to collect 20 cm³ of gas. When the temperature was increased to 35 °C, it only took 1 minute to collect the gas. The reaction was faster.

When the temperature is increased, the rate of reaction is increased.

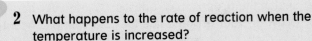 **2** **What happens to the rate of reaction when the temperature is increased?**

Explaining the effect of temperature

Particles move around faster when you heat them, so there is more chance of them bumping into each other. This means there are more collisions in a certain time and the rate of reaction increases. It's a bit like the dancers on the dance floor again. If they dance very fast, they are more likely to bump into each other.

There is another reason why the rate of reaction increases when the temperature increases. Some particles don't have enough energy to react when they collide with other particles. There is a minimum (least) amount of energy that particles need to react, called the **activation energy**. At higher temperatures, the particles have more energy and bang into each other harder. This means that the collisions are more likely to produce a reaction, because more particles will have reached the activation energy.

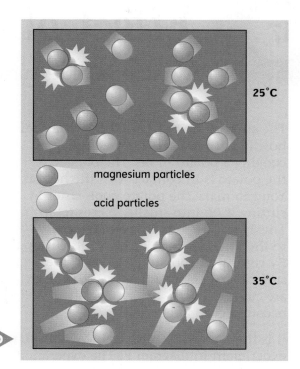

25°C

magnesium particles

acid particles

35°C

D

3 What is activation energy?

4 Give two reasons why the rate of reaction increases when the temperature increases.

5 Look at graph E. The rate of the reaction doubles for every 10 °C rise in temperature.

 a) How long do you think it would take to make 20 cm³ of gas if the temperature was 45 °C?
 b) Sketch the graph in diagram E. Draw a line on your graph to show the rate of reaction at 45 °C.
 c) How long do you think it would take to make 20 cm³ of gas if the temperature was 15 °C?
 d) Draw a line on your graph to show the rate of reaction at 15 °C.

Look at the experiment in diagram B. Graph E shows the results.

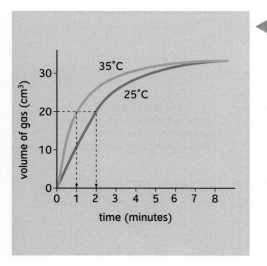

E

Remember, the student was timing how long it took to collect 20 cm³ of gas, even though more was actually made in the reaction. When the temperature is higher, the reaction is faster, so the 20 cm³ of gas is made faster.

Summary

If the temperature is increased, the rate of reaction is _____. Increasing the temperature means that the particles move around _____. This means that there are more _____ in a certain time. Also, when the temperature is increased, the particles have more _____. This means that they are more likely to _____ when they collide. The minimum amount of energy needed for particles to react is the _____ energy.

| activation | collisions | energy |
| faster | increased | react |

17

Effect of surface area

What effect does surface area have on the rate of reaction?

The **surface area** of something measures how much surface is exposed. Imagine cooking a potato in oil. The outside of the potato is in contact with the hot oil. You can make the potato cook faster by cutting it up into smaller pieces (chips!). This is because more surface is exposed to the hot oil when the potato is cut up. By cutting the potato into chips, the surface area becomes larger. If the chips are cut into crisps, the surface area becomes even larger!

A

It is the same with chemical reactions. Look at the experiment in diagram B. The experiment is carried out twice – first with large marble chips and then with small marble chips. The small chips have a larger surface area. The total mass of chips is kept the same (5 g) to make it a fair test. The volume of acid must also be kept the same in each experiment.

1 What happens to the surface area of a solid when it is cut into smaller pieces?

Choose the correct answer from the list.

the surface area is bigger
the surface area is smaller
the surface area stays the same

B

cotton wool to stop acid 'spray' escaping

Experiment 1
5 g of large chips

Experiment 2
5 g of small chips

5 g of marble chips

dilute hydrochloric acid

70.00 g — balance

2 Look at the experiment in diagram B. What two things must be kept the same to make it a fair test?

After all the results have been collected, a graph can be drawn. This is shown in graph C.

C

3 **a)** How long did the reaction take with large chips?
b) How long did the reaction take with small chips?
c) How long would the reaction take if the chips were crushed into a powder?

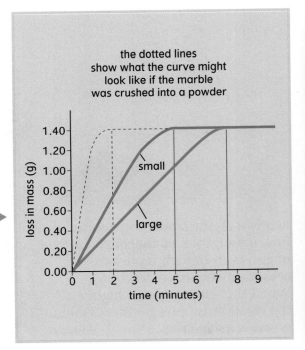

the dotted lines show what the curve might look like if the marble was crushed into a powder

small

large

loss in mass (g)

1.40
1.20
1.00
0.80
0.60
0.40
0.20
0.00

0 1 2 3 4 5 6 7 8 9
time (minutes)

P How could you investigate the effect of surface area on rate of reaction?

- How will you change the surface area of the marble chips?

- What will you need to do to make it a fair test?

- How will you measure the rate of reaction?

D

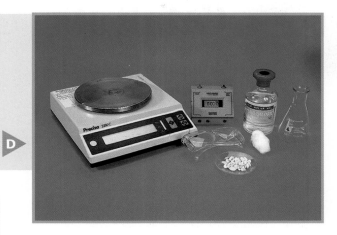

The smaller the particles can be made, the bigger the surface area is and the faster the rate of reaction will be.

Explaining the effect of surface area

When the marble chips are broken into small pieces, the surface area is bigger. There are more particles on the surface for the acid particles to react with, so the reaction is faster. When the surface area is increased, the rate of reaction increases.

E

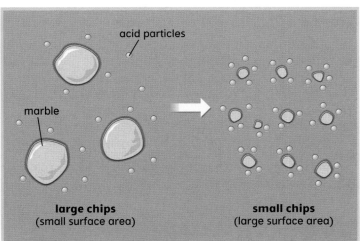

acid particles

marble

large chips
(small surface area)

small chips
(large surface area)

?

4 Copy and complete the sentence below by choosing the correct word in the brackets.

The rate of reaction (decreases/increases/stays the same) when the surface area of a solid is increased.

5 Explain why the fine flour dust in a flour mill sometimes explodes.

! Coal dust can cause explosions in mines, if it catches fire. The surface area of the dust is very large and so, if it is ignited, the reaction is so fast it causes an explosion. This can also happen with substances like flour. In 1878 a flour mill in Minneapolis exploded when the flour dust caught fire. It killed 18 people and flattened nearby buildings.

Summary

The surface area of a solid can be made bigger by breaking it into _____ pieces. When a solid is broken into smaller pieces, the _____ area is bigger. Increasing the surface area _____ the rate of reaction. In the reaction between marble chips and acid, the small marble chips will react _____ with the acid than the large chips. The reaction can be made even faster by crushing the marble chips into a _____ . Crushing solids into a powder makes the surface area even _____ .

bigger	faster	increases	powder
	smaller	surface	

18 Catalysts

What is a catalyst?

Some chemical reactions are very slow. This is sometimes useful. For example, iron rusts very slowly and food rots slowly. We would not want iron bridges to rust away quickly or for our food to go off quickly!

But there are some reactions that we might want to speed up. A **catalyst** is a substance that speeds up a chemical reaction. Catalysts are used a lot in factories which make chemicals. Modern cars use platinum as a catalyst in the exhaust. This part of the exhaust is called a **catalytic converter**. Its job is to quickly turn poisonous gases into less harmful ones.

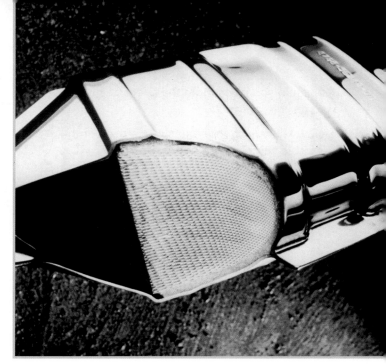

 A *The inside of a catalytic converter in a car.*

1 What is a catalyst?
2 What is the job of a catalytic converter in a car?

Look at the experiment in diagram B. Hydrogen peroxide breaks down slowly to make water and oxygen:

$$\text{hydrogen peroxide} \longrightarrow \text{water} + \text{oxygen}$$
$$2H_2O_2 \longrightarrow 2H_2O + O_2$$

A catalyst (manganese (IV) oxide) is added to the second test tube. The reaction is much faster with the catalyst. The catalyst is still there at the end of the reaction and does not get used up. It can be used over and over again.

3 Does a catalyst get used up in a chemical reaction?
4 How can you tell that the reaction is faster with the catalyst?

B

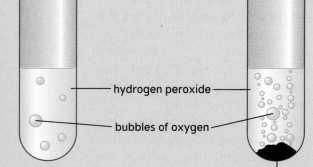

hydrogen peroxide

bubbles of oxygen

manganese dioxide (catalyst)

Hydrogen peroxide solution sterilises these contact lenses. But you might forget to rinse the lenses before putting them back in your eyes. A catalyst at the bottom of the container quickly breaks down hydrogen peroxide into water and oxygen. **C**

P How could you investigate the effect of different catalysts?

- How will you make it a fair test?
- How will you decide which is the best?

potato

liver

manganese oxide (IV)

Catalysts in industry

Catalysts are important for speeding up chemical reactions in industry. This saves a lot of money because the factory does not need to operate for as long to produce the same amount of chemicals. There are lots of different types of catalyst. Different reactions need different catalysts.

E *Iron is the catalyst used to make ammonia. Ammonia is an important chemical for making fertilisers.*

F *Platinum is the catalyst used to make nitric acid. Nitric acid is another important chemical used to make fertilisers.*

G *Nickel is the catalyst used to make margarine.*

Summary

A catalyst _____ up a chemical reaction. It is not _____ up in the reaction but remains _____ at the end. Different catalysts are used for different _____ . For example, _____ is used in car exhausts to quickly change poisonous gases into less dangerous ones.

platinum   reactions   ~~speeds~~   ~~unchanged~~   ~~used~~

?

5 Why are catalysts useful in industry?

6 Why are many catalysts made into small pellets or crushed into powders?

Enzymes

What are enzymes?

All living things are made from cells. There are chemical reactions going on inside every cell, keeping them alive. The chemical reactions have to be speeded up by catalysts made by the cell. These catalysts are called **enzymes**. Enzymes are catalysts from living things. Sometimes they are called 'biological catalysts'.

? 1 What is an enzyme?

Look at the experiment in diagram B. Hydrogen peroxide breaks down slowly into water and oxygen.

$$\text{hydrogen peroxide} \longrightarrow \text{water} + \text{oxygen}$$
$$2H_2O_2 \longrightarrow 2H_2O + O_2$$

Liver has enzymes in it that speed up the reaction. **B**

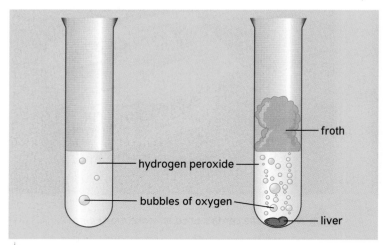

- froth
- hydrogen peroxide
- bubbles of oxygen
- liver

? 2 What do enzymes do to the rate of reaction?

Effect of temperature

The chemical reactions in cells actually happen faster when it is warm rather than hot. Enzymes are large protein molecules and they are affected by temperature. If it is too hot (above 45 °C), they are damaged and do not work. Biological washing powders contain enzymes. The enzymes in the washing powder break down stains. They work best at about 40 °C.

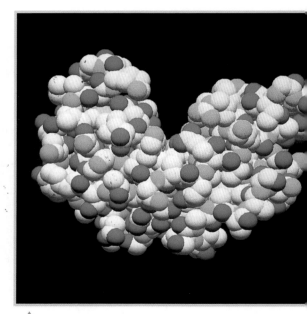

A *A computer model of an enzyme molecule.*

The bombardier beetle uses an enzyme to break down hydrogen peroxide into water and oxygen. It happens so quickly, like an explosion, that it frightens away any predators. **C**

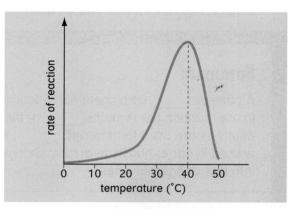

rate of reaction

temperature (°C)

D *The rate of reaction of enzymes breaking down stains on dirty clothes is affected by temperature.*

P How could you study the effect of temperature on enzymes?

E

- Think how you could destroy the enzymes in the liver.
- How will you know if the enzymes have stopped working?
- How will you make it a fair test?

3 What happens to enzymes if the temperature is too high?

Effect of pH

Enzymes can be affected by how much acid or alkali is present. Remember, pH is a measure of how acidic or alkaline a substance is. The graphs in diagram F show how two different enzymes, X and Y, are affected by pH.

4 What conditions does enzyme X work best in?

5 What conditions does enzyme Y work best in?

F
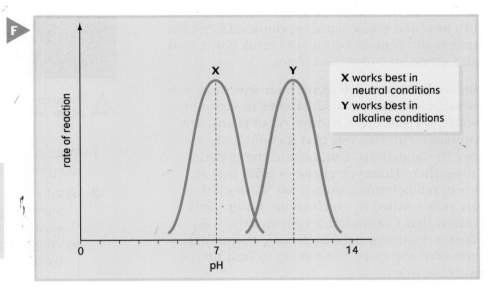

X works best in neutral conditions
Y works best in alkaline conditions

P How could you investigate the effect of pH?

G
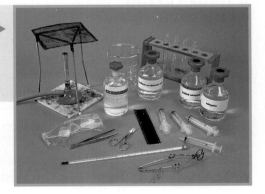

- Protease breaks down proteins into smaller molecules
- How will you change the pH to see what effect it has?

Summary

Enzymes are _____ from living things. They are sometimes called _____ catalysts. Enzymes are large _____ molecules. They work best when the temperature is _____ rather than hot. They are damaged and do not work if the temperature is higher than about 45°C. Enzymes are also affected by _____ .

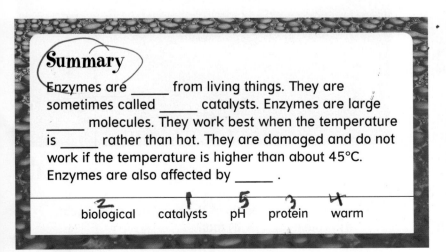

biological   catalysts   pH   protein   warm

6 When you are ill you sometimes get a high temperature. If your body temperature goes too high, you can die. Explain why a high body temperature is dangerous. (Hint: look at the first paragraph of this topic.)

Uses of enzymes

How are enzymes useful to us?

Enzymes have many uses and are used at home and in industry.

Enzymes in the home

Some washing powders are called 'biological detergents' because they contain enzymes. The enzymes in the washing powder break down stains, like food and grease stains on clothes. Dishwasher tablets also contain enzymes to break down food and grease on cutlery and plates.

Before biological detergents were invented, you would have to wash your clothes in very hot water to clean them and get rid of stains. The problem with this was that it could make the dye in the material run, or ruin the material altogether. However, enzymes work best at lower temperatures, usually 40 °C, so clothes are now washed in much cooler water. This means that clothes last longer and the wash does not damage delicate fabrics. It also means you save energy by not having to heat up the water so much.

How do enzymes help to clean clothes and dishes?

Most foods contain **proteins** and **fats**, which are insoluble. Also, stains like sweat contain protein. Protein and fat molecules are very big and they stick to clothes and dishes. To clean the clothes and dishes, the large molecules have to be broken down into smaller molecules. This is called **digestion**. The smaller molecules are soluble and so dissolve in the wash.

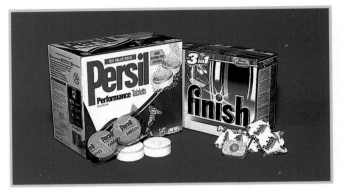

 Biological washing powders and dishwasher tablets both contain enzymes.

1 Write down two useful things that are made using enzymes.

2 a) Why are you able to wash clothes at much lower temperatures with biological washing powders?
b) What are the advantages of using biological washing powder?

3 a) What is digestion?
b) Why do large molecules like protein have to be digested?

A biological detergent will probably have protein-digesting enzymes in it called **proteases**. It will also have fat-digesting enzymes called **lipases**.

4 What are the names of the enzymes that digest:
a) proteins?   **b)** fats?

Enzymes in industry

Enzymes are used in industry to make all sorts of foods.
Table C shows the uses of some of these enzymes.

Type of enzyme	Proteases	Carbohydrases	Isomerases
Use	To 'pre-digest' the protein in some baby foods.	To turn starch syrup into sugar syrup for making chocolates, cakes and other food products.	To turn glucose syrup into fructose syrup, which is used in slimming foods. Fructose and glucose are both sugars.
Why is it used?	The baby may not be able to digest all the protein itself.	Sugar syrup is sweet and makes the food 'taste nice'.	Fructose is twice as sweet as glucose. This means it can be used in smaller quantities in slimming foods.

Using enzymes in industry means that lower temperatures and pressures can be used for the reactions. This means that a company does not have to buy expensive equipment that also uses a lot of energy. This saves money.

One problem in the 1970s was that workers in washing-powder factories developed allergies to the enzymes and came out in a rash. The problem was solved in the factories, but some people using washing powders at home still get rashes and allergies from the enzymes.

Summary

Washing powders contain enzymes called _____ and lipases. Proteases digest proteins and lipases digest _____ . Enzymes are used to make baby food and lots of sweet sugary foods like cakes and _____. Slimming foods contain _____ syrup, which is sweeter than glucose syrup.

chocolate   fats   fructose   proteases

5 What are each of these enzymes used for in industry?
   a) proteases.
   b) carbohydrases.
   c) isomerases.

6 A fat-digesting enzyme found in a fungus can be used in washing powders. It can act at low temperatures. The enzyme breaks down after a few days into carbon dioxide, nitrogen and water.
   a) Why is the fungus useful for making washing powder?
   b) Why do you think the enzyme is 'environmentally friendly'?

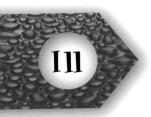

Enzymes and food

How else can enzymes be useful to us?

Our bodies need enzymes to speed up chemical reactions in our cells and to help digest our food. We can also use enzymes to make some foods and drinks.

 1 Write down three examples of foods or drinks that can be made with the help of enzymes.

Enzymes are used to make all these things.

Yeast is a living thing. Enzymes in the yeast cells can turn sugars into carbon dioxide and alcohol. This process is called **fermentation**.

 Yeast cells

 2 What is fermentation?

Making beer and wine

Beer and wine contain **alcohol** and are made by fermentation. Look at diagram C. The yeast cells are fermenting the glucose solution. Since fermentation is a chemical reaction we can write it as a word equation:

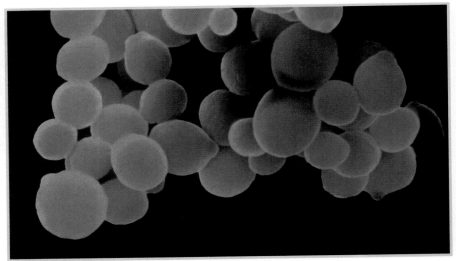

Limewater is used to test for carbon dioxide. If you breathe out through a straw into a test tube of limewater it will turn milky (cloudy). This is because you breathe out carbon dioxide, made in respiration. If the limewater turns milky in diagram C, then carbon dioxide has been made and we know that fermentation has taken place.

glucose → carbon dioxide + ethanol
(a type of sugar)   (a type of alcohol)

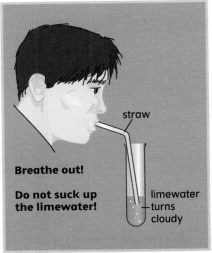

D

straw

Breathe out!

Do not suck up the limewater!

limewater turns cloudy

 3 Imagine you had a test tube full of gas with a bung in the top. You think it is carbon dioxide.

a) What would you do to test if it were carbon dioxide gas?

b) What would be the result if it were carbon dioxide?

C

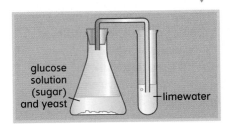

glucose solution (sugar) and yeast

limewater

How could you find out which temperature yeast works fastest at?

- How will you trap the carbon dioxide?
- How will you know which is the best temperature?
- How will you make it a fair test?

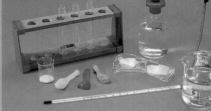

Making bread

Yeast has also been used for thousands of years by people all around the world, to make bread. Yeast is added to the dough mixture. The dough is warmed so that the enzymes in the yeast can work properly. It slowly makes bubbles of carbon dioxide. These bubbles of carbon dioxide make the dough rise. The bread can then be baked in a hot oven.

4 Why does dough rise?

! The ancient Egyptians found out that yeast makes bread rise around 4000 BC!

5 What are microbes?

Using microbes to make food

Microbes are very small living things, usually only one cell big. Yeast and bacteria are both microbes. We have seen how the enzymes in yeast are used to make food and drink.

Making yoghurt

People have made yoghurt for thousands of years. Yoghurt is made from milk, which contains a sugar called **lactose**. There are bacteria in milk. Enzymes in the bacteria change lactose into **lactic acid**. The lactic acid makes the milk curdle and turn thick.

G Straining yogurt makes it thicker.

Summary

Enzymes in _____ can be used to make lots of things like _____ and bread. The enzymes in the yeast turn _____ into alcohol and _____ _____. This process is called _____. To test for carbon dioxide, the gas is passed into _____. The lime water turns _____. Enzymes can also be used to make yoghurt, which is made from _____.

beer   carbon dioxide   fermentation
limewater   milk   milky   glucose   yeast

6 What is yoghurt made from?

7 What is the lactose in milk changed into to make yoghurt?

8 Naan bread, pitta bread and chapattis are all 'flat' breads. They have not risen like other breads. What is the difference between the way they are made and the way ordinary bread is made?

Changing the rate of reaction

What factors affect the rate of reaction?

There are four factors that affect the rate of a chemical reaction. The rate of a chemical reaction can be increased by:

- increasing the surface area of solids
- increasing the concentration of solutions (or pressure, if gases are reacting)
- increasing the temperature
- using a catalyst.

Look at photograph A. It shows marble chips (calcium carbonate) reacting with hydrochloric acid. The marble chips are quite large.

Temperature

Increasing the temperature of the hydrochloric acid will speed up the reaction. Increasing the temperature increases the speed of the acid particles so that:

- they collide with the marble particles more often
- they also have more energy and so the collisions are more likely to result in a reaction.

A

Catalyst

Using a catalyst could speed up the reaction. Different reactions need different catalysts. The catalyst is not used up and can be used over and over again. It remains unchanged at the end of the reaction.

Concentration

Increasing the concentration of the hydrochloric acid also makes the reaction go faster. There are more acid particles in the same volume of liquid and so there are more collisions.

Surface area

Breaking the large chips into smaller chips will increase the surface area and speed up the reaction.

1 a) How can you increase the surface area of a solid like marble?
   b) What could you do to small marble chips to make the reaction go even faster?

2 Why does increasing the temperature increase the rate of reaction?

Enzymes

Enzymes are biological catalysts. They are large protein molecules found in living things. They speed up chemical reactions. The enzymes in yeast speed up chemical reactions like fermentation. The enzymes in bacteria turn milk into yoghurt.

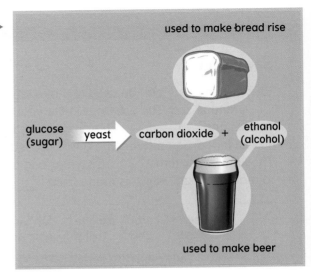

B

used to make bread rise

glucose (sugar) — yeast → carbon dioxide + ethanol (alcohol)

used to make beer

Enzymes are affected by:

- pH – some enzymes work best in acidic conditions, others prefer alkaline conditions
- temperature – the enzymes are usually damaged by temperatures above 45 °C.

Enzymes can be used both at home and in industry.

Using enzymes to bring about chemical reactions has advantages and disadvantages.

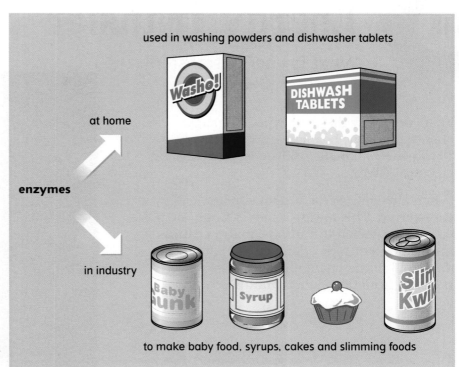

used in washing powders and dishwasher tablets

enzymes

at home

in industry

to make baby food, syrups, cakes and slimming foods

Advantages	Disadvantages
Home	**Home**
- Using enzymes in detergents means less water and energy are needed for washing. - Delicate fabrics are not damaged.	- The enzymes in detergents can cause skin allergies and rashes.
Industry	**Industry**
- Using enzymes in industry means lower temperatures and pressures can be used. This saves money on energy bills and means that expensive equipment is not needed.	- Careful controls are needed to keep the right temperature and pH.

3 Write down three foods that enzymes can be used to make.

4 Write down two things that are made by enzymes that are not foods.

Summary

Four _____ affect the rate of a reaction. These are temperature, surface area, concentration and using a _____. Enzymes and _____ can be used to make lots of useful things. Enzymes can be used to make detergents like washing powders and _____ tablets. They can also be used to make foods and drinks like baby food, cakes and _____ foods. The enzymes in _____ are used to make beer and bread.

catalyst   dishwasher   factors   microbes   slimming   yeast

Energy transfer

What is energy transfer?

There are many different types of energy: chemical energy, heat energy, light energy, sound energy, kinetic (movement) energy and electrical energy.

When a chemical reaction takes place, energy is **transferred**. This means it moves from one place to another. When it transfers, it also changes into a different type of energy. It's a bit like a football player changing clubs. The player transfers from one club to another.

A

The chemical energy stored in these fireworks is transferred to light, heat, movement and sound energy.

 1 Write down six different types of energy.

B

Heat from an exothermic reaction can be used to cook food.

Exothermic reactions

An **exothermic** reaction *gives out* heat energy to the surroundings. The surroundings get hotter. **Combustion** (burning) is an exothermic reaction.

 2 What is an exothermic reaction?

Endothermic reactions

An **endothermic** reaction *takes in* heat energy from the surroundings. The surroundings get colder.

 3 What is an endothermic reaction?

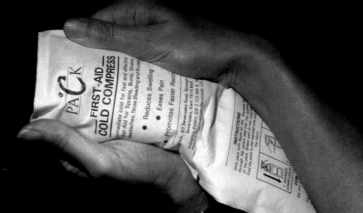

C

This 'ice pack' does not contain any ice at all. An endothermic reaction between two chemicals takes place, making the surroundings colder.

P How could you tell whether a reaction was endothermic or exothermic?

- What measurements will you take?
- How will you make it a fair test?
- How will you know which reactions are exothermic and which are endothermic?

D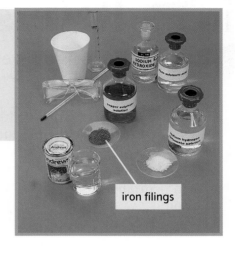

iron filings

Temperature changes in endothermic and exothermic reactions

Look at diagram E. It shows an exothermic reaction and an endothermic reaction. The surroundings could be air, a test tube or water that chemicals have dissolved in, or even your leg!

E

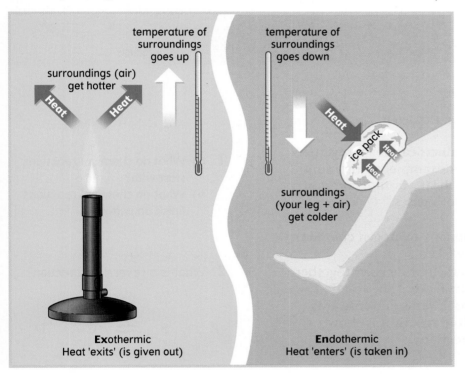

temperature of surroundings goes up

surroundings (air) get hotter

Heat   Heat

temperature of surroundings goes down

Heat

ice pack

Heat   Heat

surroundings (your leg + air) get colder

Exothermic
Heat 'exits' (is given out)

Endothermic
Heat 'enters' (is taken in)

? **4 a)** What happens to the temperature of the surroundings in an exothermic reaction?

b) What happens to the temperature of the surroundings in an endothermic reaction?

? **5 a)** Write down whether each of these chemical reactions is exothermic or endothermic.

Reaction	Temperature at start (°C)	Temperature at end (°C)
A+B	25	30
C+D	20	40
E+F	25	20

b) Explain your answers.

Summary

When a chemical reaction takes place, _____ is transferred to or from the _____. An _____ reaction gives out _____ energy to the surroundings. The temperature of the surroundings _____. An _____ reaction takes in heat energy from the surroundings. The temperature of the surroundings _____.

energy	endothermic
exothermic	falls	heat
rises	surroundings

Reversible reactions

What is a reversible reaction?

A chemical reaction starts off with reactants. The reactants react together to make the products.

reactants ⟶ products

For example, when an acid neutralises an alkali:

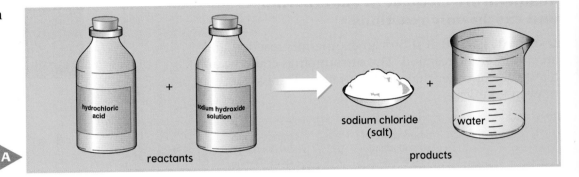

hydrochloric acid + sodium hydroxide solution ⟶ sodium chloride (salt) + water

A reactants   products

Sometimes there is only one reactant:

hydrogen peroxide ⟶ water + oxygen

In some chemical reactions, the products can react together and turn back into the reactants. For example, ammonium chloride (a solid) is broken down by heat, forming ammonia and hydrogen chloride, which are both gases.

ammonium chloride ⇌ ammonia + hydrogen chloride

Some of the ammonia and hydrogen chloride react together to make ammonium chloride, which is what the reaction started with! The reaction can go backwards and forwards. It is a reversible reaction. A **reversible reaction** is shown by half arrows pointing in both directions.

1 a) What do chemical reactions start with?
   b) What do chemical reactions finish up with?

2 What is a reversible reaction?

A + B ⇌ C + D

There are really two reactions going on at the same time, the forward reaction...

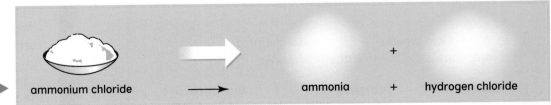

B ammonium chloride ⟶ ammonia + hydrogen chloride

and the backward reaction...

ammonia + hydrogen chloride ⟶ ammonium chloride

C

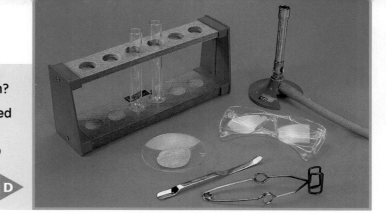

P How could you investigate a reversible reaction?

- Blue copper sulphate crystals can be changed into white powder by heating.
- How do you turn the white powder back into blue crystals (the backward reaction)?

D

Test for water

Copper sulphate crystals normally contain water as well as copper sulphate. They are called hydrated copper sulphate and are blue.

If hydrated copper sulphate is heated, it loses water and turns into anhydrous copper sulphate powder which is white.

When water is added to anhydrous copper sulphate it turns from white back to blue, forming the blue hydrated copper sulphate crystals again. The reaction is reversible. (In the equation below heat is in brackets because it is not a chemical.)

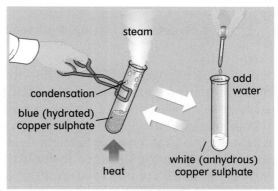

E

hydrated copper   (+ heat energy) ⇌ anhydrous copper   + water
sulphate (blue crystals)   sulphate (white powder)

You can use this to test for water. White anhydrous copper sulphate turns blue if water is present.

Energy changes in reversible reactions

If a reversible reaction is exothermic in one direction, it will be endothermic in the other direction. In the example used above:

- In the *forward reaction* energy is taken in, so this is an endothermic reaction.
- In the *backward reaction* energy is given out, so this is an exothermic reaction.

The same amount of energy is transferred in each case.

? **3** **a)** How can you turn hydrated copper sulphate into anhydrous copper sulphate?

    b) How can you turn white copper sulphate back to blue?

? **4** Look at this reaction:

A + B ⇌ C (+ heat)

a) Is the forward reaction endothermic or exothermic?

b) Explain your answer to part a.

c) How can you turn C back into A + B?

Summary

A reversible reaction is one that can go _____ and forwards. Hydrated copper sulphate is _____ in colour. When it is heated, it changes into anhydrous copper sulphate, which is _____ in colour. When water is added, blue _____ copper sulphate is formed again. This can be used to test for _____ . In a reversible reaction, the amount of energy transferred in both directions is the _____ .

backwards	blue	hydrated
same	water	white

Nitrogen – a very useful gas!

What is nitrogen used for?

The air around us is made up of a mixture of different gases. Pie chart A shows how much of each gas there is in the air.

 1 What percentage of the air is nitrogen?

Plants need nitrogen, which they use to make proteins for growth. Even though the air is nearly 80% nitrogen, plants cannot use this nitrogen. Plants get their nitrogen from **nitrates** in the soil. Special bacteria living in the soil can turn the nitrogen in the air into nitrates. Nitrates are dissolved in water in the soil and the plants get them when they absorb water through their roots.

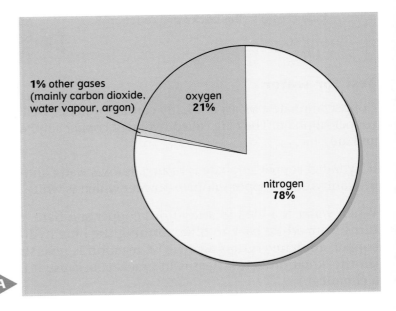

1% other gases (mainly carbon dioxide, water vapour, argon)

oxygen **21%**

nitrogen **78%**

A

Nitrogen can be used to make lots of useful chemicals, like **fertilisers**. Fertilisers are made from nitrates. Using fertilisers adds nitrates to the soil. Fertilisers are used by farmers to increase the **yield** of crops (to get the crops to grow better and produce more food or other useful materials).

 2 What can nitrogen be used to make?

Farmers add fertiliser to the soil. The fertiliser gives crops nitrogen, which they need for growth. **B**

 Lightning can turn nitrogen in the air into nitric acid. Nitric acid falls to the ground and ends up as nitrates in the soil.

 3 Why do farmers add fertilisers to the soil?

4 Write down two ways that nitrates get into the soil.

Crops take nitrates from the soil as they grow. When they are harvested, the crops are cut down and taken away. They are not allowed to rot back into the soil. This means there are less nitrates in the soil. Farmers have to add fertilisers to replace the missing nitrates.

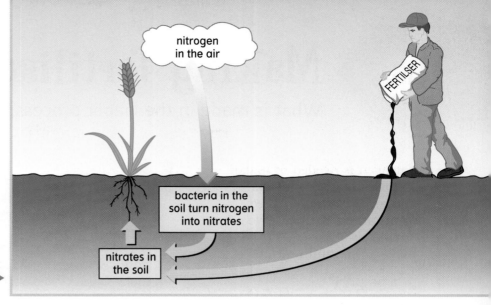

Two ways that a plant can get nitrates. **C**

The 'pros and cons' of using fertilisers **D**

There are advantages of using fertilisers but also disadvantages. Diagram D compares the advantages and disadvantages.

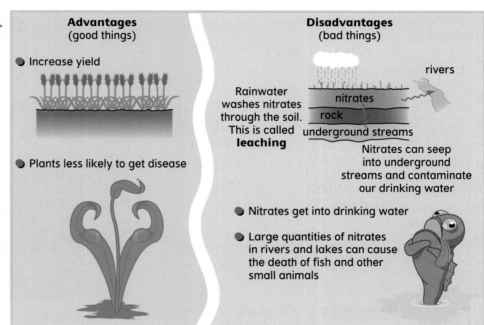

5 a) Write down one advantage of using nitrate fertilisers.

b) Write down one disadvantage of using nitrate fertilisers.

Summary

The air is nearly 80% _____ . Plants need nitrogen to make _____ for growth. Fertilisers have _____ in them. Nitrates can also be made by special _____ in the soil. Fertilisers increase the _____ of a crop. One problem with nitrate fertilisers is that they can seep into _____ and lakes and contaminate our drinking _____ .

bacteria   nitrates   nitrogen   proteins
rivers   water   yield

6 Many years ago farmers used to 'rotate' their crops. They would leave one of their fields without a crop and grow clover instead. Clover roots contain lots of bacteria, which turn nitrogen into nitrates. The clover was ploughed into the field before planting the seeds for a new crop.

Explain why this was a good idea.

Making fertilisers – part 1

What is made in the Haber process?

Nitrogen is needed to make fertilisers. Most fertilisers contain a chemical called **ammonium nitrate**. Two chemicals are needed to make ammonium nitrate:

- ammonia
- nitric acid.

Both these chemicals contain nitrogen.

 1 What chemical is found in most fertilisers?

Fritz Haber won the Nobel Prize for Chemistry in 1918 for making ammonia from nitrogen and hydrogen. But he also made poisonous gases, which were used to kill many soldiers in the trenches during World War One. His wife killed herself because he would not stop making these poisonous gases.

 A

In this topic we will look at how ammonia is made. Ammonia is made by using the **Haber process** which was invented by Fritz Haber.

Two chemicals are needed to make ammonia – nitrogen and hydrogen.

These British soldiers were blinded by poisonous gases. B

$$\text{nitrogen} + \text{hydrogen} \rightleftharpoons \text{ammonia}$$
$$N_2 + 3H_2 \rightleftharpoons 2NH_3$$

The reaction is reversible. Some of the ammonia breaks back down into nitrogen and hydrogen. Special conditions are needed to make as much ammonia as possible:

- Catalyst: iron
- Temperature: 450 °C
- Pressure: about 200 atmospheres. C

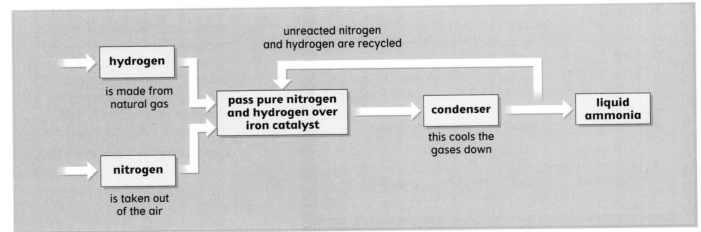

unreacted nitrogen and hydrogen are recycled

hydrogen
is made from natural gas

nitrogen
is taken out of the air

pass pure nitrogen and hydrogen over iron catalyst

condenser
this cools the gases down

liquid ammonia

 Part of the Haber plant at Billingham in North East England.

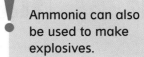 Ammonia can also be used to make explosives.

 2 a) What catalyst is used?
b) What is the temperature?
c) What is the pressure?

Making ammonia uses up huge amounts of energy – about 1% of the world's energy production. But a new catalyst recently discovered in Germany means that less pressure is needed and so less energy is used up.

3 Look at diagram C.
The nitrogen and hydrogen used in the Haber process come from raw materials (natural materials from the Earth).
a) What raw material is used to supply hydrogen?
b) What raw material is used to supply nitrogen?

These conditions are chosen to get a reasonable amount (yield) of ammonia quite quickly. The higher the temperature, the faster the rate of reaction, but the lower the yield. High pressures help the forward reaction (more ammonia made), but involve using much more expensive equipment. Also, if the pressure is too high it can be dangerous. The factory might explode! The nitrogen and hydrogen that have not reacted are recycled and fed back into the start of the process.

1.5 million tonnes of ammonia are made in the UK every year, but over 100 million tonnes are made world-wide.

 4 In the Haber process, a temperature of about 450 °C is used. If the temperature is increased, less ammonia is made. If the temperature is decreased, more ammonia is made. Why do you think the temperature is not lowered below 450 °C, even though more ammonia would be made? (Hint: think about the rate of reaction.)

Summary

Ammonia is one of the chemicals needed to make _____. To make ammonia, _____ and hydrogen are reacted together. This process is called the _____ process. The reaction is _____. Unreacted gases are _____ to make sure there is no waste. A temperature of _____ and a _____ of about 200 atmospheres is used. An _____ catalyst is also needed.

---

450 °C   fertilisers   Haber
iron   nitrogen   pressure
recycled   reversible

Making fertilisers – part 2

How is ammonium nitrate fertiliser made?

Two chemicals are needed to make ammonium nitrate:

- ammonia
  (made in the Haber process)
- nitric acid
  (made from ammonia).

Some of the ammonia from the Haber process can be used to make the nitric acid needed.

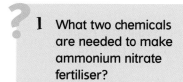 **1** What two chemicals are needed to make ammonium nitrate fertiliser?

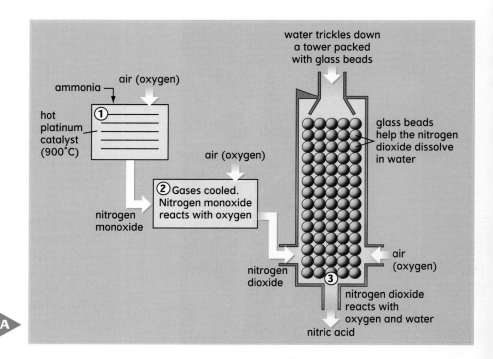

A

Making nitric acid

There are three stages to the process, shown in the diagram.

1 The ammonia is oxidised.
A hot platinum catalyst is needed to speed up the reaction.

ammonia + oxygen ⟶ nitrogen monoxide + steam
$4NH_3$ + $5O_2$ ⟶ $4NO$ + $6H_2O$

2 The nitrogen monoxide is cooled and then reacted with oxygen to make nitrogen dioxide.

nitrogen monoxide + oxygen ⟶ nitrogen dioxide
$2NO$ + O_2 ⟶ $2NO_2$

3 The nitrogen dioxide reacts with oxygen and water to make nitric acid.

nitrogen dioxide + oxygen + water ⟶ nitric acid
$4NO_2$ + O_2 + $2H_2O$ ⟶ $4HNO_3$

Nitric acid can be used to make lots of chemicals. Most of the nitric acid made is used to make fertiliser.

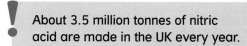 About 3.5 million tonnes of nitric acid are made in the UK every year.

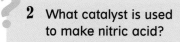 **2** What catalyst is used to make nitric acid?

B *The nitric acid plant at Billingham. It uses ammonia so it is built next to the Haber plant.*

Making ammonium nitrate fertiliser

Ammonium nitrate is a salt. It is made in a **neutralisation** reaction between ammonia and nitric acid. Diagram C shows how this is done.

$$\text{acid} + \text{alkali} \longrightarrow \text{salt}$$
$$\text{nitric acid} + \text{ammonia} \longrightarrow \text{ammonium nitrate}$$

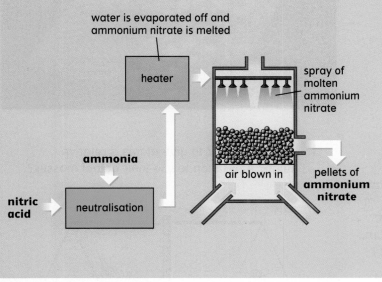

water is evaporated off and ammonium nitrate is melted

heater

spray of molten ammonium nitrate

ammonia

air blown in

pellets of **ammonium nitrate**

nitric acid

neutralisation

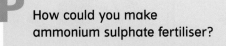 Ammonium nitrate crystals.

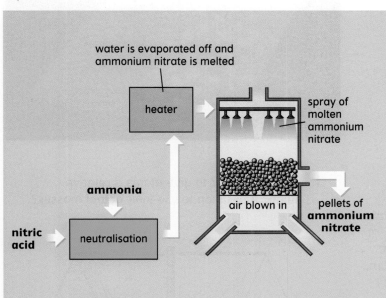

P How could you make ammonium sulphate fertiliser?

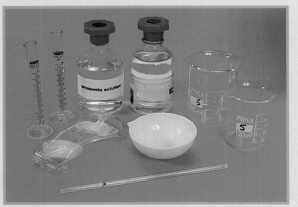

E

4 Jane says that you only need ammonia to make fertiliser.

a) Why does Jane think this?

b) Explain why she is wrong.

3 What type of reaction takes place to make ammonium nitrate? Choose from this list.

combustion
neutralisation
decomposition

Summary

To make nitric acid there are _____ stages. First, the ammonia is _____ to make nitrogen monoxide. The nitrogen monoxide is _____ and reacted with _____ to make nitrogen dioxide. The nitrogen dioxide reacts with water and oxygen to make _____ _____. Now ammonium nitrate can be made in a _____ reaction. The nitric acid is reacted with _____ (an alkali) to make ammonium nitrate. This is then used in _____.

ammonia	cooled	fertilisers
neutralisation		nitric acid
oxidised	three	oxygen

Relative atomic mass

What is relative atomic mass?

All chemicals are made of atoms. The mass of an atom is too small to measure.

Atoms are very small.

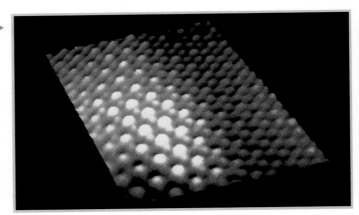

> ! The mass of a nitrogen atom is about 0.00000000000000000000000023 g!

Working with such small numbers would be too difficult. So, it is easier to give each atom a number on a scale and see how heavy they are compared to each other. This number is called the **relative atomic mass**.

The relative atomic mass can be called **R.A.M.** for short and it has a symbol, A_r. The lightest atom is hydrogen, so it is given a relative atomic mass of 1. Carbon is 12 times heavier than a hydrogen atom, so it is given a relative atomic mass of 12. Magnesium is 24 times heavier than hydrogen so it has a relative atomic mass of 24.

Each element in the Periodic Table has a symbol with two numbers. The relative atomic mass is the bigger number of the two. Look at diagram C. It shows two symbols from the Periodic Table. From this we can see that carbon atoms are three times heavier than helium atoms.

? 1 Why is it easier to give atoms a relative atomic mass than to use their actual masses?

The mass of 12 hydrogen atoms equals the mass of one carbon atom.

? 2 Use the Periodic Table on page 246 to find the relative atomic mass of:
   a) oxygen
   b) sulphur
   c) magnesium.

3 Use the Periodic Table on page 246 to answer this question. How many times heavier than an oxygen atom is a sulphur atom?

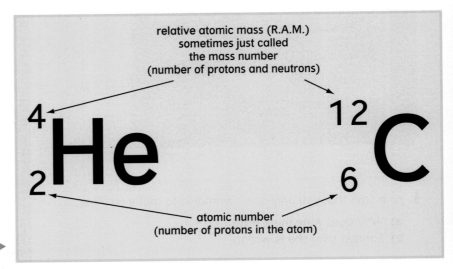

relative atomic mass (R.A.M.)
sometimes just called
the mass number
(number of protons and neutrons)

atomic number
(number of protons in the atom)

Carbon atoms are three times heavier than helium atoms.

Relative formula mass

The chemical formula for water is H_2O. If the relative atomic masses of the atoms in water are added together, you get the **relative formula mass**. It can be called **R.F.M.** for short and has the symbol M_r.

Worked examples

A What is the R.F.M. of water?

Water = H_2O

(R.A.M.s: H = 1, O = 16)

$$2 \text{ hydrogen} = 2 \times 1 = 2$$
$$1 \text{ oxygen} = 1 \times 16 = \underline{16}$$
$$\underline{18}$$

So, the relative formula mass of water is 18.

Ammonium nitrate = NH_4NO_3.

B What is the R.F.M. of ammonium nitrate?

(R.A.M.s: H = 1, N = 14, O = 16)

$$2 \text{ nitrogen} = 2 \times 14 = 28$$
$$4 \text{ hydrogen} = 4 \times 1 = 4$$
$$3 \text{ oxygen} = 3 \times 16 = \underline{48}$$
$$\underline{80}$$

So the relative formula mass of ammonium nitrate (NH_4NO_3) is 80.

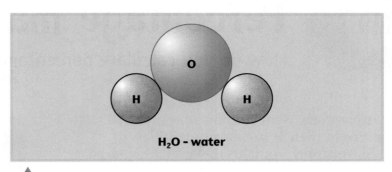

H_2O - water

D   *H_2O is 18 times heavier than one H atom.* E

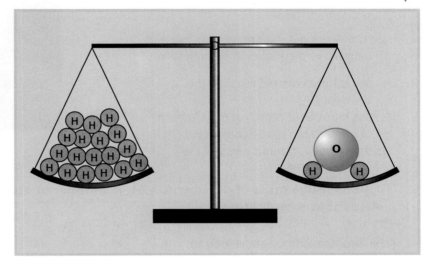

4 Work out the relative formula masses for these compounds:
  a) carbon dioxide – CO_2
  b) ammonia – NH_3
  c) nitric acid – HNO_3
  d) magnesium sulphate – $MgSO_4$.

! Some enzymes have a R.F.M. of about 4 000 000!

5 Element X has a R.A.M. of 20. Element Y has a R.A.M twice that of X and half that of Z.

  a) What is the R.A.M. of element Y?
  b) What is the R.A.M. of element Z?
  c) Write down the name of elements X, Y and Z

6 Work out the R.F.M.s of these.

  a) aluminium sulphate – $Al_2(SO_4)_3$
  b) lead nitrate – $Pb(NO_3)_2$.
     (Hint: $(SO_4)_3$ means there are three lots of SO_4 in the compound.)

Summary

Relative atomic mass is called _____ for short and has the symbol A_r. Hydrogen has a R.A.M. of 1 and carbon has a R.A.M. of 12 which means that a carbon atom is _____ times heavier than a hydrogen atom. We can work out the _____ _____ _____ by adding up all the relative atomic masses in a chemical formula.

| 12 | R.A.M. | relative formula mass |

Percentage mass

How do you calculate percentage mass?

Farmers may want to know how much nitrogen there is in different fertilisers to see which one contains the most. They need to be able to calculate the **percentage mass** of nitrogen in the fertilisers.

A

E You can work out the percentage mass of an element in a compound if you know:

- the relative atomic mass of the element (A_r)
- the number of atoms of the element in the formula of the compound (n)
- the relative formula mass of the compound (M_r)

$$\text{percentage mass of an element in a compound} = \frac{\text{R.A.M.} \times \text{number of atoms (of that element)}}{\text{R.F.M.}} \times 100$$

The equation can be shortened to:

$$\% \text{ mass} = \frac{A_r \times n}{M_r} \times 100$$

Worked examples

A Calculate the percentage mass of hydrogen in water.

The formula for water is H_2O. This means that in a molecule of water, there are two hydrogen atoms and one oxygen atom.

The A_r of hydrogen = 1 and the A_r of oxygen = 16.

The relative formula mass (M_r) of water is:

$$2 \times 1 = 2$$
$$1 \times 16 = \underline{16}$$
$$\underline{18}$$

You then use the relative formula mass in the equation.

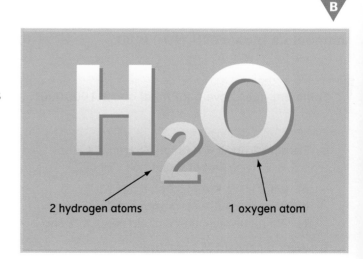

B

2 hydrogen atoms   1 oxygen atom

To work out the percentage mass of hydrogen:

A_r of H   there are 2 H atoms in the formula

% mass $= \dfrac{1 \times 2}{18} \times 100 = 11.1\%$

M_r of H_2O

So the percentage mass of hydrogen in water is 11.1%.

?

1 Find the percentage mass of oxygen in magnesium oxide MgO.

2 Find the percentage mass of nitrogen in ammonia NH_3.

3 Find out the percentage mass of sodium in sodium carbonate – Na_2CO_3.

4 Find out the percentage mass of sulphur in sulphuric acid – H_2SO_4.

5 Find out which one of these fertilisers has the highest percentage mass of nitrogen.

a) ammonium sulphate – $(NH_4)_2SO_4$

b) ammonium nitrate – NH_2NO_3

c) urea – $CO(NH_2)_2$.

(Hint: $(NH_4)_2$ means two lots of NH_4 in the compound.)

B Calculate the percentage of sodium in sodium sulphate – Na_2SO_4.

First work out the relative formula mass (M_r):

2 sodium $= 2 \times 23 = 46$
1 sulphur $= 1 \times 32 = 32$
4 oxygen $= 4 \times 16 = \underline{64}$
$ 142$

Now put the numbers into the equation:

% mass $= \dfrac{A_r \times n}{M_r} \times 100$

% mass $= \dfrac{23 \times 2}{142} \times 100 = 32.4\%$

So, the percentage mass of sodium in sodium sulphate is 32.4%.

Summary

To work out the percentage mass of an element in a compound, three pieces of information are needed; the _____ _____ _____ of the element, how many _____ of the element there are in the compound and the _____ _____ _____ . This information is then put into an _____ to work out the percentage mass of the element.

---

atoms   equation   relative atomic mass (A_r)
relative formula mass (M_r)

Further questions

1 a) This symbol is found on labels for substances like bromine.

Which word from this list completes the sentence below?

| corrosive | harmful | oxidising | toxic |

This symbol tells us bromine is _____. (1)

b) This symbol tells us that a substance is highly flammable.

Name one substance you know that is highly flammable. (1)

2 James is investigating the reaction between zinc and hydrochloric acid.

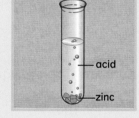

— acid

— zinc

a) Write down four ways James could increase the rate of reaction. (4)

b) Copy and complete the following sentence.

During the experiment the test tube became warm because an _____ reaction was taking place. (1)

3 Yeast is used to make wine and beer. Yeast cells use glucose and produce two new substances.

a) Which word from this list completes the word equation?

| ethanol | oxygen | glucose | starch | water |

glucose → carbon dioxide + _____ (1)

b) What is the name given to this reaction? (1)

c) Why is yeast also used in bread-making? (1)

d) What is the test for carbon dioxide? (1)

4 Marble chips (calcium carbonate) react with dilute hydrochloric acid as shown in this equation:

$CaCO_3 + 2HCl \longrightarrow CaCl_2 + H_2O + CO_2$

The rate at which this reaction takes place can be studied by measuring the amount of carbon dioxide gas produced. The graphs below show the results of four experiments, 1 to 4. In each experiment, the amount of marble chips, the volume and the concentration of the acid were kept the same. The temperature of the acid was changed each time. Small marble chips were used for the experiment.

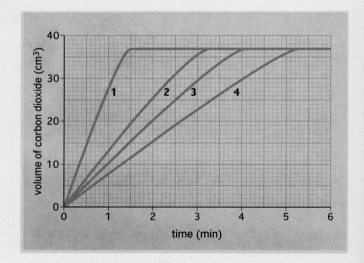

a) Which graph, 1 to 4, shows the results for the highest temperature? Explain fully how you know. (2)

b) Explain what happens to the particles in a reaction when they are heated and why this speeds up the reaction. (2)

c) i) What was the total volume of gas made in each experiment? (1)

ii) Why was it the same volume for each experiment? (1)

iii) How could you increase the volume of gas made in each experiment? (1)

5 The table below shows the results from the reaction between marble chips with (A) 20 cm^3 of dilute hydrochloric acid and (B) 10 cm^3 of dilute hydrochloric acid + 10 cm^3 of water.

Time (min)	Total mass of carbon dioxide produced (g)	
	(A) 20 cm^3 dilute HCl	(B) 10 cm^3 dilute HCl 1 10 cm^3 H$_2$O
0	0.00	0.00
1	0.54	0.27
2	0.71	0.35
3	0.78	0.38
4	0.80	0.40
5	0.80	0.40

a) Plot two graphs on the same grid (time along the bottom). Label the first graph (A) and the second graph (B). (3)

b) Sketch, on the same grid, the curve you might have expected for the reaction (A) if it was carried out at a higher temperature. Label this curve (C). (1)

c) Sketch, on the same grid, the curve you might have expected for reaction (B) if the marble chips had been ground into a powder. Label this curve (D). (1)

d) Explain your answer to part c). (1)

6 An investigation was carried out to see how the rate of this reaction could be speeded up.

hydrogen peroxide $\longrightarrow$ water + oxygen

Powdered manganese(IV) oxide was added to the hydrogen peroxide.

a) The manganese(IV) oxide speeded up the reaction. What name is given to this type of chemical? (1)

b) What would happen to the rate of reaction if:

i) the concentration of the hydrogen peroxide is increased? (1)

ii) lumps of manganese(IV) oxide are used instead of powder? (1)

7 Copy and complete these sentences using the words from the box. You may use each word once, more than once or not at all.

baby foods   carbohydrates   catalysts money   protein slimming foods   temperatures   time washing powders

Enzymes are used to speed up chemical reactions. They are called biological _____. Enzymes are made of _____ and can be damaged by high _____. Enzymes are used in industry to make foods such as _____ _____ and _____ _____. They are used at home in _____ _____, which allow clothes to be washed at lower temperatures. In industry the use of enzymes saves _____. (7)

8 Ammonia is manufactured by the Haber process. Nitrogen and hydrogen react together as shown in the equation below.

nitrogen + hydrogen $\rightleftharpoons$ ammonia

a) What is meant by the symbol $\rightleftharpoons$? (1)

b) Name one compound made from ammonia on a large scale. (1)

c) Why is iron used in the Haber process and what effect does it have? (2)

d) Some of the unreacted nitrogen and hydrogen is recycled. Why is this? (1)

9 Look at the table. It gives some relative atomic masses (A_r).

Atomic symbol	Relative Atomic Mass (A_r)
H	1
O	16
S	32
Zn	65

Sulphuric acid has the formula, H$_2$SO$_4$. It has a relative formula mass (M_r) of 98.

Zinc sulphate has the formula ZnSO$_4$. Work out the relative formula mass (M_r) of zinc sulphate. (2)

Changing state

Why do materials change state?

Water has three different **states**. Ice is the **solid** state of water, and steam is water in its **gas** state. What we normally call water is a **liquid**. All substances are either solids, liquids or gases.

? 1 What are the three states of matter?

Ice, liquid water and steam are all made of the same kind of **particle**. The three states of water are very different, because of the way the water particles are arranged.

In solids, the particles are held together in a fixed arrangement. There are strong forces between the particles, holding them together. The particles can vibrate, but they cannot move around.

? 2 Describe the arrangement of particles in a solid.

A

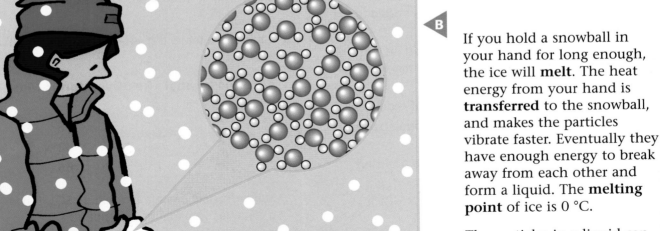

B

If you hold a snowball in your hand for long enough, the ice will **melt**. The heat energy from your hand is **transferred** to the snowball, and makes the particles vibrate faster. Eventually they have enough energy to break away from each other and form a liquid. The **melting point** of ice is 0 °C.

The particles in a liquid can move around, but they are still very close to each other. There are still quite strong forces holding them together.

3 What happens to the particles in a solid when the solid melts?

P How could you investigate what happens to the temperature of a solid when it is melting?

Some particles in water move fast enough to escape from the liquid and become a gas. This is called **evaporation**. If you heat the liquid, more particles have enough energy to escape and the water will evaporate faster. If it is hot enough, all the particles have enough energy to turn into a gas.

When a liquid is evaporating as fast as possible, little bubbles of gas form inside the liquid, and the liquid **boils**. The **boiling point** of water is 100 °C.

C

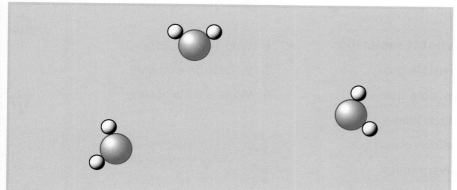

D

4 Explain why putting wet gloves on a radiator helps to dry them.

In a gas, the particles can move around freely. There are only weak forces between them.

5 Describe the arrangement of particles in a gas.

6 a) What does melting point mean?
 b) What does boiling point mean?

7 If some petrol is spilled in a garage, it soon disappears. Describe what is happening to the particles, in as much detail as you can.

8 a) What are the properties of solids, liquids and gases?
 b) Explain these properties using ideas about the arrangements of particles and the forces between them.

9 Spilled petrol usually dries up a lot faster than a puddle of water. What does this tell you about the boiling points of the two liquids? Explain your answer.

Summary

When a solid is heated, the particles in it vibrate _____, and when the solid reaches its _____ point, the particles have enough energy to _____ away from each other and form a liquid. Particles in the _____ that are moving _____ enough may evaporate and form a _____. When the temperature is higher, _____ happens faster. When the _____ of the liquid reaches its _____ point, lots of particles form gas _____ inside the liquid.

---

boiling   break   bubbles   evaporation   fast
faster   gas   liquid   melting   temperature

Elements and compounds

What are different materials made from?

Carbon dioxide is an invisible gas, and water is a clear liquid. Green plants like grass can turn these substances (with a few other things) into new leaves and roots. A cow can turn grass into milk and beef.

A

These changes are possible because everything is made from **atoms**. Atoms are very tiny particles. There are about 100 different kinds of atoms, which can join together in different ways to form millions of different substances.

A substance containing just one kind of atom is called an **element**. When two or more atoms join together, they form a **molecule**.

Elements can look very different, and each one has its own **symbol**.

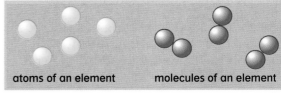

C

atoms of an element   molecules of an element

B

Element	Symbol	What it looks like
hydrogen	H	invisible gas
oxygen	O	invisible gas
carbon	C	black solid
chlorine	Cl	yellow/green gas
sodium	Na	silvery metal
calcium	Ca	grey/white metal

 1 What is an atom?

2 What is an element?

3 What is a molecule?

D

When two or more *different* kinds of atom combine, they form a **compound**. A compound can look quite different to the elements it is made from.

Sodium is a soft, shiny metal. Chlorine is a green, poisonous gas. When they react together they form sodium chloride, which is a white solid.

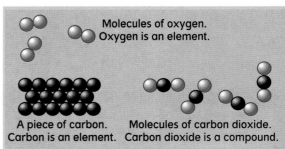

Molecules of oxygen.
Oxygen is an element.

A piece of carbon.   Molecules of carbon dioxide.
Carbon is an element.   Carbon dioxide is a compound.

4 What is the difference between an element and a compound?

E

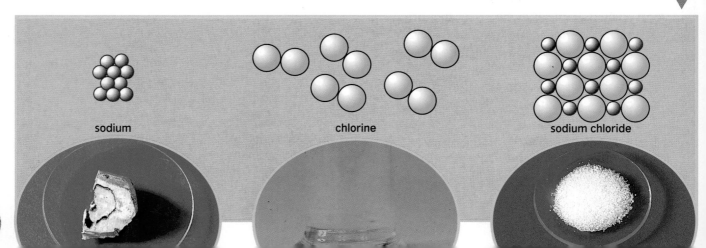

sodium   chlorine   sodium chloride

A compound is only formed when two or more different kinds of atoms **react** together. Oxygen and hydrogen can be mixed together, but they do not form a compound until they react.

F

5 What is the difference between a mixture and a compound?

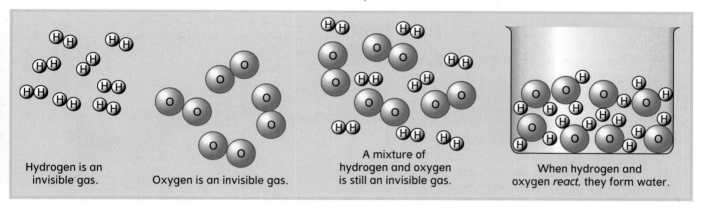

Hydrogen is an invisible gas.

Oxygen is an invisible gas.

A mixture of hydrogen and oxygen is still an invisible gas.

When hydrogen and oxygen *react*, they form water.

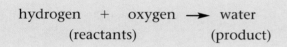

hydrogen + oxygen → water
(reactants)   (product)

G

A reaction can be described using a **word equation**. The arrow shows that the **reactants** change into the **products**.

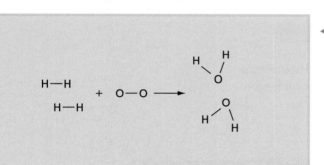

$$H-H$$
$$H-H$$
$$+ \quad O-O \longrightarrow$$

H
O
H

O
H
H

H

We can also represent reactions using symbols for the different elements.

The most common compound in the Universe is water.

6 Look at diagram D.
  a) Write a word equation for the reaction between carbon and oxygen.
  b) Now show the reaction between carbon (C) and oxygen (O) using symbols.

7 Nitrogen is an invisible gas. Hydrogen and nitrogen react together to form ammonia.
  a) Write a word equation for this reaction.
  b) Show the reaction in a particle drawing.
  c) Show the reaction using symbols.

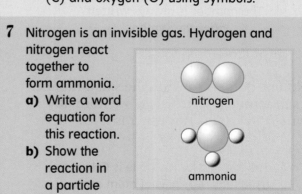

nitrogen

ammonia

I

Summary

Everything is made from _____. There are about _____ different kinds of atom. An _____ is a substance that contains only _____ kind of atom. A _____ is a substance that is made of _____ or more different kinds of atoms _____ together.

| 100 | atoms | compound | element |
| joined | one | two |

Formulae

How do we know which atoms are in a compound?

The names of some compounds make it easy to tell which atoms are in it. One **molecule** of hydrogen chloride is made from one atom of hydrogen and one atom of chlorine.

Some compounds do not have such useful names. The name 'water' does not tell you anything about which atoms are in water. A better way of describing a compound is to use a formula. A formula shows which atoms are in a compound (or in a molecule of an element), and how many atoms of each kind there are.

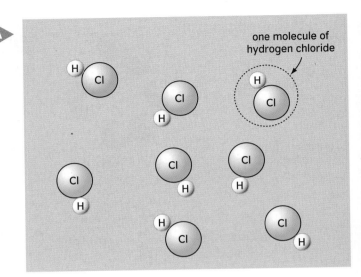

one molecule of hydrogen chloride

A

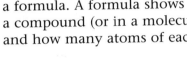 **1** What does the formula for a compound tell you?

The formula for water is H_2O_1.

> This number means that there is one oxygen atom.

> This number means that there are two hydrogen atoms. The number is always written after the symbol.

No one bothers to write the small number 1s in formulae, so the way we normally write the formula for water is H_2O.

2 The formula for methane is CH_4.
  a) Which two kinds of atom are in methane?
  b) How many of each kind of atom are there?

B A model of a water molecule and how it is drawn.

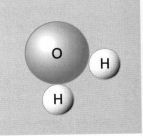

We show the state of an element or compound by putting 's', 'l' or 'g' in brackets after the formula. These are called **state symbols**.

Mg(s) shows us that magnesium is a solid.

H$_2$O(l) shows us that water is a liquid.

Br$_2$(g) shows us that bromine is a gas.

! The letters 'aq' stand for aqueous, which is Latin for 'dissolved in water'.

? **3** Write down the formula for:
  a) oxygen gas
  b) nitrogen gas.

We can also show when a chemical is dissolved in water, by putting (aq) after the formula. NaCl(aq) is salty water!

Some elements have a formula as well. In most elements and compounds that are gases at room temperature, the atoms form molecules. Oxygen, nitrogen and hydrogen all form molecules with two atoms joined together. The formula for hydrogen is H$_2$(g).

We can use formulae instead of words to show what happens in a reaction.

$$\text{magnesium} + \text{chlorine} \longrightarrow \text{magnesium chloride}$$
$$\text{Mg(s)} + \text{Cl}_2\text{(g)} \longrightarrow \text{MgCl}_2\text{(s)}$$

Summary

The _____ of a compound shows which _____ are in the compound, and how _____ of each kind there are. State _____ can be used to show whether the substance is a _____ (s), a liquid _____, or a _____ (g). The symbol (aq) means that the substance is _____ in _____.

atoms   dissolved   formula
gas   (l)   many   solid
symbols   water

? **4** Which elements are in these compounds, and how many atoms of each element are there?
  a) magnesium oxide (MgO)
  b) ammonia (NH$_3$)
  c) calcium chloride (CaCl$_2$).

5 This is the equation for the reaction between sulphuric acid and magnesium.

sulphuric acid + magnesium $\longrightarrow$ magnesium sulphate + hydrogen
H$_2$SO$_4$(aq) +   Mg(s) $\longrightarrow$ MgSO$_4$(aq)   +   H$_2$(g)

For each substance in the reaction, write down:
  a) which atoms are in it, and how many of each kind there are
  b) what state it is in.

6 What would you see if you watched the reaction in question 5? (Hint: look at the state symbol for hydrogen.)

Balancing equations

How do we know how much of a chemical is needed?

When you bake a cake or make biscuits, you follow a recipe that tells you how much of each ingredient to use. In the same way, chemists who make new materials need to know how much of each chemical to use to get the right reaction. They need to work out a **balanced equation** for the reaction.

When a chemical reaction happens, there are always the same number of atoms there at the beginning and at the end. Only the arrangement of the atoms has changed.

A

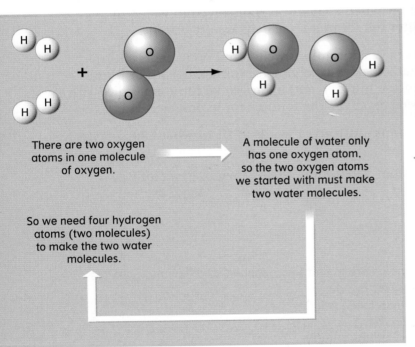

There are two oxygen atoms in one molecule of oxygen.

A molecule of water only has one oxygen atom, so the two oxygen atoms we started with must make two water molecules.

So we need four hydrogen atoms (two molecules) to make the two water molecules.

B

Picture B shows what happens when hydrogen and oxygen react to form water.

We show that two molecules of something are needed by putting a 2 in *front* of the formula.

$$2H_2(g) \quad + \quad O_2(g) \longrightarrow 2H_2O(l)$$

This equation is **balanced**. It shows how many molecules of each substance react together.

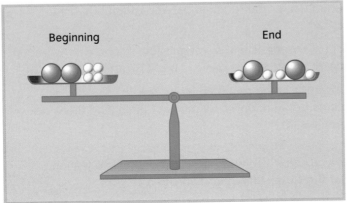

Beginning   End

C

 1   Why do we need to balance equations?

If you could find the mass of hydrogen and oxygen that reacted, their total mass would be the same as the mass of water that forms. In any reaction, the total mass of the reactants is always equal to the total mass of the products.

You can balance an equation by counting the number of atoms of each element on each side of the equation.

For instance, carbon burns in hydrogen to form methane.

$$C(s) \quad + \quad H_2(g) \quad \longrightarrow \quad CH_4(g)$$
$$1\ C \qquad\qquad 2\ H \qquad\qquad\qquad 1\ C,\ 4\ H$$

There are not enough hydrogen atoms on the left-hand side, so we add another hydrogen *molecule* by writing a 2 in front of it.

$$C(s) \quad + \quad 2H_2(g) \quad \longrightarrow \quad CH_4(g)$$
$$1\ C \qquad\qquad 4\ H \qquad\qquad\qquad 1\ C,\ 4\ H$$

Now the equation is balanced.

Remember:

- you can only add whole molecules
- you cannot change the formula of a compound!

P Copper reacts with oxygen to form copper oxide (CO). How could you find out what mass of oxygen reacts with a certain mass of copper?

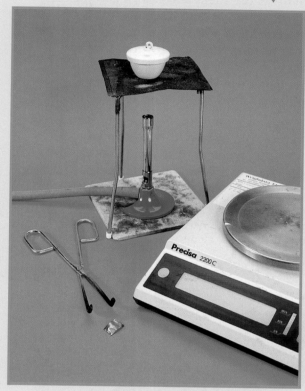

Summary

At the end of a _____, there are always the _____ numbers of _____ as there were at the _____. The _____ of the products is always the same as the mass of the _____. We can show this using a _____ equation.

---

atoms   balanced   beginning   mass
reaction   reactants   same

Ideas about atoms

How have ideas about atoms changed?

Chemists use ideas about atoms to develop new materials. There have been lots of different ideas about what materials are made from. Some of these ideas were linked to people's religions. The earliest scientific ideas came from thinkers in Greece, around 2500 years ago.

? 1 Look at picture A. Write down the four 'elements' that some Greeks thought the world was made from.

A *Empedocles' idea.*

? 2 Which two Greek thinkers had the first ideas about atoms?

B *The first ideas about atoms came from Leucippus, and his pupil Democritus.*

People who investigated chemicals and chemical changes were called alchemists. They tried different ways of treating chemicals to try to make new substances. They were usually trying to turn ordinary metals into gold, or to discover a chemical that would let people live forever. They did not use theories to work out how to make new substances.

? 3 Who used chemistry thousands of years ago?

? 4 What were most alchemists trying to make?

Another very famous scientist called Aristotle believed the ideas about earth, air, fire and water. Most scientists thought that Aristotle was right.

Not many people bothered to think about atoms. The people who actually used chemistry thousands of years ago were the perfume and dye makers, and metal workers, and they did not need theories to help them.

In the 1650s, an English scientist called Robert Boyle did some experiments on gases. He did not just try to make new substances, but made lots of careful measurements. He thought that the results of his experiments could be explained if air was made of separate particles.

5 What was Boyle's idea about gases?

Robert Boyle in his laboratory with his assistant

In 1785, the French chemist Louis-Joseph Proust discovered that all compounds had simple, fixed ratios of different elements in them, measured by mass. For instance, a compound could contain three times as much of one element as another, but never 3.2 times as much, or 2.8 times as much.

Our modern ideas about atoms started with an English scientist called John Dalton. He agreed with Boyle's idea that gases were made of tiny particles. He thought that if all substances were made of particles, and each element was made of a different kind of particle with a different mass, this would explain Proust's discovery.

 E *John Dalton collecting gas from a marsh.*

Dalton's theory was accepted by most scientists because it could explain what happened in experiments. There were still some scientists who were not convinced about atoms until Einstein proved that atoms existed in 1905.

Summary

The earliest _____ ideas came from the ancient Greeks. Some of these scientists suggested that everything was made of _____. It wasn't until the 17th century that scientists started making very careful _____ in experiments. When _____ suggested his _____ about atoms, most scientists believed him because his theory could _____ the results of experiments.

---

atoms   Dalton   explain   ideas
measurements   scientific

6 Why did most scientists believe Dalton's ideas about atoms?

7 How are our modern ideas about atoms different to the ancient Greeks' ideas?

Atomic structure

What are atoms made from?

New and useful materials are being invented all the time. Scientists need to know what is inside atoms, and how they join up, to help them to develop new chemicals.

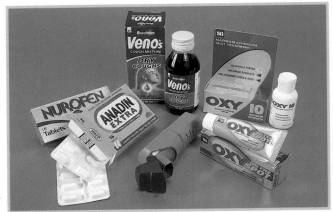

These medicines were all developed using knowledge about atoms and how they join up. **A**

Atoms are made up of three different kinds of particles, called **protons**, **neutrons** and **electrons**.

 1 What are atoms made from?

The masses of these particles are very tiny, so we do not use units like grams. We say that protons and neutrons both have a mass of 1. Electrons are even smaller. They do have a mass, but it is so small that we can ignore it. We say that electrons have a **negligible** mass.

Protons and electrons have **electric charges**. Protons have a **positive** (+) charge, and electrons have a **negative** (−) charge. Neutrons are 'neutral', they have no charge. Atoms always have the same number of protons and electrons, so the charges cancel each other out. Atoms have no overall electrical charge.

All elements are made from these three kinds of particles. Each atom in an element has the same number of protons. A different element will have a different number of protons in its atoms. The number of protons in an atom is called its **atomic number**, or **proton number**.

 3 If an atom has four protons, how many electrons does it have?

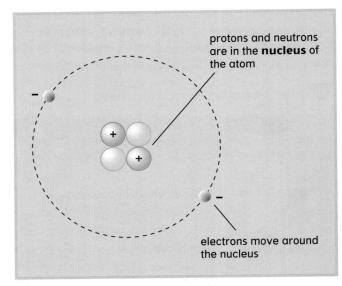

protons and neutrons are in the **nucleus** of the atom

electrons move around the nucleus

B *The structure of a helium atom.*

 2 Why do we say that electrons have a negligible mass?

C

	Mass	**Charge**
proton	1	+1
neutron	1	0
electron	negligible	−1

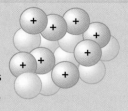

A hydrogen nucleus. Hydrogen atoms always have just one proton in the nucleus. The atomic number of hydrogen is 1.

A carbon nucleus. Carbon atoms always have six protons. The atomic number of carbon is 6.

An oxygen nucleus. Oxygen atoms always have eight protons. The atomic number of oxygen is 8.

D

The mass of an atom depends on the number of protons and neutrons. The total number of protons and neutrons in an atom is called its **mass number**. Look at picture D. Carbon has six protons and six neutrons, so it has a mass number of 12.

4 Look at picture D.
   a) What is the mass number of oxygen?
   b) What is the mass number of hydrogen?

This is the mass number of the element. It is the total number of protons and neutrons in the atom.

This is the atomic number of the element. It is the number of protons in the atom.

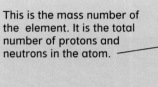

This is the way that information about elements is shown on the Periodic Table.

E

F

Sometimes atoms of an element have different numbers of neutrons. Picture F shows two different carbon atoms. They are both carbon, because they both have six protons in the nucleus. These two atoms are **isotopes** of carbon. Isotopes are atoms of the same element that have different numbers of neutrons. Most elements have different isotopes.

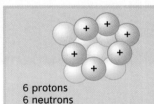

6 protons 6 neutrons

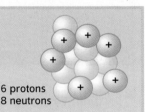

6 protons 8 neutrons

Summary

Copy and complete the following table and sentences.

Particle	Location	Mass	Charge
Proton			
	nucleus		0
		negligible	

The atomic ____ of an atom is the number of ____ in the ____. The total number of ____ and neutrons is called the ____ number. Atoms normally have the ____ number of ____ and electrons, so they have no overall ____. Atoms with the same ____ of protons but ____ numbers of neutrons are called ____ of an element.

charge   different   isotopes   mass
nucleus   number   protons   same   electron
neutron   -1   1   +1   outside nucleus

5 What are isotopes of an element?

6 The element sodium can be shown like this:

23
Na
sodium
11

G

   a) What is the atomic number of sodium?
   b) How many protons does a sodium atom have in its nucleus?
   c) What is the mass number of sodium?
   d) How many neutrons does a sodium atom have?
   e) How many electrons does a sodium atom have?

7 Find out why many Periodic Tables show chlorine with a mass number of 35.5. (Hint: you cannot have half a proton or neutron in a nucleus.)

Electronic structure

How are the electrons arranged inside an atom?

Some elements are very reactive, and some hardly react at all. Elements behave differently because of the way their electrons are arranged.

Calcium reacts very quickly with weak acid.

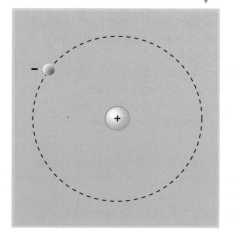

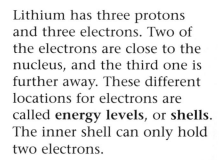

B *Neon does not react in these lighting tubes, even though it is so hot that it is glowing*

Electrons have a negative charge, and protons have a positive charge. An atom normally has the same number of protons and electrons, so it has no overall charge.

1 What kind of charge do electrons have?

2 Boron is an element that has five protons in its nucleus. How many electrons does it have?

Lithium has three protons and three electrons. Two of the electrons are close to the nucleus, and the third one is further away. These different locations for electrons are called **energy levels**, or **shells**. The inner shell can only hold two electrons.

Helium has two protons and two neutrons in its nucleus. It has two electrons moving around the nucleus.

Hydrogen has just one proton. One electron moves around it.

A hydrogen atom. **C**

A helium atom. **D**

A lithium atom. **E**

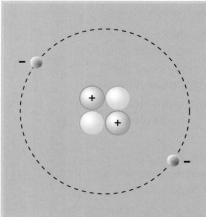

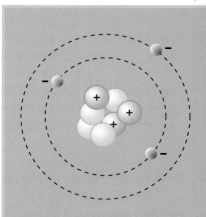

The second shell can hold eight electrons. When this is full, the third shell starts to fill up. The third shell can also hold eight electrons. The inner shells always fill up first. Bigger atoms have even more shells of electrons.

When we are thinking about electrons, we usually draw each electron as a cross, and show the whole nucleus as a circle.

 G *You can think of electrons as boxes that have to be put onto shelves. Each shelf (or shell) can only hold a certain number of boxes (or electrons).*

2,1

2,8,1

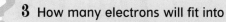 **3** How many electrons will fit into
a) the inner shell?
b) the second shell?
c) the third shell?

 F *A potassium atom.*

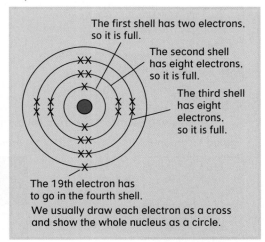

The first shell has two electrons, so it is full.

The second shell has eight electrons, so it is full.

The third shell has eight electrons, so it is full.

The 19th electron has to go in the fourth shell.

We usually draw each electron as a cross and show the whole nucleus as a circle.

We can show the electronic structures of all the elements by drawing diagrams like diagram F. Some elements have nearly 100 electrons, so these diagrams could get very big! An easier way of showing the **electron structure** is to write the number of electrons in each shell. We can show the electronic structure of potassium as 2,8,8,1.

4 Look at diagram F.
a) Make a neat copy of the diagram for potassium.
b) Write the electronic structure for potassium in numbers.

5 Sulphur has an atomic number of 16.
a) How many electrons does an atom of sulphur have?
b) Draw a diagram to show how the electrons are arranged.
c) Write the electronic structure for sulphur in numbers.

6 Lithium and potassium are metals. Sulphur is a non-metal.
a) What do you notice about the numbers of electrons in the outer shells of the metal atoms?
b) What is different about the non-metals?

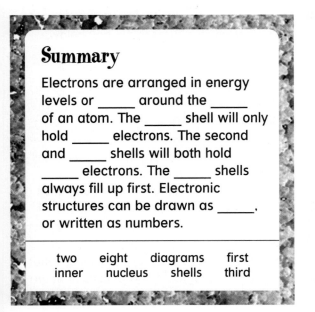

Summary

Electrons are arranged in energy levels or _____ around the _____ of an atom. The _____ shell will only hold _____ electrons. The second and _____ shells will both hold _____ electrons. The _____ shells always fill up first. Electronic structures can be drawn as _____, or written as numbers.

| two | eight | diagrams | first |
| inner | nucleus | shells | third |

139

The Periodic Table

What does the Periodic Table tell us about different elements?

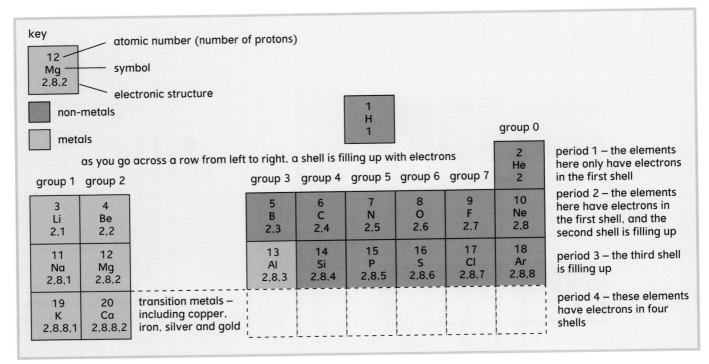

The elements are arranged in the Periodic Table in order of their atomic numbers.

Part of the Periodic Table (the whole table is shown on page 246).

A

?**1** Look at Table A.
   a) If you know which period of the Periodic Table an element is in, what does that tell you about its electronic structure?
   b) If you know how far across a row an element is, what does that tell you about its electronic structure?

The position of an element in the Periodic Table can also tell us something about how the element reacts. Look at table A again. You can see that the elements in a **group** have the same number of electrons in the outer shell. Only the electrons in the outer shell of an atom will take part in chemical reactions. Because all the elements in a group have a similar arrangement of electrons, they usually have similar properties and reactions to each other. They also form compounds with similar formulae.

?**2** Look at Table A. Why do lithium and sodium have similar reactions?

3 Match up the groups with the descriptions of their electron structures in the box below, and write out the correct sentences.
   a) Group 1 elements ...
   b) Group 2 elements ...
   c) Group 7 elements ...
   d) Group 0 elements ...

   | ... all have two electrons in their outer shell |
   | ... all have full outer electron shells |
   | ... all have one electron in their outer shell |
   | ... all have just one gap in their outer shell |

4 Argon is not a reactive element. It is very difficult to make it react with anything. What can you predict about the reactions of neon?

Some properties change as you go down a group. For instance, elements at the top of a group may have lower melting and boiling points than ones at the bottom.

The elements can be split up into **metals** and **non-metals**. Look at the large Periodic Table on page 246. Over three quarters of the elements are metals, and these are shown on the left-hand side of the Periodic Table. The non-metals are shown on the right-hand side of the Periodic Table.

> Some elements, like boron and silicon, are called semi-metals, because they have some properties of metals, and some properties of non-metals.

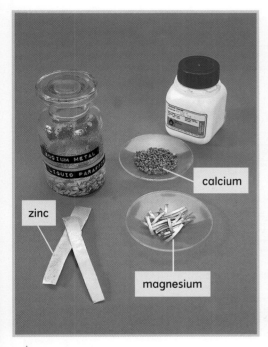

B *Metals.*

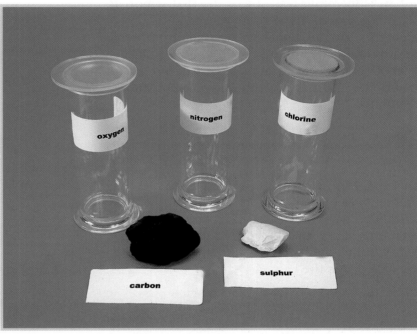

C *Non-metals.*

Summary

The position of an _____ in the Periodic _____ can tell us about its electronic _____. The elements are arranged in order of their _____ numbers. From left to _____ across each row, a particular _____ is being filled with _____. Elements in each group have similar _____ to each other, because they have the _____ number of electrons in their _____ shells. Over three _____ of the elements are metals, and are found on the _____ hand side of the Periodic Table. Non-metals are on the _____ hand side.

---

atomic   electrons   element   left   outer   quarters
   reactions   right   same   shell   structure   Table

5 a) Where are the metals found on the Periodic Table?
b) Where are the non-metals found?

6 If you were drawing a Periodic Table, there are several places you could put hydrogen.
a) Explain why you might want to put it at the top of Group 1.
b) Explain why you might want to put it at the top of Group 7.
c) Why do you think it is usually shown on its own?

Looking for patterns

How was the Periodic Table discovered?

One way that scientists can learn more about the world is to look for patterns, and then try to explain *why* these patterns exist.

Johan Döbereiner was one of the first scientists to look for patterns of properties in the elements. He noticed that chlorine, bromine and iodine had similar properties. He noticed two other triads (or groups of three), but he could not find a pattern in any more of the elements.

 1 Write down the elements in Döbereiner's triads.

In 1864, John Newlands decided to put all the elements in order of the masses of atoms (mass numbers). When he did this he found that the elements could be divided into groups, with every 8th element having similar properties. He called this the Law of Octaves.

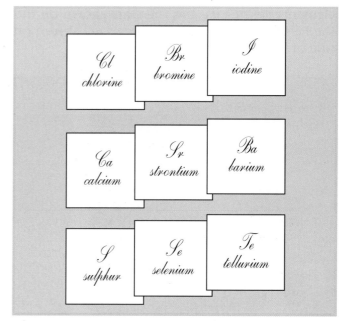

A Döbereiner's triads.

1	H	F	Cl	Co & Ni	Br	Pd	I	Pt & Ir
2	Li	Na	K	Cu	Rb	Ag	Cs	Tl
3	G	Mg	Ca	Zn	Sr	Bd	Ba & V	Pb
4	Bo	Al	Cr	Y	Ce & La	U	Ta	Th
5	C	Si	Ti	In	Zr	Sn	W	Hg
6	N	P	Mn	As	Di & Mo	Sb	Nb	Bi
7	O	S	Fe	Se	Ro & Ru	Te	Au	Os

B Newlands' octaves. Not all the symbols are the same as the modern symbols.
The colours show which elements are grouped together in the modern Periodic Table.

Most scientists took no notice of Newlands' ideas, because his law did not work for all the elements. This was partly because the mass number for some elements had not been measured correctly, and partly because he had not allowed for any new elements that might be discovered.

 2 Look at Table B, and look at the Periodic Table on page 246. Describe one way that Newlands' table is different to our modern Periodic Table.

3 Why didn't scientists agree with Newlands' ideas?

142

A Russian scientist called Dmitri Mendeleev arranged the elements in something like their 'modern' order in 1869. Mendeleev arranged the elements in order of their mass numbers, but he also looked at their properties. If the order of mass numbers put elements in the wrong place for their properties, he ignored the masses. He also left gaps in the table where there was no element that fitted the pattern. He predicted the mass numbers and other properties of these 'missing elements'.

4 Mendeleev did two things to make his elements 'fit' into his table. What were they?

The Periodic Table was useful because it could be used to *predict* the properties of undiscovered elements. In 1874, a French scientist called Paul-Emile Lecoq discovered gallium, one of the 'missing' elements, and found that it had properties very similar to the properties predicted by Mendeleev.

It was not until the structure of the atom was discovered in 1910 that scientists realised that Mendeleev's order for the elements depended on atomic number (the number of protons in the nucleus) rather than mass number. Today, the Periodic Table is a useful way of summarising the structure of atoms.

C Dmitri Mendeleev.

Today, a compound of gallium is used in fighter aircraft to confuse radar.

Summary

Many scientists tried to find _____ in the properties of the _____. The Periodic _____ drawn by Mendeleev was the closest to our modern _____ Table. He left _____ for elements that had not been discovered. Mendeleev's table could be used to _____ the properties of _____ elements. Today, our Periodic Table is based on atomic _____, and is a useful summary of the structure of _____.

atoms   elements   gaps
number   patterns   Periodic   predict
Table   undiscovered

5 Why did scientists start to think that Mendeleev's Periodic Table was useful?

6 What do scientists use to decide the order of elements in the modern Periodic Table?

7 Look at the Periodic Table on page 246. Which pairs of elements are in the 'wrong' place according to their mass numbers?

8 Explain why Döbereiner's triads and Newlands' octaves were not very useful to scientists.

Metals and non-metals

Why are metals and non-metals different?

Metals and non-metals have very different **properties**.

Metals:

- have high melting and boiling points (all except mercury are solid at room temperature)
- are strong, and can be bent or hammered into shape without breaking
- are good conductors of heat and electricity.

Non-metals:

- have low melting and boiling points (nine are gases at room temperature, and one is a liquid)
- are brittle and crumbly when solid
- are poor conductors of heat and electricity.

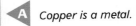
A *Copper is a metal.*

B *Sulphur is a non-metal.*

> Diamond and graphite are unusual non-metals. They are both made of pure carbon, but diamond is very hard and graphite conducts electricity!

 1 **a)** Write down three properties of metals.
   b) Write down three properties of non-metals.

Metals and non-metals are different because of their electronic structures. The electrons in an atom's outer shell form **bonds** that hold different atoms together. Different electronic structures mean that different kinds of bonds are formed. Atoms of metal elements have only a few electrons in their outer shell. Atoms of non-metal elements have outer shells that are full, or nearly full.

2 Why do metals and non-metals have different properties?

Group 0

The elements in Group 0 are non-metals. They are all gases at room temperature. It is very hard to make them react with anything. We say they are very **unreactive**. They are sometimes called the **noble gases**.

Atoms of Group 0 elements all have full outer shells of electrons. When an atom has a full outer shell, it tends to stay that way. If atoms had feelings, you could say that they 'liked' to have a full outer shell. Elements that do not have full outer shells react with other atoms to get full shells.

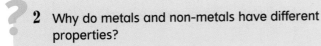

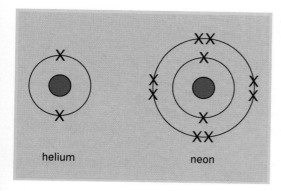

helium   neon

Atoms of the elements in Group 0 all have full outer shells.

C

Argon is used inside light bulbs to stop the hot filament reacting with anything.

E

The noble gases are useful because they do not react.

Helium is much less dense than air. It is used in balloons. The only other gas that can be used in balloons is hydrogen, and that is dangerous because it burns very easily.

Helium is used inside this weather balloon.

D

4   Why are noble gases used inside lights?

5   Why is helium used in balloons instead of hydrogen?

6   Look at picture F, which shows the electron shells of three different elements. For each element, say whether it is a metal or a noble gas. Explain your answers.

F

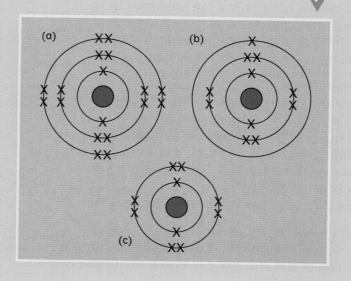

(a)   (b)

(c)

Summary

Most metals have _____ melting and _____ points. They are strong, and conduct heat and _____ well. Metal atoms all have only a few _____ in their outer shells. Non-metals have _____ melting and boiling _____. Solid non-metals are crumbly and _____. They do not conduct _____ or electricity very well. They all have full or nearly _____ outer shells. The noble _____ are very unreactive because they have _____ outer shells. They are useful in lighting, and _____ is used in balloons.

boiling	brittle	electricity
electrons	full	gases	heat
helium	high	low	points

Metallic bonding

How do the atoms in metals stay together?

People have been using metals for thousands of years, to make tools, jewellery and even weapons. Picture A shows some of the properties of metals, and why these properties are important. Metals have these properties because of the way their atoms are held together.

malleable – metals can be hammered into shape.

ductile – metals can be pulled into wires.

metals are strong

A

Gallium is a metal with a melting point of 30 °C. If you hold a piece in your hand it will melt!

1 Write down four properties of metals.

B Metals conduct heat and electricity.

Lithium atoms form lithium ions by losing one electron. Lithium ions have a full outer shell of electrons. **C**

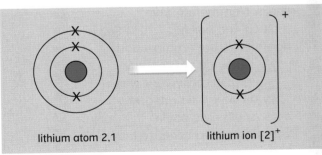

lithium atom 2,1 → lithium ion [2]⁺

All metals have only a few electrons in their outer shells. Metal atoms need to lose electrons if they are to have full outer shells (like the electron structure of a noble gas).

An atom normally has the same number of protons and electrons. The positive charges on the protons are balanced by the negative charges on the electrons. If a metal atom loses some electrons it will have a positive charge, because there are no longer enough electrons to balance out the protons. An atom that has lost (or gained) electrons is called an **ion**.

When you are writing out the electronic structure of an ion you put brackets around the numbers and the charge outside the brackets, for example $[2,8]^{2+}$.

2 a) What is an atom called if it has lost or gained some electrons? Choose the correct answer:
   A isotope **B** electron **C** ion.
   b) Why does an atom that has lost electrons have a positive charge?

In a piece of metal, all the metal atoms lose their outer electrons. The electrons move around between the metal ions. The negative electrons attract the positive metal ions, and hold them together in a regular arrangement called a **giant structure**. There are strong forces holding all the ions in place.

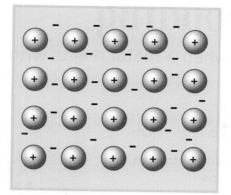

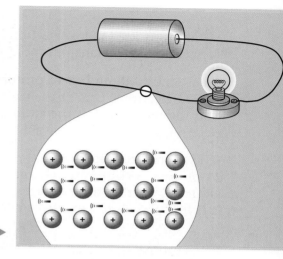

3 Why are the ions in a metal held together?

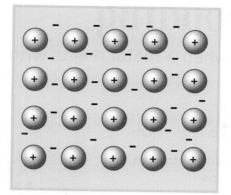
D In a metal the ions are arranged in a regular pattern.

Metals are very good at conducting electricity because the outer electrons can move. If a voltage is applied across a piece of metal, all the electrons drift along in the same direction, forming an electric current. The moving electrons can also transfer heat energy, and this is what makes metals so good at conducting heat.

E

4 a) Why are metals good at conducting electricity?
b) Why are metals good at conducting heat?

Metals are strong because the forces holding the ions together are strong. They can be hammered into shape because of the regular arrangement of ions in the metal. If a metal is hit, layers of ions can slide over each other. The ions are still held together by the electrons between them, so the metal bends instead of breaking.

F

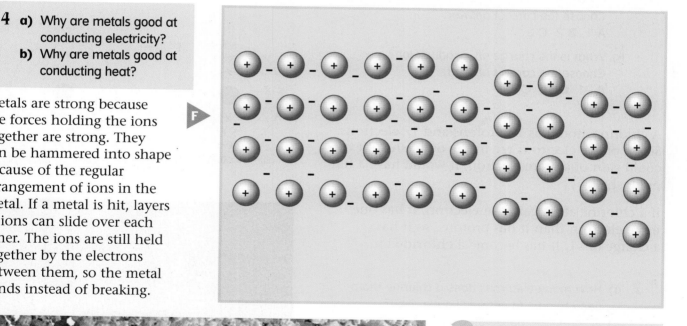

Summary

Metal _____ lose their outer _____ to form positive ions. The electrons move between the _____ and _____ them together. These _____ electrons allow _____ to conduct heat and _____.

---

atoms   electricity   electrons   hold   ions   metals   moving

5 Why are metals:
a) strong?
b) malleable?

6 Mercury is a liquid metal, not a solid. Do you think that some of the electrons in mercury move around easily? Explain your answer.

Ionic bonding

What happens when a metal reacts with a non-metal?

Metal atoms need to lose electrons to gain full outer shells, and non-metal atoms need to gain electrons.

An atom of sodium has 11 protons in its nucleus, and 11 electrons. One of the electrons is in the outer shell. If the atom could lose that electron, it would then have a full outer shell.

If a sodium atom loses an electron, it still has 11 protons with positive charges, but only 10 electrons with negative charges to balance them. It is now a sodium ion with a charge of +1.

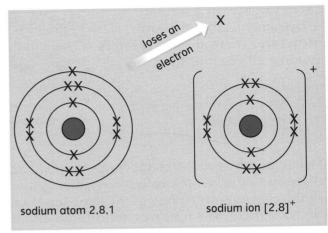

loses an electron X

sodium atom 2,8,1   sodium ion [2,8]⁺

A   **B**

1 a) How many electrons does a sodium atom need to lose to get a full outer shell?
Choose the correct answer:
A 1 **B** 2 **C** 3

b) What is the charge on a sodium ion?
Choose the correct answer:
A −1 **B** +1 **C** +2

A chlorine atom has 17 protons and 17 electrons. Seven of the electrons are in the outer shell. If it could gain one more electron, it would have a full outer shell.

If a chlorine atom gains an electron, it has one more electron than it has protons, so it has a charge of −1. It has become a **chloride** ion.

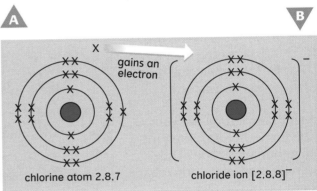

X gains an electron

chlorine atom 2,8,7   chloride ion [2,8,8]⁻

2 a) How many electrons does a chlorine atom need to gain to get a full outer shell?

b) What is the charge on a chloride ion?

When sodium and chlorine react together, the sodium atoms lose electrons and the chlorine atoms gain them. The sodium ions and chloride ions have opposite charges, so they are attracted to each other. The forces holding them together are called **ionic bonds**. A salt is an ionic compound formed by a reaction between an acid and a base.

The reaction of a sodium with chlorine is very violent. This is not how sodium chloride is made. Much of it is found naturally in sea water.

C

Some metals need to lose more than one electron to get a full outer electron shell. Diagram D shows what happens when calcium reacts with chlorine.

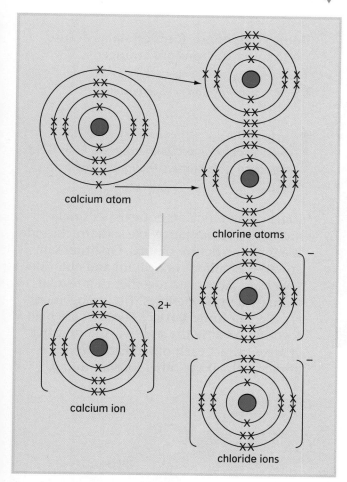

calcium atom

chlorine atoms

2+

calcium ion

−

−

chloride ions

Some non-metals need to gain more than one electron to get a full outer shell. Diagram F shows what happens when magnesium reacts with oxygen.

 Magnesium burning.

F Magnesium reacting with oxygen.

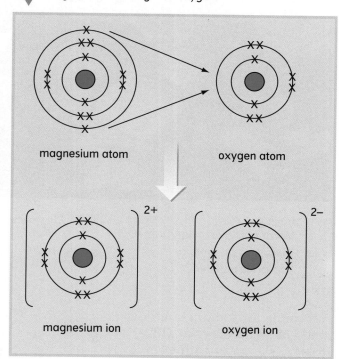

magnesium atom

oxygen atom

2+

2−

magnesium ion

oxygen ion

Summary

Metal atoms need to ____ one or ____ electrons to get a full ____ shell. Non-metal ____ need to gain ____ or more ____ to get a full outer ____. When an atom gains or ____ an electron it becomes an ____ with an electric ____. Positive and ____ ions are attracted to each other. The ____ holding ions together are called ionic ____.

atoms	bonds	charge
electrons	forces	ion	lose	loses
more	negative	one	outer	shell

3 When sodium and chlorine react, what happens to the electrons that the sodium atoms lose?

4 Look at diagram D. Explain why the formula for calcium chloride is $CaCl_2$.

5 Look at diagram F. Explain why the formula for magnesium oxide is MgO.

6 Lithium reacts with chlorine to form lithium chloride. Draw diagrams to show what happens to the electrons in this reaction, and write down the formula of lithium chloride. (You may need to look back at Topic J11.)

Giant structures

How are ions arranged in an ionic compound?

Ionic compounds form crystals because of the way the ions are arranged.

A *Iron sulphide is an ionic compound.*

> **!** Iron sulphide is sometimes called 'Fools Gold' because gold hunters thought it was gold.

Ionic compounds do not exist as single molecules. A substance like sodium chloride is a **giant structure** of ions. One tiny salt crystal has billions of sodium and chloride ions in it, all packed together in a regular arrangement. Sometimes this arrangement is called an **ionic lattice**. The ions are held together because the positive and negative charges attract each other. Each ion is attracted to all the other ions around it.

 1 What is the arrangement of ions in an ionic compound called?

B *The structure of sodium chloride.*

A formula for sodium chloride could be written as $Na_{50}Cl_{50}$, or $Na_{1000}Cl_{1000}$, or with even bigger numbers, depending on how many ions there are in a crystal. For compounds like this, the formula is written as NaCl. This means that for every sodium ion (Na^+), there is one chlorine ion (Cl). The formula for ionic compounds shows us the **ratio** of the different ions.

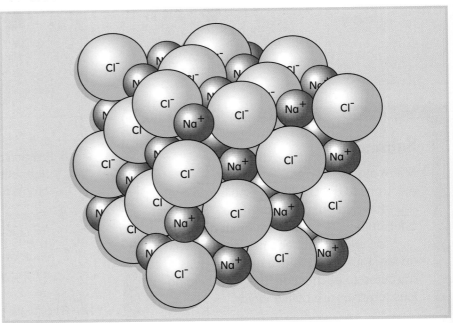

2 If there are a million sodium ions in a piece of sodium chloride, how many chloride ions will there be?

The forces between the ions are very strong. It takes a lot of energy to make the ions break away from each other, so ionic compounds have very high melting points. Ionic compounds are solid at room temperature.

An ionic solid does not conduct electricity. There are no free electrons to move, and the charged ions cannot move.

If the ionic compound is melted, the ions can move around. Because they carry an electric charge, they can conduct electricity.

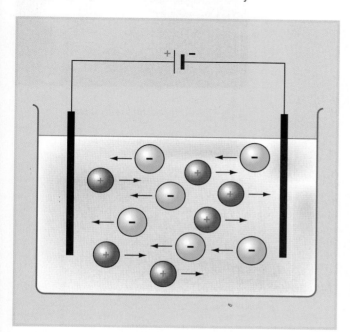

C A molten ionic substance can conduct electricity.

! The melting point of NaCl is 800 °C.

? **3** Are the forces between ions in a compound weak or strong?

4 Do ionic compounds have high or low melting points?

Some ionic compounds dissolve in water. When this happens the positive and negative ions break away from each other, and can move around in the water. A solution of an ionic compound can conduct electricity.

P How could you test some different chemicals to find out which ones are ionic compounds?

D

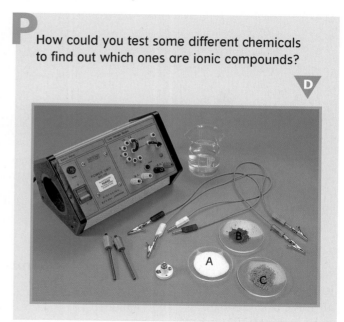

? **5** A solid ionic compound cannot conduct electricity. Explain why not.

6 a) How can you make an ionic compound conduct electricity? (Hint: there are two ways.)
  b) Explain why these methods work.

7 Ions in metals also form giant structures. Explain why solid metals conduct electricity, but solid ionic compounds do not.

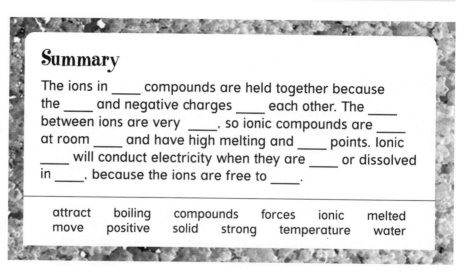

Summary

The ions in ____ compounds are held together because the ____ and negative charges ____ each other. The ____ between ions are very ____, so ionic compounds are ____ at room ____ and have high melting and ____ points. Ionic ____ will conduct electricity when they are ____ or dissolved in ____, because the ions are free to ____.

attract	boiling	compounds	forces	ionic	melted
move	positive	solid	strong	temperature	water

The alkali metals

What are the reactions of the Group 1 elements?

The metals in Group 1 of the Periodic Table are called the alkali metals. They are very reactive. There are six elements in Group 1, and they all have just one electron in their outer shells.

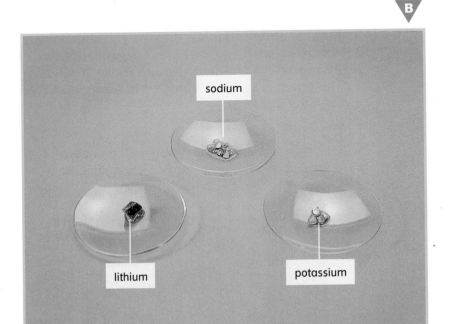

A Caesium reacting with water.

? 1 Look at table C.

a) Which element has the lowest boiling point?

b) Which has the highest melting point?

c) Which one would be the easiest to melt?

Group 1 elements react with non-metals to form ionic compounds. They all have one electron in their outer shell, and so they all lose one electron to form ions with a +1 charge.

The elements in Group 1. C

Element	Symbol	Atomic number	Melting point (°C)	Boiling point (°C)	Reactivity
lithium	Li	3	181	1342	**least reactive**
sodium	Na	11	98	883	
potassium	K	19	63	760	
rubidium	Rb	37	39	686	
caesium	Cs	55	29	669	**most reactive**

! Sodium gas is used in street lights. Liquid sodium is used to cool nuclear reactors.

D *Sodium chloride is an ionic compound.*

The Group 1 metals have very low densities. They float on water. They are also very reactive, and they react with the water. The equation for the reaction of lithium with water is:

lithium + water ⟶ lithium hydroxide + hydrogen

$$2Li(s) + 2H_2O(l) \longrightarrow 2LiOH(aq) + H_2(g)$$

If you collected the gas given off in this reaction, you could show it was hydrogen by testing it with a lighted splint. A test tube of hydrogen would burn with a squeaky explosion.

Lithium floats on water while it is reacting. **E**

? **2** What do the letters in brackets in the symbol equation tell us?

3 How could you show that the gas given off was hydrogen?

All the Group 1 metals form +1 ions which means that the equations for the reactions of the other metals in Group 1 are very similar. They all form hydroxides when they react with water. When Group 1 hydroxides dissolve in water they form alkaline solutions. This is why the Group 1 metals are sometimes called the **alkali metals**.

? **4 a)** Write a word equation for the reaction of sodium with water.
   b) Write a symbol equation for the reaction.

5 Why are the Group 1 metals called the alkali metals?

F *Potassium reacting with water.*

The alkali metals near the bottom of the Group are more reactive than the ones near the top. When potassium reacts with water, the heat of the reaction melts the potassium, and the ball of molten potassium moves around on the surface of the water. The hydrogen produced by the reaction catches fire and burns.

? **6** Look at photograph A. Your teacher is not allowed to show you the reaction between caesium and water. Why do you think this is?

7 Find out why the alkali metals are usually stored in bottles of oil.

8 Why is caesium much more reactive than lithium? (Hint: think about the distance between the nucleus and the outer electron.)

Summary

The metals in Group 1 of the _____ Table form ions with a _____ of +1. They form ionic _____ with non-metals. When they _____ with water they give off _____ gas, and form alkaline compounds called _____. They are known as alkali _____. The metals further down the group are _____ reactive, and have lower _____ and boiling points.

charge   compounds   hydrogen
hydroxides   melting   metals
more   Periodic   react

Covalent bonding

How are atoms of non-metals held together?

There are millions of different compounds in your body, and most of the atoms making up these compounds are non-metal atoms. Most non-metal compounds are held together by a different kind of bonding, called **covalent bonding**. In covalent bonding, atoms share electrons.

Chlorine is written as Cl_2. This is because, in chlorine gas, two chlorine **atoms** form one chlorine **molecule**. They share electrons so that both atoms can have a full outer shell of electrons.

When they are gases, most non-metal elements form molecules with two atoms in them. They are called **diatomic gases** ('di' means two). The only non-metals that do not form molecules are the noble gases. They already have full outer electron shells, so they do not need to share electrons.

Atoms can share more than one pair of electrons. Diagram B shows some molecules which share different numbers of electrons.

Two chlorine atoms can have full outer shells if they share electrons. All the electrons are the same as each other – we can use dots and crosses to make it easier to see which atoms the electrons were originally from.

? 1 What is covalent bonding?

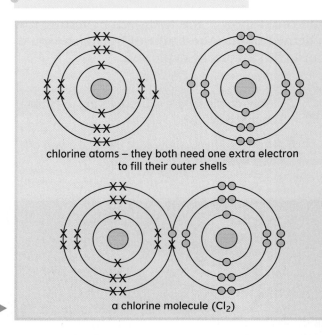

chlorine atoms – they both need one extra electron to fill their outer shells

a chlorine molecule (Cl_2)

A

? 2 Look at diagrams A and B. How many pairs of electrons do these atoms share?
a) nitrogen
b) oxygen
c) chlorine.

3 Why don't the noble gases form diatomic molecules?

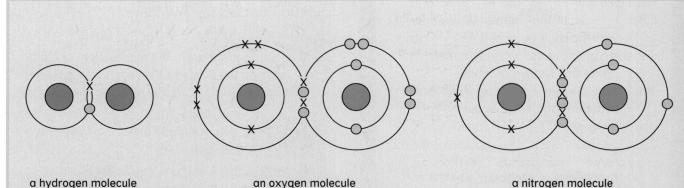

a hydrogen molecule   an oxygen molecule   a nitrogen molecule

Covalent bonds can also form between atoms of different non-metal elements. Picture C shows how hydrogen and carbon share electrons to form covalent bonds. This compound is called methane, and it is a gas.

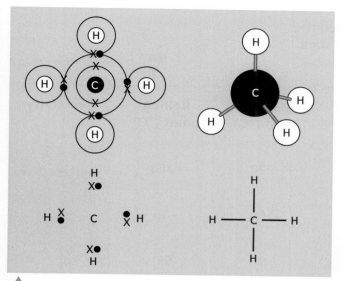

There are different ways of showing covalent bonds.

Non-metal atoms which form covalent bonds often form molecules. Substances made of molecules are often liquids or gases at room temperature. They have low melting and boiling points. They do not conduct heat or electricity well, even when they are solid or liquid, because there are no charged particles to carry the current.

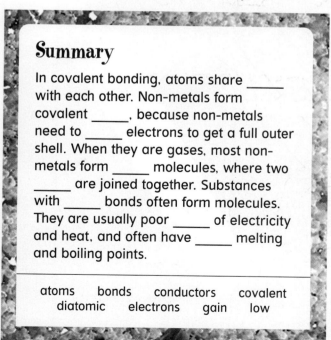

Summary

In covalent bonding, atoms share _____ with each other. Non-metals form covalent _____, because non-metals need to _____ electrons to get a full outer shell. When they are gases, most non-metals form _____ molecules, where two _____ are joined together. Substances with _____ bonds often form molecules. They are usually poor _____ of electricity and heat, and often have _____ melting and boiling points.

| atoms | bonds | conductors | covalent |
| diatomic | electrons | gain | low |

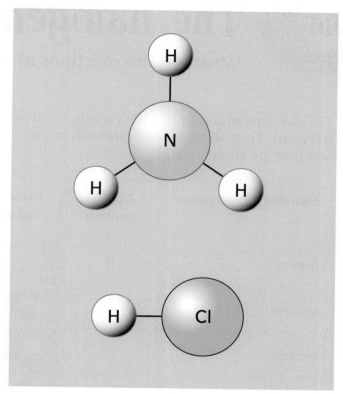

Ammonia and hydrogen chloride are both compounds made from non-metals. They are both gases at room temperature.

4 Look at picture D. Draw a diagram to show how the electrons are shared between the different atoms in hydrogen chloride.

5 This is part of the symbol equation for the reaction that forms methane.
$$C + H_2 \longrightarrow$$
a) What kind of bonding holds the atoms together in methane?
b) Finish writing the equation, balance it and add state symbols.

6 This is part of the equation for the formation of ammonia.
$$N_2 + 3H_2 \longrightarrow$$
a) Finish writing the equation, balance it, and add state symbols.
b) Draw a diagram to show how the electrons are shared between the atoms in ammonia.

7 Explain the difference between covalent and ionic bonding, in as much detail as you can.

The halogens

What are the reactions of the elements in Group 7?

The elements in Group 7 of the Periodic Table are called the **halogens**. They all have seven electrons in their outer shell and they are all non-metals.

 A The elements in Group 7.

Element	Symbol	Atomic number	Molecule of gas	Melting point (°C)	Boiling point (°C)	Reactivity
fluorine	F	9		−220	−188	most reactive
chlorine	Cl	17		−101	−35	
bromine	Br	35		−7	59	
iodine	I	53		114	184	least reactive

Fluorine and chlorine are gases at room temperature, and bromine is a liquid. All the halogens are coloured when they are gases. They all form diatomic molecules (molecules with two atoms joined together covalently).

1 Which halogen has the lowest melting and boiling points?

2 Look at Table A and photograph B. How could you tell the difference between a test tube full of nitrogen and one full of chlorine? There are two ways. (Hint: most of the air is made of nitrogen.)

! Chlorine gas is poisonous. It was used as a weapon in the first World War (1914–1918). Thousands of soldiers were killed or injured by it.

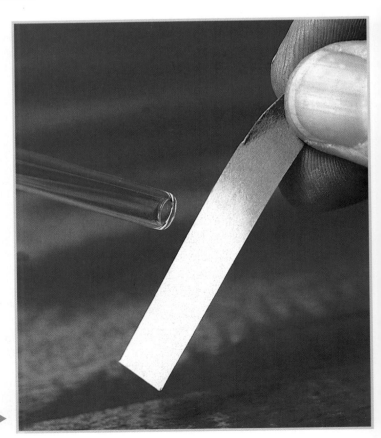

Chlorine bleaches damp litmus paper. **B**

When halogens react with metals they form ionic compounds called **salts**. Halogens all need just one electron to fill their outer shell, and so they all form negative ions with a –1 charge. The ions have a slightly different name to the atoms they were made from:

- a fluorine atom forms a fluoride ion
- a chlorine atom forms a chloride ion.

All halogen atoms form **halide** ions. Fluoride and chloride are examples of halide ions.

The halogens at the top of Group 7 are more reactive than the ones at the bottom. Halogens and metals can react to form halide salts. If a solution of one of these salts is mixed with a solution of a more reactive halogen, a **displacement reaction** happens. The more reactive halogen 'grabs' the metal.

If you mix iodine solution with potassium bromide solution, nothing happens. This is because the more reactive halogen, bromine, is already part of a salt.

Halide salts have many uses. Sodium fluoride is used in toothpaste. Sodium chloride is used to de-ice roads and silver bromide is used to make photographic paper (see topic J18).

Summary

The halogens all form _____ with pairs of atoms. They react with _____ to form salts, and their _____ all have a –1 charge. The halogens at the _____ of the group have the lowest _____ and boiling points, and are the _____ reactive. A reactive _____ will displace a less reactive one from a solution of its salt.

halogen	ions
melting	metals
molecules	most	top

chlorine + potassium bromide $\longrightarrow$ potassium chloride + bromine

$Cl_2(aq) + 2KBr(aq) \longrightarrow 2KCl(aq) + Br_2(aq)$

Chlorine is more reactive than bromine, so chlorine ends up in the compound.

Bromine is less reactive than chlorine, so it is displaced (pushed out) from the salt.

Gritting lorries spread sodium chloride onto roads to de-ice them. **C**

? 3 What is the name of the ion that is formed when a bromine atom gains an electron? Choose the correct answer:

A bromine
B halogen
C bromide

? 4 Copy and complete these word equations. If there is no reaction, write 'no reaction'.
a) iodine + potassium bromide $\longrightarrow$
b) chlorine + potassium iodide $\longrightarrow$
c) bromine + sodium chloride $\longrightarrow$

5 Halides form ionic compounds with metals. Draw a diagram to show the bonding in sodium fluoride.

157

Using sodium chloride

How do we use sodium chloride?

Sodium chloride is the salt you are probably most familiar with, as you put it on your food. It is also the main substance in sea water that makes it taste 'salty'. It is often called **common salt**. Sodium chloride is also very important because of the other chemicals that can be made from it.

> **!** Sodium chloride is an essential chemical in your body. Your body contains about 250 g of salt.

A salt mine.

Sodium chloride is obtained from underground deposits or from sea water.

Sodium chloride is an ionic compound, so it conducts electricity when it is dissolved. Sodium chloride is dissolved in water to make **brine**.

Electrolysis is used to split up the chemicals in brine. Chlorine gas is given off at the **anode** (the positive **electrode**). Hydrogen (from the water in the solution) is given off at the **cathode** (the negative electrode). Sodium ions are left in the solution and form sodium hydroxide (the hydroxide comes from the water).

Salt being obtained from sea water.

1 What is the name for a solution of sodium chloride in water?

2 Name the three products formed when sodium chloride is electrolysed.

chlorine gas (Cl_2)

hydrogen gas (H_2)

sodium hydroxide (NaOH) is left in solution

anode

cathode

D *Uses of chlorine.*

E *Uses of hydrogen.*

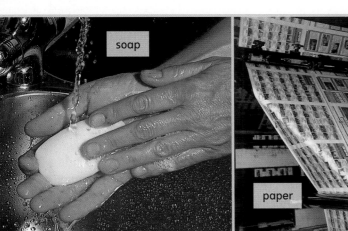

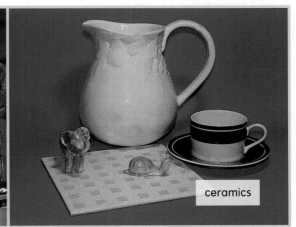

Uses of sodium hydroxide. **F**

Summary

Brine is a solution of _____ chloride in _____. It can be electrolysed to form _____, hydrogen and sodium _____ solution. Chlorine is used to kill _____ in water that is used for drinking or _____ in. It is also used to make hydrochloric _____, disinfectants and _____, and to make PVC (a _____). Hydrogen is used to make _____ and ammonia. Sodium hydroxide is used to make _____, soap and ceramics.

acid	bacteria	bleach
chlorine	hydroxide	margarine
paper plastic	sodium	swimming water

3 Give three uses of chlorine.

4 Give two uses of hydrogen.

5 Give three uses of sodium hydroxide.

6 Hydrogen can also be used as a fuel.
   a) Which element does hydrogen combine with when it is used as a fuel?
   b) Write a balanced symbol equation to show this reaction.

Halogen compounds

How are halogen compounds useful?

Halogens can form covalent bonds with other non-metals, or ionic bonds with metals. Compounds of the halogens are useful in industry and for photography.

Acids

The halogens react with other non-metals to form molecules with covalent bonds. For instance, chlorine reacts with hydrogen to form hydrogen chloride. Hydrogen chloride is a gas at room temperature.

Hydrogen chloride can be dissolved in water. When it dissolves, it splits up and forms positive hydrogen ions and negative chloride ions. A solution that contains hydrogen ions is an acid. When hydrogen chloride dissolves in water it forms hydrochloric acid.

The other hydrogen halides also form acids when they dissolve in water. Acids are useful for making lots of other chemicals, for cleaning metals before they are rust-proofed, and for making printed circuit boards that are used in computers.

A

Fluorine reacts with sodium to form sodium fluoride. Sodium fluoride can help to stop teeth decaying, particularly in children. It is sometimes added to drinking water. It is also added to many toothpastes.

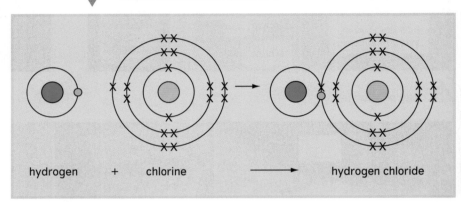

hydrogen + chlorine ⟶ hydrogen chloride

? 1
a) Is hydrogen chloride a molecule or a giant structure?
b) What kind of bonding holds the two atoms together?

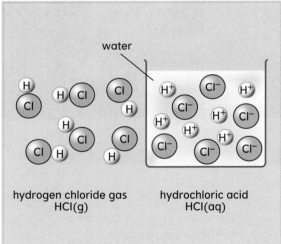

water

hydrogen chloride gas
HCl(g)

hydrochloric acid
HCl(aq)

B

 C *A printed circuit board.*

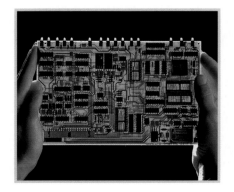

? 2 Look at picture B. What charge is on a chloride ion?

3 Hydrogen bromide dissolves in water to form an acid. What do you think this acid is called?

Photography

Silver can react with chlorine, bromine or iodine to form salts, called **silver halides**. The silver and the halide ions are held together with ionic bonds. If light shines on one of the compounds, it breaks apart and silver is formed again. The same thing happens when X-rays shine on them, or the radiation from radioactive substances.

For instance, silver bromide forms silver and bromine when light shines on it:

$$\text{silver bromide} \longrightarrow \text{silver} + \text{bromine}$$
$$2AgBr(s) \longrightarrow 2Ag(s) + Br_2(g)$$

This reaction is useful in photography. Tiny particles of silver look black, and any silver bromide that does not react can be removed with other chemicals.

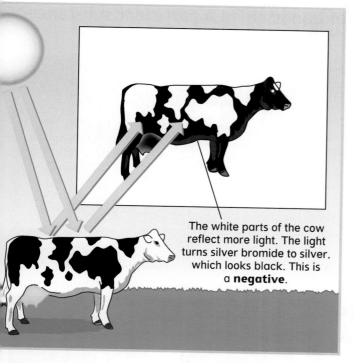

The white parts of the cow reflect more light. The light turns silver bromide to silver, which looks black. This is a **negative**.

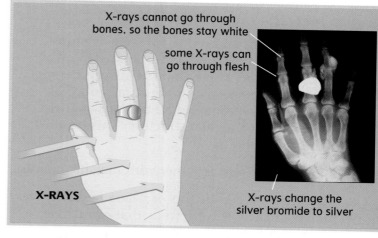

X-rays cannot go through bones, so the bones stay white

some X-rays can go through flesh

X-RAYS

X-rays change the silver bromide to silver

D This is what happens when a photograph is taken. Afterwards, the film is treated with other chemicals to stop the rest of the silver bromide changing.

P A piece of photographic paper goes dark when light shines on it. How could we investigate what affects the darkness of the paper?

F

Summary

Hydrogen reacts with the halogen elements to form _____ halides. These are gases with _____ bonds, but when they _____ in water they form acids. Hydrogen chloride forms _____ acid.

Silver halides are used in _____. When light or other forms of _____ shine on them, the _____ compound is converted into silver, which appears _____ on the film.

| black | covalent | dissolve | hydrochloric |
| hydrogen | photography | radiation | silver |

?

4 a) Which chemical is used on photographic film?

b) What colour does this turn when light shines on it?

c) Which chemical causes this colour?

5 If you have an X-ray, your bones show up white on the film. Explain why this happens in as much detail as you can.

6 a) Write a word equation to show what happens when silver iodide (AgI) splits up.

b) Write a balanced symbol equation for the reaction. Put in the state symbols.

Structures and bonding

How do we know which type of bonds are in a particular substance?

The type of bonding in a substance depends on the type of atoms in it. Substances with different bonding have different properties.

Metals – metallic bonding

Metal atoms all need to lose one or more electrons to get a full outer shell of electrons. The electrons move around between the metal ions. The positive ions are attracted to the negative electrons and all the ions are held together in a regular structure. This is called metallic bonding.

Substances held together with metallic bonding:

- are good conductors of heat and electricity, because of the electrons that can move
- are strong and malleable, because the layers of ions can move over each other
- usually have high melting and boiling points, because of the strong forces holding the ions together.

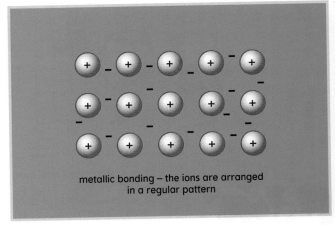

metallic bonding – the ions are arranged in a regular pattern

Metals have metallic bonding.

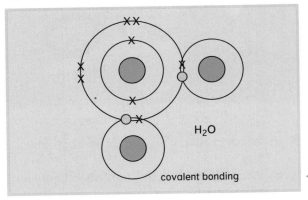

H_2O

covalent bonding

Non-metals – covalent bonding

The noble gases are non-metals. They are very unreactive because they already have full outer electron shells. All other non-metals need electrons to give them a full outer shell. When different non-metal elements react with each other, they share electrons and form covalent bonds.

Compounds made of non-metals often form molecules. They usually:

- have low melting and boiling points
- are poor conductors of heat and electricity, because none of the electrons are free to move

Water and most of the gases in the air all have covalent bonds.

Metals and non-metals – ionic bonding

When a metal reacts with a non-metal, the metal atoms lose electrons to form positive ions, and the non-metal atoms gain electrons to form negative ions. The positive and negative ions are attracted to each other, and held together with strong forces. This is ionic bonding.

Substances with ionic bonding:

- form giant structures
- have high melting and boiling points, because of the strong forces between ions
- conduct electricity when they are molten or dissolved, because the electrically charged ions can move around.

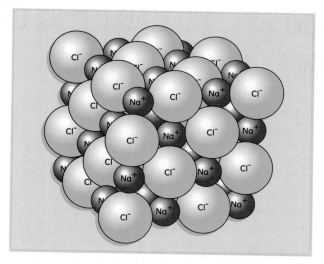

E

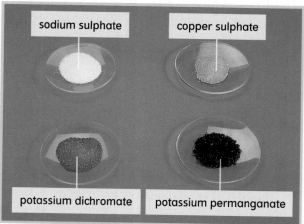

F

These substances all have ionic bonds.

sodium sulphate

copper sulphate

potassium dichromate

potassium permanganate

1 Which kind of bonding is formed between:
  a) two non-metal elements?
  b) a metal and a non-metal?

2 a) Why are metals good conductors of electricity?
  b) Why do ionic substances conduct electricity when they are melted or dissolved in water?
  c) Why don't covalent substances conduct electricity?

3 Why do metals and ionic substances usually have high melting and boiling points?

4 Which kind of bonding produces molecules?

5 a) Why are solid metals good conductors of heat?
  b) Why are covalent and ionic substances poor conductors of heat?

6 Draw electronic diagrams to show how atoms or ions are arranged in the following substances.
  a) copper
  b) hydrogen chloride
  c) sodium chloride.

Summary

Atoms in metals are held together by _____ bonding, where all atoms lose electrons to form _____ ions. Covalent _____ form between two non-metal atoms, when they share _____ to get full outer _____. When a metal and a _____-_____ react, electrons move (from the metal to the _____-_____) to form _____ bonds. The _____ of a substance depend on the type of _____ in the substance.

bonding   bonds   electrons   ionic
metallic   non-metal   positive
properties   shells

Further questions

1 This diagram represents an atom.

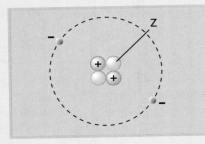

a) What is represented by Z? (1)

b) Copy and complete this table to show the relative masses and charges of the particles in atoms.

	Mass	**Charge**
proton	1	
neutron		
electron	negligible	−1

(3)

2 This symbol represents an atom of chlorine.

$$^{35}_{17}\text{Cl}$$

a) How many protons does a chlorine atom have? (1)

b) How many electrons does it have? (1)

c) How many neutrons does it have? (1)

d) A different isotope of chlorine has a mass number of 37. How many protons does this isotope have? (1)

e) How many neutrons does this isotope have? (1)

3 A magnesium atom has 12 electrons.

a) Draw a diagram to show the electronic structure of a magnesium atom. (3)

b) Will the atom gain or lose electrons when it forms an ion? (1)

c) Choose the correct way of writing the electronic structure of a magnesium ion from the list.

$[2,8,1]^+$ $[2,8]^{2+}$ $[2,8,1]^-$ $[2,8,8]$ $[2,8]^{2-}$ (1)

4 Hydrogen and oxygen react together to form water. A hydrogen atom has one electron, and an oxygen atom has eight electrons.

a) Hydrogen forms molecules with the formula H_2. What kind of bonding holds the two hydrogen atoms together? (1)

b) Draw a diagram to show the electronic structure of a hydrogen molecule. (1)

c) Copy and complete this equation to show the reaction. Balance the equation and add state symbols.

$$H_2 + O_2 \longrightarrow$$ (3)

5 These diagrams show the electronic structures of calcium and fluorine atoms.

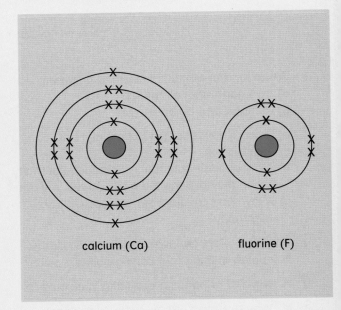

calcium (Ca)   fluorine (F)

a) Which of these two elements is a non-metal? (1)

b) How many electrons does calcium need to lose to gain a full outer shell? (1)

c) What will be the charge on a calcium ion? (1)

d) How many electrons does fluorine need to gain to get a full outer shell? (1)

e) Write down the formula for calcium fluoride. (1)

f) Will solid calcium fluoride conduct electricity? (1)

6 This diagram shows part of the Periodic Table.

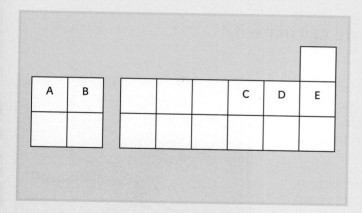

a) Write down the letters of two elements that you would expect to be metals. (2)

b) Which element will have a full outer shell of electrons? (1)

c) Which two elements will form molecules when they are gases? (2)

d) Which element will have the highest mass number? (1)

7 Helium, neon and argon are called noble gases. They are in Group 0 of the Periodic Table.

a) Which of these diagrams shows a noble gas? (1)

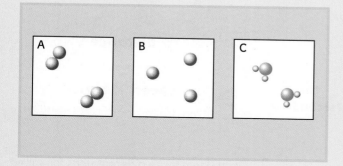

b) Give one use for helium. (1)

c) Name one other noble gas and give a use for it. (1)

8 Sodium chloride is a compound of a metal and a non-metal.

a) Which element in sodium chloride is a metal? (1)

b) What kind of bonding holds sodium chloride together? (1)

c) Name two places that large quantities of sodium chloride can be found. (2)

d) What is brine? (1)

e) Electrolysis can be used to split up brine into chlorine, hydrogen and sodium hydroxide solution. Give one use for each of these products. (3)

f) How could you test a gas to see if it was chlorine? (1)

9 Three of the elements in Group 7 of the Periodic Table are fluorine, chlorine and bromine. Fluorine and chlorine are gases at room temperature.

a) Which diagram represents chlorine gas?

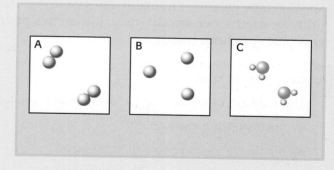

b) Which of these three Group 7 elements is the most reactive? (1)

c) Copy and complete these word equations to show what will happen. If there is no reaction, write 'no reaction'.

   i)   sodium fluoride solution + chlorine $\longrightarrow$

   ii)   sodium bromide solution + chlorine $\longrightarrow$ (2)

10 What sort of bonding would you expect to find in each of the following?

a) sodium bromide   b) hydrogen chloride gas
c) carbon dioxide   d) water
e) iron   f) chlorine gas

K1 Speed

What is speed and how can we calculate it?

Even when we are standing still on the Earth we are actually travelling at extremely high speeds. This is because the Earth is constantly spinning on its axis and travelling around the Sun. Even the Sun isn't standing still; it is travelling at an incredibly high speed around our galaxy.

Speed tells us how far something travels in a certain length of time. The faster something is going, the higher its speed, and the further it will travel in a certain time.

! The fastest land mammal (the cheetah) and the fastest fish (the sailfish) have the same highest recorded speed of 110 km/h.

? 1 Which mammal can travel at the highest speed?

A

Speed can be measured in many different units. The most common units are **metres per second** (m/s), **kilometres per hour** (km/h) and **miles per hour** (mph).

E **Calculating speed**

The speed of an object can be worked out if you know:

- the distance it covered
- the time it took to cover that distance.

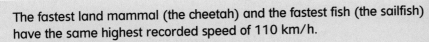

$$\underset{\text{(metres per second, m/s)}}{\text{speed}} \; \blacktriangleright = \; \underset{\text{(metres, m)}}{\text{distance}} \; \div \; \underset{\text{(seconds, s)}}{\text{time}} \; \blacktriangleright$$

```
        distance
    ──────────────────
     speed × time
```

Worked examples

A An athlete runs 100 metres in 10 seconds. What is the speed of the athlete?

speed = distance ÷ time
      = 100 m ÷ 10 s
      = 10 m/s

B A car travels 200 kilometres in 4 hours. What is the speed of the car?

speed = distance ÷ time
      = 200 km ÷ 4 h
      = 50 km/h

Note: the units for speed depend on the units you have used for distance and time.

? 2 Write down three different units for speed.

P How can you make an elastic band car? How can you make it go faster?

Velocity

Scientists often talk about **velocity** instead of speed. Velocity and speed both tell you how fast something is moving. If you only know the speed of an object you can't guess where it will be an hour later because you don't know which direction it is travelling in. Velocity tells us the speed and *direction* of an object's movement. Look at picture C.

- The speed of rabbit A is 2 metres per second.
- The velocity of rabbit B is 2 metres per second going north.

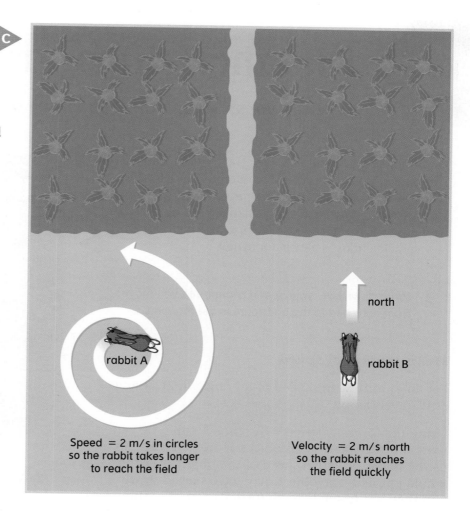

Speed = 2 m/s in circles so the rabbit takes longer to reach the field

Velocity = 2 m/s north so the rabbit reaches the field quickly

3 What does velocity tell you about the movement of an object that speed does not?

Summary

The _____ of an object tells us how far it will travel in a certain _____. To calculate speed we can use the equation:

speed = _____ ÷ _____

The higher the speed of an object the _____ it will travel in a certain time. Speed is measured in _____, km/h or mph. Velocity tells us an object's speed and _____.

direction   distance
speed   time   further
m/s

4 Copy and complete the table below:

Speed (m/s)	Distance (m)	Time (s)
	100	5
	45	9
	40	20
	20	2
	6	3

5 Choose the correct answer to complete this sentence. Two trains are travelling at 100 km/h. One train is travelling north and the other south. The trains have . . . . .

  A the same speed but different velocities.
  B the same velocity but different speeds.
  C both the same speed and the same velocity.

6 Work out how far the following people will travel:

  a) A man walking at 2 miles per hour for 3 hours.
  b) A student running at 5 metres per second for 10 seconds.
  c) A baby crawling at 0.1 metres per second for half a minute.

Distance–time graphs

How can we show an object's journey on a graph?

At the start of a Grand Prix race the cars are stationary. They speed up at an incredible rate but have to slow down to take each corner. It is hard to think of any journey that is travelled at the same speed all the way. Sometimes it is useful to know how the movement of a vehicle changes along a journey.

A

1 Write down how your speed changes as you move from your bed to the bathroom in the morning.

Mean (average) speed

For any journey, the speed of an object may change as it travels along.

Using the formula: speed = distance ÷ time, we can work out the speed of an object. However, this tells us the **mean** (average) speed of the object over the whole journey. The object may have started slowly and then got faster, but the formula can only show us the mean speed. To show how the movement changes during a journey we can use a **distance–time graph**.

2 Why is the mean speed often different from the actual speed of an object at a certain point on a journey?

Distance–time graphs

Distance–time graphs show how far an object has moved at different times. Time is plotted on the *x*-axis and distance is plotted on the *y*-axis.

3 On a distance–time graph, what type of line shows an object that is stationary?

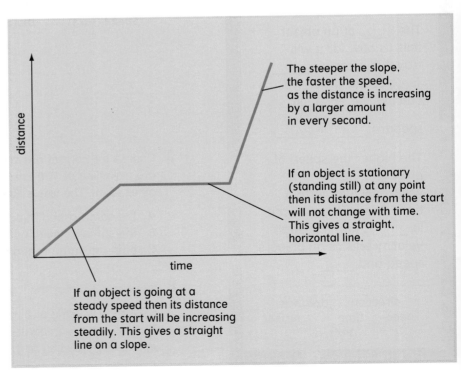

The steeper the slope, the faster the speed, as the distance is increasing by a larger amount in every second.

If an object is stationary (standing still) at any point then its distance from the start will not change with time. This gives a straight, horizontal line.

If an object is going at a steady speed then its distance from the start will be increasing steadily. This gives a straight line on a slope.

B

If an object is getting faster, the slope must get steeper so the line curves upwards. If the object is slowing down the line must get less steep.

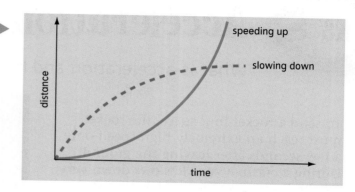

? **4** On a distance–time graph, what happens to the line on the graph if an object speeds up?

P How could you draw a distance–time graph for a car on a track?

? **5** Draw a sketch of a distance-time graph for the following journeys:

a) A girl runs at a steady speed to a bus stop, where she suddenly stops. She gets on a bus. The bus travels at a steady speed that is faster than the girl's running speed.

b) A driver parks the car on a hill but forgets to leave the hand-brake on. The car starts to move and speeds up until it reaches a steady speed. Unfortunately there is a river at the bottom of the hill which the car rolls into. The car slows down and falls at a slower, steady speed in the water until it hits the bottom where it stops.

6 **a)** Describe the following journey travelled by a snail, using the distance–time graph E:

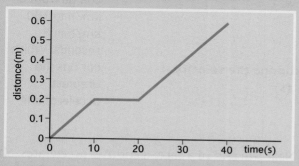

b) For how long was the snail stationary?

c) What was the mean speed of the snail over the whole journey?

d) What was the actual speed of the snail when it was moving at the start of its journey?

! Cheetahs can only run at 110 km/h for short distances. The fastest mammals over very long distances are sled dogs. Teams of these can cover 1000 km in less than 10 days.

D *The Iditarod race covers 1000 km.*

Summary

During most journeys, the speed of an object _____. We can work out the _____ (average) speed using a formula, but to see how the movement changes over a journey we can draw a _____–_____ graph. A stationary object is shown on the graph as a straight, _____ line. An object moving at a _____ speed is shown by a straight, sloped line. The steeper the slope the _____ the speed of the object.

changes distance faster horizontal
mean steady time

169

K3 Acceleration

What is acceleration and how can we calculate it?

To send a rocket into space, the rocket must reach an extremely high speed only a few seconds after leaving the ground. During a crash, a vehicle slows down very quickly compared to a vehicle that stops when it brakes gently.

These things involve an object changing velocity, but it is not just the new velocity that is important, it is how *quickly* the object *changes* velocity.

A

? 1 Put the following objects in order, starting with the object that can change velocity most quickly.

lorry	fighter plane
bicycle	steam roller

! In 1975, the fastest recorded bowler, Jeffrey Robert, accelerated a cricket ball to just over 160 km/h.

The **acceleration** of an object tells us how quickly its velocity is changing. The more the velocity of an object changes in a certain time, the greater the acceleration. Acceleration is measured in **metres per second squared (m/s²)**.

? 2 A Mini car can go from 0 km/h to 100 km/h in 10 seconds, whereas a Ferrari can go from 0 km/h to 100 km/h in 5 seconds. Which car has the greatest acceleration?

E Calculating acceleration

The acceleration of an object can be worked out if you know:

● the change in velocity of the object

● the time it took to change velocity.

acceleration = change in velocity ÷ time taken to change the velocity
(m/s²)   (m/s)   (s)

Worked examples

A At take-off, a plane accelerates from rest to 40 m/s in 10 seconds. What is the acceleration of the plane?

Change in velocity = final velocity − velocity at start
= 40 − 0
= 40 m/s.

Acceleration = change in velocity ÷ time taken
= 40 m/s ÷ 10 s
= 4 m/s².

B Near the end of a race, a sprinter accelerates. She was running at 7 m/s but accelerates to 9 m/s in 4 seconds. What is the acceleration of the sprinter?

Change in velocity = final velocity − velocity at start
= 9 − 7
= 2 m/s.

Acceleration = change in velocity ÷ time taken
= 2 m/s ÷ 4 s
= 0.5 m/s².

P How can you find the acceleration of an object using light?

? **3** What is the unit for acceleration?

acceleration of 2 m/s²

B

Deceleration

When we talk about acceleration we usually think of things speeding up. However, there are just as many situations where objects are slowing down. This is called **deceleration**. To calculate deceleration we can use exactly the same formula as for acceleration. The only difference is that the answer will be a negative number if the object is slowing down.

C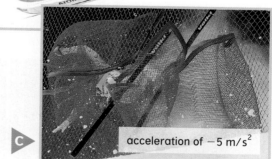

acceleration of −5 m/s²

? **4** Copy and complete table D.

D

Velocity at start (m/s)	Final velocity (m/s)	Change in velocity (m/s) = final velocity − velocity at start	Time taken (s)	Acceleration (m/s²)
0	10		5	
5	4		0.5	
3	9		2	
12	5		7	
4	8		1	

5 In the table above which of the answers show an object which is decelerating?

6 Which has the greatest deceleration, a runner going from 10 m/s to 2 m/s in 5 s or a runner going from 10 m/s to 5 m/s in 2 s?

Summary

Acceleration tells us how quickly something is _____ velocity. The _____ the acceleration the bigger the change in _____ in a certain _____. The acceleration of an object can be calculated using the formula:

_____ = change in velocity ÷ _____ taken to change velocity

Acceleration is measured in _____. When something is slowing down it is _____.

acceleration   changing   decelerating   greater
velocity   time   m/s²

Velocity–time graphs

How can we show the change in speed of an object on a graph?

The distance an object travels can be represented on a distance–time graph. You can also show how the velocity of an object changes, using a **velocity–time graph**. This can tell us more information about the movement of the object, including its acceleration.

Mount St. Helens erupted in 1980, causing rocks to travel at velocities up to 400 km/h (250 mph).

B

? 1 Write down three times today when you have accelerated.

A

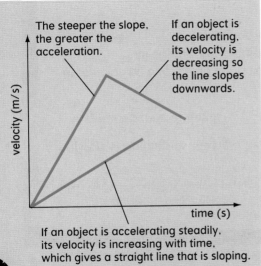

Velocity–time graphs

Velocity–time graphs show how the velocity of an object has changed at different times. Time is plotted on the *x*-axis and velocity is plotted on the *y*-axis.

C

The steeper the slope, the greater the acceleration.

If an object is decelerating, its velocity is decreasing so the line slopes downwards.

velocity (m/s)

time (s)

If an object is accelerating steadily, its velocity is increasing with time, which gives a straight line that is sloping.

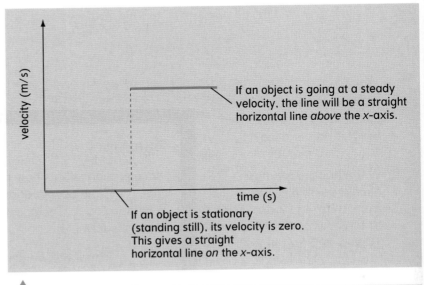

velocity (m/s)

If an object is going at a steady velocity, the line will be a straight horizontal line *above* the *x*-axis.

time (s)

If an object is stationary (standing still), its velocity is zero. This gives a straight horizontal line *on* the *x*-axis.

D

? 2 On a velocity–time graph, what type of line shows an object that is:
a) stationary?
b) travelling at a steady velocity?
c) accelerating?

It is easy to confuse distance–time graphs with velocity–time graphs. Always check the axes on the graph to see which sort it is before answering a question.

P How can we find the speed of an object using ticker tape?

E

3 On a distance–time graph, what is plotted on the *x*-axis?

4 On a velocity–time graph, what is plotted on the *y*-axis?

Here is a journey with both graphs drawn to point out the differences:

A child starts an egg and spoon race, accelerating steadily (A) until reaching a steady velocity (B). He then drops the egg and suddenly stops to pick it up (C). He accelerates again (D) and reaches a steady velocity that is slower than the last time (E), until he reaches the end of the race where he gently decelerates (F) before stopping (G).

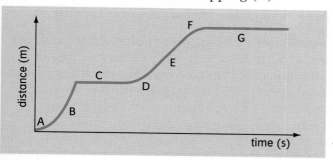

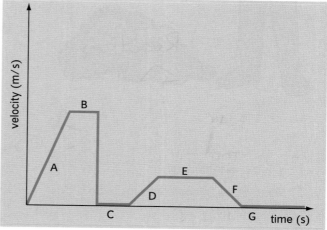

F *A distance–time graph.* *A velocity–time graph.* **G**

Summary

A velocity–time graph shows us how the _____ of an object changes as time goes by. For a stationary object the line is _____ on the *x*-axis. If an object is accelerating steadily, the line will _____ upwards. The greater the acceleration, the _____ the slope. If the object _____ the line will slope downwards. For an object travelling at a _____ velocity the line is horizontal.

---

decelerates   horizontal   slope
steeper   steady   velocity

5 Draw a velocity–time graph for the following journey:

A boy taking part in a 100 m race accelerates steadily for the first 4 seconds, reaching a velocity of 8 m/s. He runs at this steady velocity for 6 seconds before finally accelerating to 10 m/s during the remaining 3 seconds of the race.

6 For the race described in question 5, what was:

a) the acceleration of the boy during the first 4 seconds of the race?

b) the acceleration of the boy during the last 3 seconds of the race?

Balanced forces

What happens when forces are balanced?

A

? 1 What is the force?

2 What three things can a force do?

B

The world could not exist without forces. The forces in our skeletons and muscles hold our bodies up so that we are not floppy lumps on the floor. The forces in the Universe keep the planets in their positions around the Sun and hold the stars together.

! The strongest muscle in the human body is called the masseter. It produces the force needed to raise the lower jaw for biting and chewing.

What is the force?

A **force** is a **push** or a **pull**. This means a force can:

- change the speed of an object
- change the shape of an object
- change the direction that an object is moving in.

When we talk about forces, we say that a force **acts** on an object. This means the force is either pushing or pulling the object. There are very few situations where there is only one force acting on an object. We need to be able to work out what happens to objects when there is more than one force acting.

Forces are measured in **newtons**, **N**. This unit is named after a scientist called Sir Isaac Newton.

Balanced forces

If the forces acting on an object are **balanced** they will cancel each other out. Forces can only cancel out if they are acting in opposite directions, so the forces must be parallel to each other.

In a tug of war competition the teams are pulling in opposite directions. If both teams pull with exactly the same force, then the force to the left cancels out the force to the right so there is no movement in either direction. The forces are balanced.

For forces to balance they must be the same size but act in opposite directions.

? 3 What is the unit of force?

If forces are balanced it is as if there is no force at all. The movement of the object will not change because there is no remaining force to change the movement.

Equal and opposite forces

When an object is resting on a surface, the **weight** of the object is pushing down on that surface. Something has to stop the object sinking down into the surface. There is another force pushing up on the object that cancels out the object's weight. This force comes from the surface.

Whenever an object rests on a surface, the weight pushing down on the surface is cancelled out by an equal force pushing up on the object.

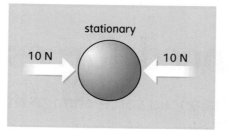

stationary

10 N → ← 10 N

 C *If an object is stationary and the forces acting on it are balanced then the object will remain stationary.*

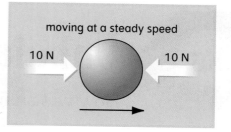

moving at a steady speed

10 N → ← 10 N

 D *If an object is moving and the forces acting on it are balanced then it will carry on moving at the same speed. There is no force to speed it up or slow it down.*

E

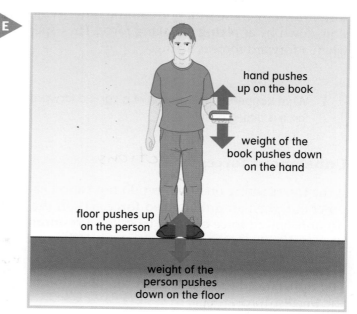

hand pushes up on the book

weight of the book pushes down on the hand

floor pushes up on the person

weight of the person pushes down on the floor

P

How could you investigate whether still water can push?

F

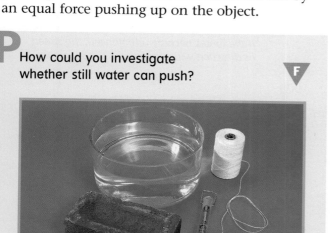

4 a) If forces are balanced, what two things can you say about them?
b) A force of 20 N acts downwards on a stationary object. What force must act upwards on the object for it to remain stationary?

5 Explain how a book can rest on a table, without falling through the table. Use the following words in your answer:

weight   force   balanced
opposite   cancel

Summary

A force is a _____ or a pull. It can _____ the shape or _____ of an object or change the direction an object is moving in. _____ forces cancel each other out. Balanced forces are the same _____ but act in opposite _____. If the forces on an object are balanced, or if no force acts on an object, its motion will not change. It will either remain _____ or continue at a steady _____. When an object is resting on a surface its _____ is cancelled out by the surface pushing up on the object.

balanced   change   directions   push
size   speed   stationary   weight

175

Unbalanced forces

How will an unbalanced force change the way an object moves?

If balanced forces act on an object then its movement will not change. We need to be able to work out what happens when **unbalanced** forces act on an object. You will already have a good idea about this as you are surrounded by these situations all the time. Vehicles slow down by applying a braking force. They speed up when a forward force is acting.

 1 What happens to the motion of a car if a forward force is acting on it?

Unbalanced forces

If the forces acting on an object do not cancel each other out, then an **unbalanced force** acts on the object. An unbalanced force can also be called a **resultant** force. (Remember: Forces can only cancel out if they are parallel to each other.)

The unbalanced force will be in the direction of the biggest force.

 C

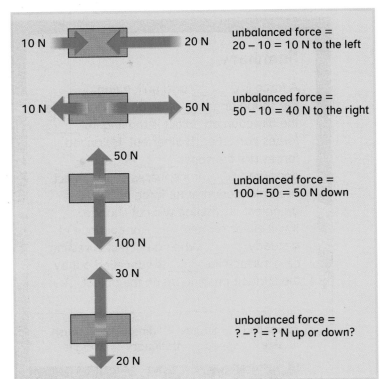

10 N   20 N   unbalanced force = 20 − 10 = 10 N to the left

10 N   50 N   unbalanced force = 50 − 10 = 40 N to the right

50 N   100 N   unbalanced force = 100 − 50 = 50 N down

30 N   20 N   unbalanced force = ? − ? = ? N up or down?

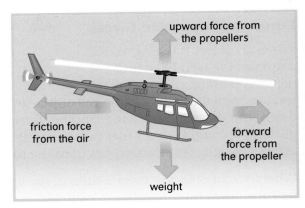

upward force from the propellers

friction force from the air

forward force from the propeller

weight

A When all the forces are balanced, the speed and direction of the helicopter stays the same. If the forces become unbalanced, the speed or direction will change.

About 50,000 years ago, a rock from space hit the Earth with enough force to destroy a whole city. Luckily it landed in an isolated region of Arizona, USA. **B**

 2 The answer to the last part in diagram C has been left out. Draw the box and forces and complete the answer to give the unbalanced force on the box.

3 True or false?

'Forces that are at right angles to each other cannot cancel each other out.'

Changing movement

When an unbalanced force acts on an object, it will change the way the object moves. There are four things to remember that tell us how the movement will change:

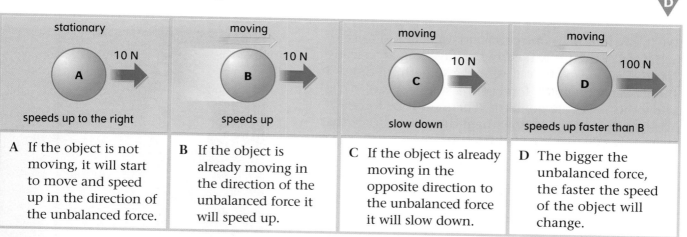

stationary	moving	moving	moving
A 10 N	**B** 10 N	**C** 10 N	**D** 100 N
speeds up to the right	speeds up	slow down	speeds up faster than B
A If the object is not moving, it will start to move and speed up in the direction of the unbalanced force.	**B** If the object is already moving in the direction of the unbalanced force it will speed up.	**C** If the object is already moving in the opposite direction to the unbalanced force it will slow down.	**D** The bigger the unbalanced force, the faster the speed of the object will change.

4 Draw a diagram showing the friction force and forward force on a car that is speeding up. Remember, the size of the force arrows can show which of the forces is the largest.

5 a) Work out the resultant force in each of the situations in diagram F.

b) Describe how the motion of the objects will change using the following words:

accelerate   decelerate   stay still

F

a)
200 N → 300 N
moving forward

b)
10 N ← 20 N
moving backwards

c)
50 N → 40 N
stationary

d)
200 N → 200 N
stationary

6 a) What is the unbalanced force on the box in diagram G?

b) What direction is the unbalanced force acting in?

G

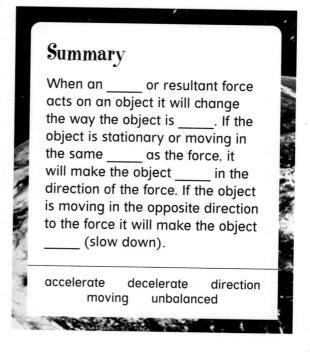

2 N   5 N
3 N
3 N
5 N
10 N

P
How could you power a rocket with water?

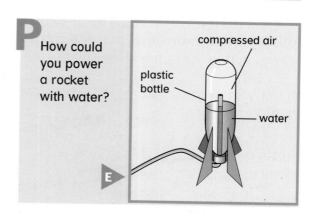

compressed air
plastic bottle
water

E

Summary

When an _____ or resultant force acts on an object it will change the way the object is _____. If the object is stationary or moving in the same _____ as the force, it will make the object _____ in the direction of the force. If the object is moving in the opposite direction to the force it will make the object _____ (slow down).

accelerate   decelerate   direction
moving   unbalanced

Friction

What is friction and how does it affect how an object moves?

We know that if an object has no unbalanced force acting on it then it will carry on travelling at a steady speed. This means that if we make something move, it should carry on going forever at a steady speed! We all know this isn't true on Earth. There must be forces acting on objects that slow them down. The force that slows things down is called **friction**.

? **1 a)** What part of a car provides the forward force that can speed the car up?
b) What force tries to slow a car down?

Friction is a force. It is caused by surfaces sliding over each other. Friction always tries to *slow things down*. Friction always acts in the opposite direction to any movement.

sledge movement

friction of the snow on the runners

B

A *This is Voyager 1 which was sent to fly past the planets in the Solar System. It keeps going at a steady speed because there is no friction in space to slow it down.*

? **2 What is friction?**

Useful friction

Sometimes friction can be helpful. Here are some examples:

 C *Friction stops the ladder falling down.*

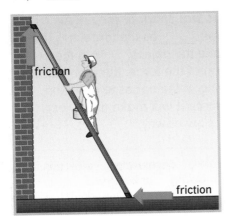

friction

friction

 D *Friction between the brake pad and the wheel stops the wheel turning.*

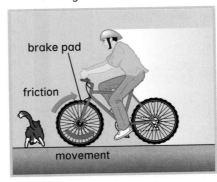

brake pad

friction

movement

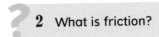 **E** *Friction between the bottle and the fingers stops the bottle slipping.*

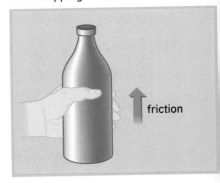

friction

? **3** Use the word 'friction' in your answers to these questions.

a) Why do trainers have rubber on the soles?
b) Why do toothbrushes often have rubber strips on their handles?

How could you find out what combination of surfaces produces the most friction?

Bicycles and cars have tyres made of rubber to help them grip the road. Water on the road reduces friction. There are grooves in the tyres called 'tread' to help push water out of the way when it is wet. Racing cars use tyres with deep, wide grooves in wet weather. If there is not enough friction, the wheels on a vehicle will go round without the vehicle moving forward. This is what happens when a car tries to travel on ice.

4 Why is it hard to walk on ice?

Unwanted friction

Friction is not always useful. In a car engine, friction can make parts of the metal wear away. Oil is used to reduce friction; it acts as a **lubricant**. Friction also makes surfaces heat up. Try rubbing your hands together quickly. Can you feel the heat energy? If there is not enough oil in a car engine to lubricate the parts, the engine can get too hot. This will damage parts of the engine.

! Teflon is used to coat non-stick frying pans. However, it is used on many other surfaces to reduce friction, including saws, zips and even bullets.

5 Look at each of the following pictures. For each picture:

a) write down whether the friction is useful or unwanted
b) explain your answer.

walking   car engine   removing a lid

6 What are the units for friction?

7 Explain why:
a) mountain bike tyres are made from rubber
b) the tyres have grooves in them.

Summary

Friction is a _____. It always acts in the _____ direction to the motion of an object. Brakes use friction to slow _____ down. The brake pad _____ on part of the wheel of the vehicle.

Friction:

- tries to _____ things down.
- will cause surfaces to _____ up.
- can _____ things down.

These affects can be reduced by using a _____ on rubbing surfaces. This will _____ friction.

force   heat   lubricant
opposite   reduce   rubs
slow   vehicles   wear

Braking and stopping

What affects the time it takes for a vehicle to slow down?

It is not long before you can start learning to drive. Driving has obviously got a lot to do with moving, but more importantly you need to be able to stop. This is not as easy as it sounds. It is hard to work out how much space you need to stop a car, because it depends on how fast you are travelling, your **reaction** time, the type of car you have and the type of road you are driving on.

A

1 a) Is it harder or easier to stop a vehicle on an icy road than a normal dry road?

b) Use your knowledge of friction to explain your answer to part a).

! When travelling at 30 mph you are travelling the length of an articulated lorry every second.

Stopping distance

The distance it takes for a car to slow down and stop is divided into two parts:

- **Thinking distance** – the distance the car travels while the driver thinks about braking.
- **Braking distance** – the distance the car travels after the brakes have been pressed.

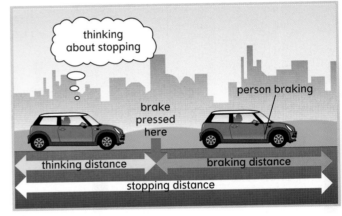

thinking about stopping

brake pressed here

person braking

thinking distance

braking distance

stopping distance

B

P Can you find your reaction time? C

E The total stopping distance of a vehicle is the thinking distance and the braking distance added together:

stopping distance = thinking distance + braking distance

Thinking distance

When a driver sees a red light, it takes time for the brain to send a message to the foot to press the brake. This is the driver's **reaction time**. While this is happening the vehicle is still moving forward at its original speed.

- The faster the vehicle is moving, the further it will travel during the reaction time.
- The longer it takes the driver to react, the further the vehicle will travel during the reaction time.

2 What is the thinking distance?

A driver's reaction time will be increased if the driver is tired, has taken drugs or drunk alcohol. This is why the police are trying so hard to stop people driving under the influence of drugs or alcohol. The longer a person's reaction time is, the longer it will take for a vehicle to stop in an emergency.

Poor visibility, due to fog or heavy rain, makes it harder for drivers to see when they need to stop.

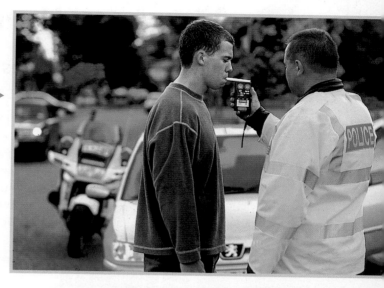

Braking distance

Once a driver has pressed the brakes, the vehicle begins to slow down.

- The faster the vehicle is moving, the longer it will take to slow down, for a certain **braking force**.

- If a bigger braking force is used to stop the vehicle, the time for the vehicle to stop will decrease.

If the road is wet or icy, this will increase the braking distance. If too big a braking force is used, the tyres may slide on the road because there is not enough friction. Vehicles must also be well maintained. If the brake pads on a vehicle are worn down it will take longer for a vehicle to slow down when the brakes are applied.

E The brake pads of a Formula 1 car glow, due to the amount of force used.

Summary

The _____ distance for a vehicle is made up of the _____ distance and the braking _____. The thinking distance is the distance travelled during the driver's _____ time. If the driver is tired or _____ this will increase the reaction time. The braking distance is increased if the road is _____ or wet, or if the vehicle is poorly _____. If a driver uses too large a braking _____ the friction between the road and tyres may not be enough to stop the car _____.

---

distance   drunk   force   icy   maintained
   reaction   skidding   stopping   thinking

4 Which of the following will increase the braking distance of a car?

   A a tired driver
   B a drunk driver
   C worn brake pads.

5 The thinking distance is 20 metres and the braking distance of a car is 30 metres. What is the stopping distance of the car?

6 A car is travelling at 30 m/s. The thinking time of the driver is 2 s. In an emergency, how far will the car travel before the driver presses the brake?

Moving through fluids

How can liquids and gases affect how an object moves?

When two solid surfaces move over each other, friction tries to stop the movement. Sometimes an object isn't moving on a solid surface, but it still experiences a friction force that slows it down. For instance, if you are swimming and you stop propelling yourself forward, the water slows you down until you stop moving. When you throw a ball it doesn't keep going forever, the air slows it down.

When a plane is flying, the air it moves through pushes against the front surfaces of the plane.

A

1 What tries to slow a plane down when it is flying?

Air resistance and drag

Liquids and gases are called **fluids**. The type of friction that objects feel when they are moving through a fluid is called **drag**. If the object is moving in the air, then this friction force is sometimes called **air resistance**. Drag is caused by the particles in a fluid hitting the front surface of the object. This makes a force that pushes in the opposite direction to the movement of the object.

2 What causes air resistance?

3 What two forces try to slow a car down when it is travelling along a road?

B

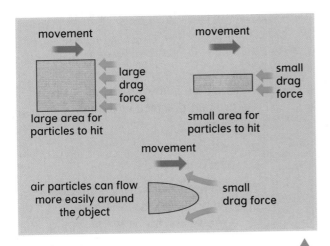

C

 When a shuttle re-enters the Earth's atmosphere, the friction caused by the atmosphere raises the surface temperature of the shuttle to over 950 °C.

The bigger the front **surface area** of an object, the more particles can hit the object. This means the drag force or air resistance will be bigger. Some objects are specially designed to reduce drag by making the area of the front surface smaller. The shape of the front surface also changes the amount of drag. Some shapes make it easier for the liquid or gas to flow over them. This is called **streamlining**. Streamlining reduces drag.

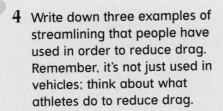

4 Write down three examples of streamlining that people have used in order to reduce drag. Remember, it's not just used in vehicles; think about what athletes do to reduce drag.

P

How could you investigate the force needed to move an object at different speeds?

D

5 a) What pushes against the front of a lorry as it travels along a motorway?

b) Will this push get larger or smaller if the lorry slows down?

Summary

When objects move through a liquid or a _____, drag tries to _____ them down. If the object is moving through air the force is also called _____ _____. It is caused by _____ hitting the front surface of the object. The bigger the front surface _____ of the object, the _____ the force will be. _____ can reduce drag by making it easier for the particles to _____ over the object. The _____ the object is travelling, the bigger the _____ will be.

air resistance	area	bigger
drag	flow	faster	gas
particles	slow	streamlining

Speed and drag

When you cycle down a hill and get faster you might have noticed that the force of the wind pushing against you gets stronger. This is the case for all moving objects. The faster they travel, the bigger the force pushing against them from the liquid or gas they are travelling through.

The higher the speed of an object, the bigger the drag or air resistance.

Imagine a submarine under water. If it travels at a low speed, water can move slowly out of the way so there is only a small amount of drag. If the submarine speeds up, the water has to be pushed out of the way faster, so the force on the front of the submarine is larger.

A new type of one man submarine. Notice the shapes of the front surfaces. **E**

6 Put the pictures in box F in order, starting with the one with the least amount of drag:

F

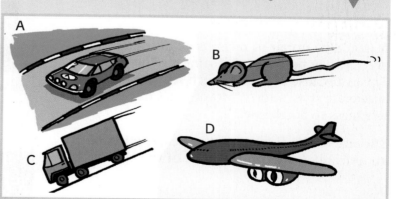

7 What happens to the air resistance on an aeroplane as it slows down?

8 A woman is running at a steady speed. The air resistance acting on her is 20 N and the friction force acting on her (between her shoes and the ground) is 2 N. What force must her legs be providing to push her forward?

Unbalanced forces and acceleration

What affects the acceleration of an object?

When car designers are working on the new cars of the future, they are constantly trying to improve the performance of the car; making it accelerate better and use as little fuel as possible. So how do designers do this?

- Streamlining the body of the car reduces air resistance, which makes the car use less fuel and accelerate more easily.
- Reducing the **mass** of the car also helps.

 1 What helps to reduce the air resistance of a vehicle?

Acceleration and force

We know that an unbalanced force will make an object speed up (accelerate) or slow down (decelerate). The size of the acceleration depends on the size of the unbalanced force.

> *For an object of a certain mass, the bigger the force the bigger the acceleration or deceleration.*

Acceleration and mass

It would be unfair to race a car against a lorry, even if they both had the same engines inside. This is because a car has much less mass to accelerate than a lorry. Motor bikes have even less mass to accelerate.

The size of the acceleration or deceleration of an object depends on the mass of the object.

2 **a)** Cyclist A is able to produce twice the forward force as cyclist B. Which cyclist will have the greatest acceleration?
   b) Both cycles have exactly the same brakes, which the cyclists press with the same force. What can you say about the deceleration of the cyclists if they have the same mass?

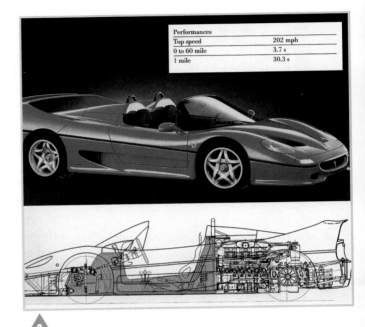

Performances	
Top speed	202 mph
0 to 60 mile	3.7 s
1 mile	30.3 s

A ▼ **B** ▼

forward force = 2500 N
acceleration = 5 m/s²

forward force = 500 N
acceleration = 1 m/s²

The bigger the mass of an object, the bigger the force that is needed to produce the same acceleration.

C

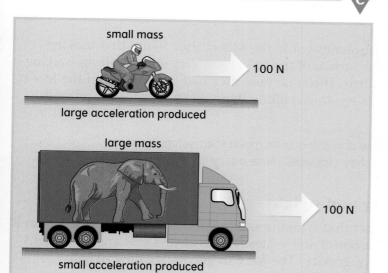

small mass

100 N

large acceleration produced

large mass

100 N

small acceleration produced

3 The same force is acting on each of the objects in the list. Put the objects in order, starting with the one with the most acceleration.

A A car of mass 2000 kg
B A mouse of mass 0.05 kg
C A person of mass 60 kg
D A plane of mass 50 000 kg

P How can you investigate what happens to the acceleration of a trolley when you increase its mass?

D

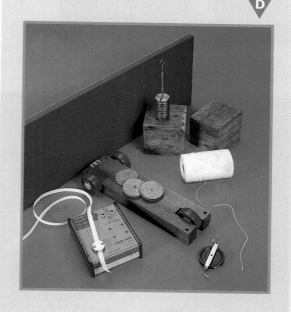

4 Copy the grid and write the correct answer to each question in the grid. What is the shaded word?

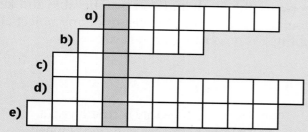

a)
b)
c)
d)
e)

a) The submarine will move in this direction if the forward force is greater than the drag.
b) This makes a vehicle accelerate.
c) This causes resistance when objects move through it.
d) Objects do this when unbalanced forces are acting.
e) If you do this to an object it will have less air resistance.

5 An elephant and an ant are about to start a race.
a) If both animals can produce the same forward force, which will accelerate the fastest? Explain your choice.
b) In fact, both animals have the same acceleration at the start of the race. Which animal produced the largest forward force?

Summary

When an unbalanced force acts on an object it will _____ or _____.
The bigger the unbalanced force the _____ the size of the acceleration.
The bigger the _____ of the object the bigger the size of the _____ needed to produce the same acceleration.

accelerate   bigger   decelerate
mass   force

Gravity, mass and weight

What is weight and how can we calculate it?

A *Astronauts have to carry oxygen and radios on the Moon, which make them heavier.*

When astronauts got to the Moon, they found that walking across the surface of the Moon was very different from walking on the Earth. This is because they had less **weight** on the Moon. There was less force pulling them down towards the ground.

> **1** How can astronauts make themselves heavier so they can walk more easily on the moon?

Gravity and weight

Any object that is falling towards the ground, will speed up as it falls. The object accelerates. This is always true and it happens because of **gravity**. The force of gravity is called weight.

All objects attract each other by gravity. You will be attracting this book and this book will be attracting you, but the force is so small that you can't detect it. The Earth is so huge that the attractive force between the Earth and you is noticeable and keeps you on the ground. The weight of any object always points to the centre of the Earth.

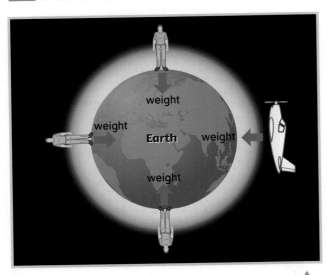

B

> **2** True or false?
>
> **a)** The force of gravity is called weight.
> **b)** Objects always fall at a steady speed.

> ! The gravitational field strength around a black hole is so strong that even light is pulled in towards it.

> **3** On the planet Pluto there is less gravity than there is on the Earth.
>
> **a)** Would your weight be more or less on Pluto than it is on the Earth?
> **b)** Would your acceleration be more or less on Pluto than on the Earth if you fell?

The strength of gravity is called the **gravitational field strength**. Gravity or gravitational field strength is measured in **newtons per kilogram (N/kg)**.

Each planet has a different gravitational field strength.

- The bigger the gravitational field strength, the faster an object will accelerate when it falls towards the surface of the planet.
- The bigger the gravitational field strength, the bigger the weight of a certain object.

The gravitational field strength on the Earth is 10 N/kg. This means that each kilogram of mass has a weight of 10 newtons.

Mass

We know that if gravity changes, the weight of an object also changes. However, the object itself does not change. The **mass** is the amount of **matter** in an object and this only changes if something is cut off or added to the object. So, if you go to the Moon you may weigh less but you won't have changed mass and so you will look exactly the same. Mass is measured in kilograms (kg).

only losing weight

C

4 Write down whether each of these events will change the mass *and* the weight of something or *only* the weight.

a) Moving an object from Earth to the Moon.
b) Cutting your hair.
c) Feeding a cat.
d) Going to Mars.

5 Copy and complete the following table:

Weight = (N)	Mass × (kg)	Gravity (N/kg)
	50	10
	100	10
	20	5
	2	3
	60	4

Calculating weight

The weight of an object can be worked out if you know:

● the mass of the object
● the gravitational field strength.

weight = mass × gravitational field strength
   (N)   (kg)   (N/kg)

Weight is a force, so it is measured in newtons (N).

Worked example

A girl of mass 65 kg goes to the Moon where the gravitational field strength is 1.6 N/kg. What will her weight be on the Moon?

weight = mass   ×   gravitational field strength
        = 65   ×   1.6
        = 104 N

6 What units is mass measured in?

7 An astronaut has a mass of 70 kg.
He travels from the Earth to the Moon, where the gravitational field strength is 1.6 N/kg.

a) What is the astronaut's weight on the Moon?
b) What is the change in the astronaut's weight as he travels from the Earth to the Moon?

Summary

Weight is a force caused by _____. Gravity or gravitational _____ _____ tells us how quickly an object will accelerate when it falls. The bigger the gravitational field strength the _____ the weight of an object. _____ is the amount of matter in an object. Mass only changes if something is _____ off or added to an object. We can work out the weight of an object using:

_____ = mass × gravitational
               field strength.

_____ field strength is measured in _____ and is always 10 N/kg on the _____.

bigger   cut   Earth   field strength
     gravitational   gravity   mass
          N/kg   weight

187

Terminal velocity

What is terminal velocity?

If an object falls, the gravitational pull of the Earth makes the object accelerate. The faster the object travels in the air the bigger the air resistance trying to slow it down. So can an object carry on getting faster forever as it falls?

The answer is no since forces become balanced, and the object will travel at a steady speed.

? 1 What is the name of the force that:
   a) pulls objects towards the Earth?
   b) tries to slow things down as they travel through the air?

2 What will happen to the speed of a falling object if the weight pulling down on the object is equal to the air resistance pushing up on the object?

Air resistance and terminal velocity

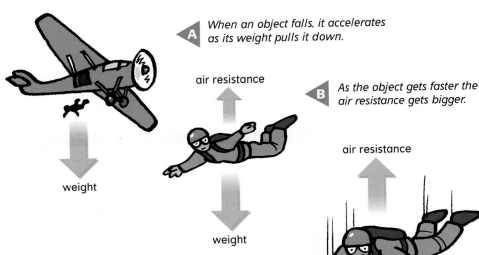

A When an object falls, it accelerates as its weight pulls it down.

B As the object gets faster the air resistance gets bigger.

air resistance

weight

air resistance

weight

air resistance

weight

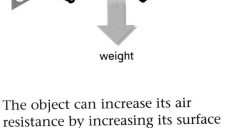

C

Eventually the object goes so fast that its air resistance is as big as the weight. The forces are balanced so the object stops accelerating and falls at a steady speed. This is called its **terminal velocity**.

? 3 What happens to the air resistance of a parachutist when the parachute is opened?

4 When an object is travelling at its terminal velocity, what can you say about the forces acting on it?

The object can increase its air resistance by increasing its surface area or by being less streamlined. Now the upward force is bigger than the downward weight. This will make the object slow down.

air resistance

weight

D

air resistance

weight

E

As the object slows down, the air resistance decreases until it reaches the same size as the weight. The forces are now balanced again so the object falls at a new steady speed. It has a new terminal velocity.

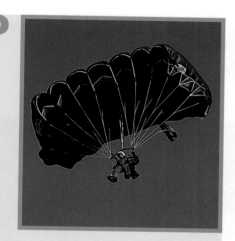

How could you find out the best shape for a parachute? **F**

5 Which car will:

a) speed up?
b) slow down?
c) stay at the same speed? **H**

A

B

C

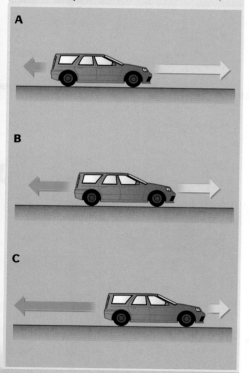

6 If you jump out of a very high aeroplane you won't accelerate all the way down to the ground. Why not?

Speed skier Harry Egger has reached a terminal velocity of 246 km/h (154 mph).

The engine in a vehicle produces a forward force that pushes the vehicle forward. This is called the **driving force**. Every vehicle has a maximum driving force that its engine can produce.

Vehicles have a terminal velocity, when the maximum driving force is cancelled out by friction and air resistance. When the forces are balanced the vehicle cannot accelerate any more and will travel at a steady speed – its terminal velocity.

Here is a general rule:

If the maximum driving forces on an object are balanced by the friction forces, the object will go at a steady speed called the terminal velocity.

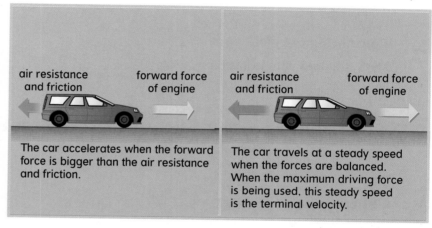

air resistance and friction — forward force of engine

The car accelerates when the forward force is bigger than the air resistance and friction.

air resistance and friction — forward force of engine

The car travels at a steady speed when the forces are balanced. When the maximum driving force is being used, this steady speed is the terminal velocity.

Summary

The faster an object moves, the greater the _____ _____ . Eventually the _____ pulling the object down, or the _____ force pushing the object forward, will be cancelled out by the _____ forces trying to slow the object down. When the forces are _____ the object will stop accelerating and will travel at a _____ speed called its _____ _____.

air resistance   balanced   driving   friction
steady   terminal velocity   weight

K13 Work and energy transfer

How can we calculate the amount of work done?

When a force moves something we say that **work** is done. This involves changing one form of **energy** into another. For instance, when an engine moves a car forward, **chemical energy** stored in the fuel is changed into **kinetic (movement) energy**. We say that chemical energy has been transferred to kinetic energy. The amount of energy that is transferred when a force moves something is known as the **work done**.

 1 'The work done is the same as the amount of energy transferred.' Is this sentence true or false?

A *These people have to do work to push the car.*

The amount of energy transferred is measured in **joules** (J). So, the work done is also measured in joules.

E **Calculating the work done**

The work done can be found if you know:

- the force applied
- the distance over which the force is applied.

work done = force applied × distance moved in the direction of the force
   (J)   **(N)**   **(m)**

 2 What are the units for work done?

Worked examples

A A car pushes itself forward with a force of 1000 N. If it moves 200 m, what is the work done by the car?

Work done = force   × distance moved in the
              applied   direction of the force
          = 1000 N × 200 m
          = 200 000 J.

 B *The force and the distance must be in the same direction.*

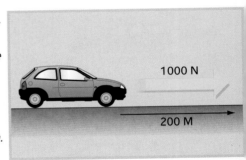
1000 N
200 M

B A crane lifts a load off the ground to a height of 20 m. If the weight of the load is 500 N, what is the work done by the crane?

Work done = force   × distance moved in the
              applied   direction of the force
          = 500 N × 20 m
          = 10 000 J.

 the crane pulls up with a force of 500 N

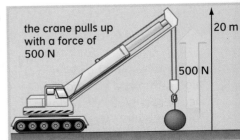
20 m
500 N

P How would you work out how much work you have done today?

 D

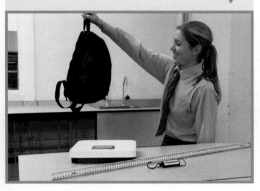

? **3** If something is lifted it gains gravitational potential energy. 100 J of chemical energy is changed into gravitational potential energy when a gardener picks up a large plant. How much work does the gardener do?

4 Copy and complete the table below:

Work done = (J)	Force applied × (N)	Distance moved in the direction of the force (m)
	23	2
	4	50
	35	4
	14	10
	10	24

Elastic potential energy

Work is done whenever a force is applied over a distance. This means that if a force changes the shape of an object, work must be done.

When you stretch a spring or elastic band, you use a force over a distance. Work is being done, so energy is being transferred. The energy that you use to do the work is changed into stored energy in the spring or elastic band. This stored energy is called **elastic potential energy**. **E**

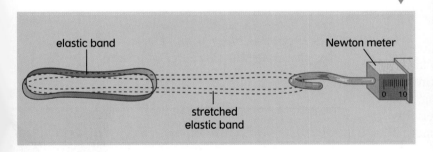

elastic band   Newton meter

stretched elastic band

? **5** Draw three situations where work is being done. Show on your diagrams the force and direction of the distance moved. Here is an example: **F**

6 Which requires more work to be done, lifting a weight of 10 N a height of 0.5 m or pushing the same weight a distance of 2 m against a friction force of 5 N?

Summary

Work done is the amount of _____ transferred from one type to another when a force moves something. The unit for work done is the _____. We can calculate the work done using:

work done = _____ applied × _____ moved in the direction of the force

When we calculate the work done, the force and distance must be in the same _____. If work is done stretching a spring, the energy stored in the spring is called _____ _____ energy.

direction   distance
elastic potential   energy
force   joule

191

K14   Kinetic energy

What is kinetic energy and how can we calculate it?

Life would be very boring if we couldn't move around. In fact all of our daily activities need movement energy, even thinking. **Kinetic energy** is the scientific name for movement energy.

 1   What is kinetic energy?

Kinetic energy and mass

If a bicycle and a lorry are driving towards you at the same speed, it is more worrying if you are standing in front of the lorry. The lorry has got more kinetic energy than the bicycle, which makes it do more damage if it hits an object. Two objects travelling at the same speed can have different amounts of kinetic energy, because they have different amounts of mass.

 2   **a)** If a hippo and a rat are both running at 1 m/s, which has the most kinetic energy?
     b) Explain your answer.

Kinetic energy and speed

Although the mass of an object affects its kinetic energy, the speed of the object is even more important. The faster a vehicle is travelling, the harder it is to stop as it has more kinetic energy to change into other forms of energy. In fact, if you double the speed of an object it will have *four* times more kinetic energy.

The greater the speed of an object, the greater its kinetic energy.

3   Why is a car travelling at 10 m/s harder to stop than a car travelling at 5 m/s?

!   The wind speed in a tornado funnel can exceed 200 mph.

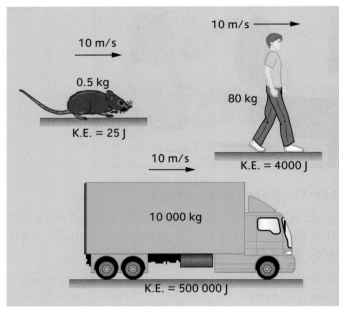

A   *Things travelling at the same speed have different amount of kinetic energy (K.E.) because they have different masses.*

The bigger the mass of an object, the greater its kinetic energy at a certain speed.

The faster the wind speed, the greater the damage it causes as it has much more energy. **B**

E Calculating kinetic energy

The kinetic energy of an object can be found if you know:

- the mass of the object
- the speed of the object.

kinetic energy $= \frac{1}{2} \times$ **mass** $\times$ **speed^2**
(J)   (kg)   (m/s)

As kinetic energy is a type of energy it is measured in joules (J).

Worked examples

A A car has a mass of 1000 kg and is travelling at 40 m/s. How much kinetic energy does it have?

$$
\begin{aligned}
\text{kinetic energy} &= \tfrac{1}{2} \times \text{mass} \times \text{speed}^2 \\
&= 0.5 \times 1000 \times (40)^2 \\
&= 800\,000 \text{ J}.
\end{aligned}
$$

B A ball with a mass of 300 g is thrown with a speed of 5 m/s. How much kinetic energy was given to the ball?

$$
\begin{aligned}
\text{kinetic energy} &= \tfrac{1}{2} \times \text{mass} \times \text{speed}^2 \\
&= 0.5 \times 0.3 \times (5)^2 \\
&= 3.75 \text{ J}.
\end{aligned}
$$

(Remember there are 1000 g in 1 kg!)

Kinetic energy and friction

The more kinetic energy an object has, the more energy it has to lose to stop it moving. Most vehicles use friction to slow them down. The kinetic energy is transferred to heat energy as the wheels do work against the friction in the brakes.

5 Copy and complete the table below:

Mass (kg)	Speed (m/s)	Speed^2	Kinetic energy (J)
10	5		
20	5		
10	10		
10	20		

6 An ice skater travelling at 2 m/s accelerates to twice this speed. What does his kinetic energy become? Choose the correct answer.

  A twice as much   **B** four times as much
  C half as much.

? 4 Look at the equation. What must you remember to do to the speed of an object when you are working out its kinetic energy?

P How could you find out how much kinetic energy you have when you run?

C

Summary

The kinetic energy of an object _____ if the speed of the object increases. If two objects are travelling at the same speed the object with the most _____ will have the largest amount of _____ energy. Kinetic energy is measured in _____. We can work out the kinetic energy of an object using:

kinetic energy $= \frac{1}{2} \times$ mass $\times$ _____ ^{2}

Kinetic energy can be changed into _____ energy when work is done against _____.

friction   heat   increases   joules
kinetic   mass   speed

The Solar System

What is in the Solar System?

Planets move around the Sun very quickly and since they are so large, they have enormous kinetic energies.

Hundreds of years ago, people believed that the Earth was the centre of the Universe, and everything else went around the Earth. It wasn't until the middle of the 1500s that a scientist called Nicolaus Copernicus showed that the planets actually travel around the Sun.

Planet	Mass	Kinetic energy
Earth	6×10^{24} kg	2.65×10^{33} J
Jupiter	2×10^{27} kg	1.62×10^{35} J
Pluto	1.2×10^{22} kg	1.34×10^{29} J

A / B

? 1 What is at the centre of our Solar System?

The Solar System

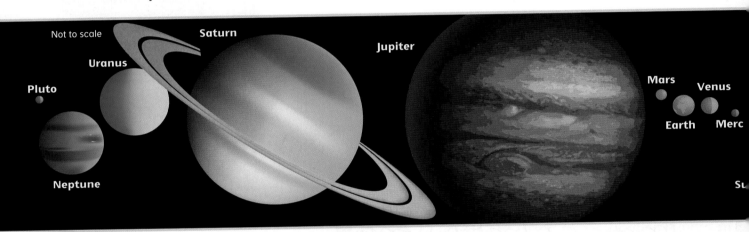

Not to scale

Pluto · Uranus · Saturn · Jupiter · Mars · Venus · Earth · Merc · Neptune · Su

In our **Solar System** there is one star which we call the Sun. Nine planets orbit (move around) the Sun at different distances from it.

Stars versus planets

In our Solar System there is only one star. However, from Earth we are able to see billions of other stars that are outside the Solar System. There are a few important differences between planets and stars.

We can see other planets from the Earth because they reflect the light from the Sun. In fact, they look just like stars. Planets are constantly moving around the Sun whereas the stars stay in fixed patterns in the sky. These fixed patterns are called **constellations**. We can tell which of the bright lights in the sky are planets because they will move across the fixed patterns of stars.

C

Planets:
- **orbit** the Sun or another star
- do not give out light
- **reflect light** from the Sun or other stars

Stars:
- stay in a fixed pattern in the sky
- give out their own light

D

The stars remain in a fixed pattern. Planets move slowly across the pattern of stars.

When we look at other planets from the Earth, the position of the planets in the constellations depends on where the planet and the Earth are in their orbits around the Sun.

2 Write down the two main differences between planets and stars.

The movement of the Earth

The Earth **orbits** (goes around) the Sun every 365¼ days. This gives us the length of our year. At the same time, the Earth spins on a **tilted axis**. It takes 24 hours for the Earth to spin around once. This gives us the length of our day. The side of the Earth that is facing the Sun is in daylight while the other side is in darkness.

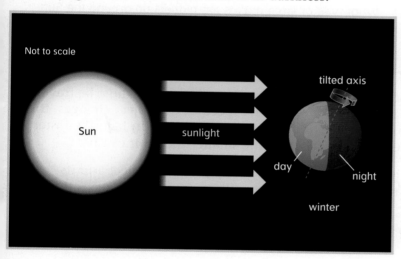

Not to scale

Sun | sunlight | tilted axis | day | night | winter

E

! The word 'planet' comes from the Greek word for 'wanderer' as scientists noticed the planets changing position against the fixed pattern of stars.

3 Copy out the sentences. Match the correct length of time to each one: either 24 hours or 365¼ days.

  a) The Earth takes this long to travel around the Sun.
  b) The Earth takes this long to spin on its tilted axis.
  c) This is the length of a day.
  d) This is the length of a year.

! As it takes 365¼ days for the Earth to orbit the Sun, every four years there is an extra day in February. This is called a leap year.

4 The diagram shows a recently discovered solar system. What are the things labelled a–d?

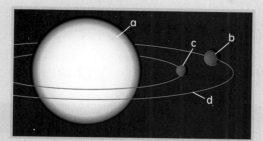

a | c | b | d

5 Explain why we have day and night on Earth.

F

6 Explain why the days are longer in the summer than in the winter.

Summary

The Solar System is a collection of _____ that orbit the _____. Stars stay in _____ patterns in the night sky called _____. Planets can only _____ light from stars. We can tell which bright lights in the night sky are planets because they _____ across the fixed patterns of _____. It takes just over 365 days (1 year) for the _____ to move around the Sun. It takes 24 hours (1 day) for the Earth to _____ on its _____ axis.

constellations   Earth   fixed   move   planets
reflect   spin   stars   Sun   tilted

Orbits

What shape are planet orbits? What affects the size of an orbit?

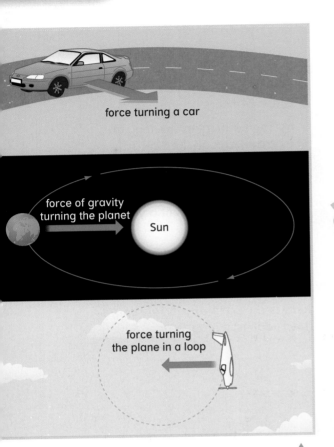

force turning a car

force of gravity turning the planet

Sun

force turning the plane in a loop

A

Planets go around the Sun, cars travel around corners and planes can do loops in the sky. Many things can move in circles, but in every case there must be a force pulling the object round, stopping it from going in a straight line.

For planets going around the Sun there is the force of gravity between the planet and the Sun, trying to pull them together. This stops the planet travelling in a straight line and makes it travel on a curved path around the Sun. This is why the planets orbit the Sun.

1 What type of force makes the planets go around the Sun, and the Moon go around the Earth?

Orbit size

For an object to stay in a particular orbit it must be travelling at the correct speed. If the speed of the object changes, then the size of the orbit will have to change. In fact, the faster the object is travelling the smaller the orbit can be.

It is the combination of the speed of an object and its gravitational attraction to a larger object that keeps it in orbit.

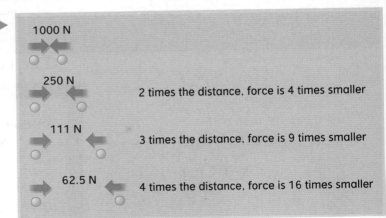

B

1000 N

250 N — 2 times the distance, force is 4 times smaller

111 N — 3 times the distance, force is 9 times smaller

62.5 N — 4 times the distance, force is 16 times smaller

Gravity and distance

The closer any objects are to each other, the stronger the force of gravity is between them. As objects move closer together they attract each other more. The increase in force is not in **proportion** with the decrease in the distance. This means that the force does not double when the distance is halved. In fact, if the distance between two planets is halved, the gravitational force between them will be *four* times larger, not twice as large.

Planet orbits

Planets do not follow circular orbits around the Sun. Instead the orbits are **ellipses** (ovals), with the Sun near the centre.

The further away the planet is from the Sun, the longer it will take to complete one orbit.

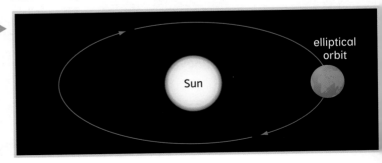

C

elliptical orbit

Sun

A **comet** is a lump of rock and ice. Comets also orbit the Sun, but their orbits are even less circular than the planets, with the Sun near to one end of the orbit. It is when the comet travels close to the Sun that the ice melts and a tail of dust and water vapour can be seen reflecting the Sun's light. **D**

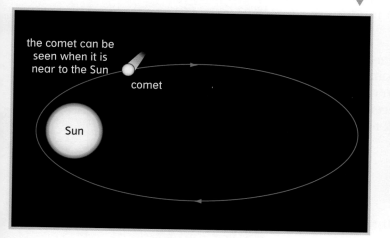

the comet can be seen when it is near to the Sun

comet

Sun

E *Comet Hale-Bopp over Stone Henge.*

P

How could you find out what happens to the size of an orbit if the force causing it changes size?

F

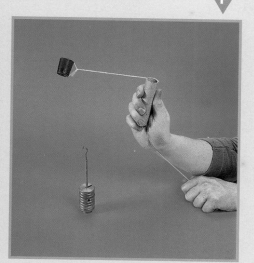

5 Why can we see comets when they are near to the Sun?

6 What would happen to the Earth's orbit if the Earth started to slow down?

2 What shape is the orbit of the Earth around the Sun?

3 When is it possible to see comets?

4 Two planets are moved so that the distance between them is halved. What will the force of attraction between them be? Choose the correct answer.

   A more than twice as large

   B twice as large   **C** less than twice as large.

Summary

Planets are held in orbit around the Sun by a _____ force. The closer two objects are together the _____ the gravitational force pulling them together. For an object to travel in a certain orbit it must be travelling at the correct _____. The _____ the speed, the larger the orbit must be. Planet and comet orbits are not _____, they have the shape of an _____. The smaller the orbit is, the shorter the _____ it takes for the orbiting body to make one complete orbit. We can see comets when they are _____ to the Sun.

bigger   circular   close   ellipse   gravitational

lower   speed   time

Satellites

What are satellites used for?

A satellite is an object that orbits another larger object. Planets are **natural satellites** of the Sun, and moons are natural satellites of the planets.

Millions of homes now have **satellite dishes**. These dishes pick up television signals that have been sent from all over the world. The signals are **emitted** (given out) in one part of the world and sent into space where they are **received** by a **satellite**. The satellite then sends the signal back to satellite dishes on a different part of the Earth.

A

? 1 Write down one use for satellites in space.

There are two main types of man-made satellites which orbit the Earth. Each type has a different orbit and different uses.

Geostationary orbit satellites

A **geostationary orbit** is one where the satellite stays above a fixed point on the Earth and follows that point around as the Earth rotates. This means that the satellite takes 24 hours to complete one whole orbit around the Earth.

Geostationary satellites are usually placed in an orbit very high above the equator. There is only a limited amount of space to put them in, so only around 400 geostationary satellites can be in orbit at any one time. If there are more than this their signals can start to affect each other.

Geostationary orbit satellites are used for communications, including satellite television and telephones.

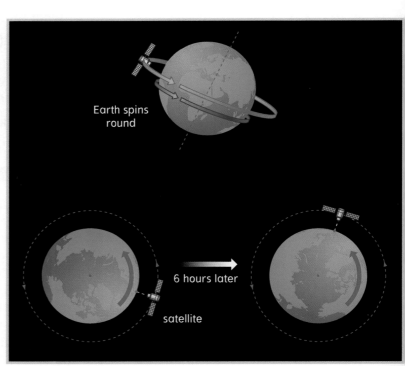

Earth spins round

6 hours later

satellite

A satellite in a geostationary orbit stays above one point on the Earth. **B**

? 2 How long does it take for a satellite on a geostationary orbit to complete one orbit? Choose the correct answer from the list.

24 hours   24 days   12 hours

3 Explain how a satellite on a geostationary orbit can always be above the same point on the Earth.

Polar orbit satellites

Satellites in a **polar orbit** move around the Earth, going over the poles during each orbit. Polar orbits are usually much closer to the Earth than geostationary orbits, and the satellite can orbit the Earth more than once a day. As these satellites move around in their orbits, the Earth is spinning around beneath them and this allows the satellites to scan the entire Earth each day.

For a satellite to stay in a particular orbit it must be travelling at the correct speed. The smaller the orbit of the satellite, the faster it must be travelling. As satellites in polar orbits are closer to the Earth than geostationary orbits they must travel more quickly.

Polar orbit satellites are used for **monitoring** the weather conditions on Earth and also for spying.

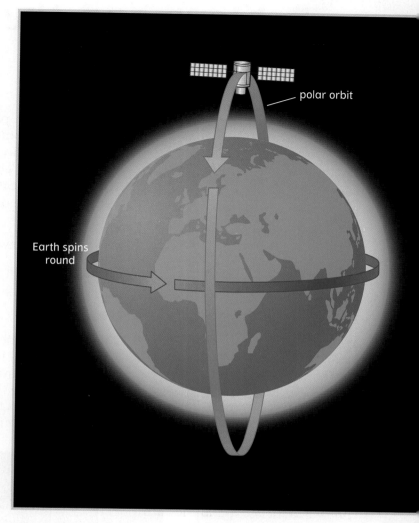

polar orbit

Earth spins round

4 Write down two differences between a polar orbit and a geostationary orbit.

5 Write down one use of a polar orbit satellite.

Satellites are above the Earth's atmosphere. This means that they can see into space far more clearly than we can from Earth. Scientists trying to find out about the Universe often use satellites to observe space without the **atmosphere** being in the way.

C *A satellite on a polar orbit can scan the whole of the Earth as it spins.*

Summary

_____ are used to send information long distances across the Earth. There are _____ types of orbits, _____ and _____ orbits. Geostationary orbits allow the satellite to stay above one _____ on the Earth. They are used for _____. Polar orbit satellites can scan the whole _____. They are used to _____ the weather.

communications	Earth	geostationary	monitor
point	polar	satellites	two

The Pegasus is the smallest rocket to launch a satellite into space. It is only 15 m long.

6 Why can a satellite see into space more easily than a telescope on Earth?

7 What is the name of the natural satellite that orbits the Earth?

8 Describe how the Olympic games being held in one country can be seen on televisions on the other side of the world.

Stars and the Universe

How are stars formed?

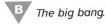

A *A galaxy.*

B *The big bang.*

C *The Orion constellation.*

Our Sun and the planets orbiting the Sun are called the **Solar System**. The Sun is just one star in a group of stars called a **galaxy**. Our galaxy is called the **Milky Way**. There are at least a billion different galaxies in the Universe. The distance between the planets in the Solar System is enormous, but the distance between stars in a galaxy is even larger. Larger still is the distance between the galaxies.

? **1** Put the following in order, starting with the largest:

Earth   Moon   Milky Way   Sun   Universe   Solar System

The Universe

Many scientists believe that the Universe began with an enormous explosion, called the Big Bang. All the energy and matter that existed was flung outwards into space. The explosion was so massive that scientists believe that the Universe is still getting larger as all the matter continues to move outwards. Over millions of years the stars and planets were formed from this matter and energy.

? **2** How do scientists believe the Universe began?

The formation of stars

Stars are made from dust and gas in space. The gravitational attraction between any particles pulls them together. As the number of particles builds up, the gravitational attraction pulling in more particles of gas gets stronger, until a star exists.

Planets form in a similar way, but don't reach such a large size. The mass of the planet can be attracted to the larger mass of a nearby star and this causes the planet to orbit the star.

? **3** What type of force makes a star form?

There are millions of stars in every galaxy. Scientists have spent centuries recording the positions of the stars in the night sky, putting them into groups called **constellation**

The life of a star

Stars are so enormous that the force of gravity pulling the gas into them is very strong. This holds the star together tightly, but also causes the temperature to get extremely hot. The high temperature makes the star try to **expand** (get bigger).

So, there is a gravitational force pulling the star inwards and another force caused by the heat pushing the star outwards. Provided that these forces are balanced, the star is **stable** and stays a similar size. Our Sun is in this stage of its life and can stay like this for billions of years.

As a star loses energy it expands until it forms a **red giant**. After more energy is lost, the star collapses as the gravitational force becomes the larger force and pulls the star in on itself. The type of star that forms next depends on the mass of the red giant.

If the red giant is not too **massive** it becomes a **white dwarf**. The matter in a white dwarf is pulled together so hard that it can be millions of times denser than materials we have here on Earth.

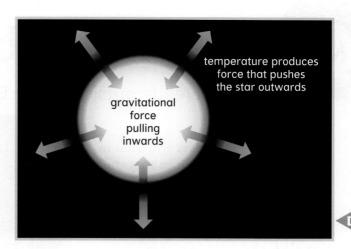

D

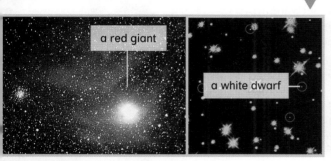

a red giant

a white dwarf

E

If the red giant is massive enough, it can **contract** (get smaller) so quickly that it causes a huge explosion. All the dust and gas in the star gets thrown into space. This is called a **supernova**. Any matter that is left behind forms a small, dense **neutron star**.

A supernova. **F**

neutron star

? **4** Explain why our Sun is in the stable stage of its life. Write about forces in your answer.

! The Crab Nebula is a star that exploded into a supernova. This produced the brightest star in the sky, visible even during the day for 3 weeks during 1054.

? **5** What is the scientific name for a group of stars?

6 When will a red giant form a neutron star instead of a white dwarf?

7 What is a supernova?

Summary

Stars are formed by the _____ of gravity pulling dust and _____ particles together. The _____ of the star is so high that it causes a force that tries to make the star _____. When the inward and outward forces are _____ the star is stable, like our _____. As the star loses _____ it expands to form a _____ _____. It can then either form a _____ _____ if it has a low mass, or a neutron star if it has a high mass.

balanced   white dwarf   energy
expand   force   gas   red giant
Sun   temperature

Life in the Universe

Is there life outside of the Earth?

Films like E.T., Star Wars and Men in Black are based on the idea that there are other life forms living on planets in space. Scientists are trying to find evidence for life on other planets and have been sending **probes** to Mars to find information to see if life could ever have existed there.

A

 1 On which other planet in the Solar System are we trying to find evidence of extra-terrestrial life at the moment?

Finding proof that there is or has been extra-terrestrial life of some kind does not just mean we actually have to see creatures face to face. There are many ways that we can prove other forms of life have existed outside of the Earth.

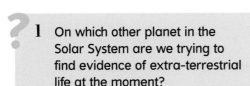 **2 a)** Do you think we can prove that dinosaurs ever existed on Earth?
b) What evidence do we have?

There are three main ways we can look for evidence of other life forms:

Finding fossils

By sending robots to the Moon and eventually to other planets, samples of rocks and other materials can be brought back to Earth for scientists to investigate. Robots can also take pictures of the planets that can be sent back to Earth. This has been done for Mars and Europa (a natural satellite that orbits Jupiter).

 3 What two things can robots bring back to Earth for scientists to investigate?

Mr and Mrs Hill from New Hampshire underwent hypnosis to remember a 3 hour period of time, during which they believed they were abducted by aliens.

Barney and Betty Hill, allegedly abducted by aliens in Virginia, USA in 1961.
B

A robot exploring Mars. C

Receiving signals from space

Radio telescopes can pick up radio signals from outer space. This is called the search for extra-terrestrial intelligence (SETI). Scientists have to try to sort out what could be meaningful signals, sent from other life forms, from the general background **noise** that is picked up. They monitor a narrow band of wavelengths to do this. They have been trying to detect signals for over 40 years, but have not found anything yet. This may be because other life forms don't have the same technology that we do.

Finding chemical changes caused by organisms

Living organisms change their environment. If these changes can be detected it can provide evidence that they exist. An example of this on Earth is the amount of oxygen in the air. If there was no life on Earth the amount of oxygen would be much lower.

The type of life that exists on Earth depends mainly on carbon and water to survive. Scientists get excited if they find these substances on other planets as it makes it more likely that life may have existed there.

D A radio telescope.

 E

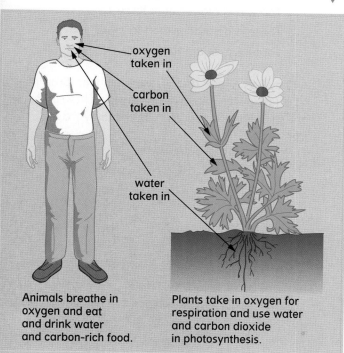

oxygen taken in

carbon taken in

water taken in

Animals breathe in oxygen and eat and drink water and carbon-rich food.

Plants take in oxygen for respiration and use water and carbon dioxide in photosynthesis.

Summary

Many scientists believe there is
_____ - _____ life. They are looking for evidence by:

- sending _____ to other planets to send back _____ and materials
- using radio- _____ to detect signals from space
- detecting changes in the _____ that may be caused by living creatures.

Living organisms on Earth need water and _____ to survive and scientists believe that if they find these substances on other _____ it is likely that life may have been there.

environment   carbon   pictures
planets   robots   telescopes
extra-terrestrial

5 What two main things do living creatures on Earth need to survive?

6 Why do you think it is easier to send a robot to Mars to look for evidence than it is to send a human? Use the words 'temperature', 'atmosphere' and 'oxygen' in your answer.

4 Why do you think we have not yet received radio signals from extra-terrestrial life in outer-space?

Further questions

1 A woman walks to work each morning. The graph shows her journey.

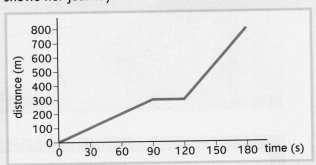

a) Between what times was the woman:

   i) standing still?

   ii) moving the fastest? (2)

b) Calculate the woman's mean (average) speed for the whole journey.
Show your working. (2)

c) Calculate the woman's fastest speed.
Show your working. (2)

2 A car accelerates from 0 m/s to 30 m/s in 5 seconds. It then travels at a constant velocity for 10 seconds, before it slows down and stops in a further 5 seconds.

a) Calculate the acceleration of the car.
Show your workings (2)

b) Draw a velocity-time graph to show the car's journey. (3)

c) What is the deceleration of the car at the end of the journey? (2)

3 The submarine in the diagram is travelling at a steady speed.

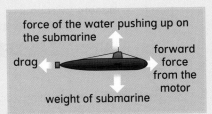

force of the water pushing up on the submarine

drag   forward force from the motor

weight of submarine

a) Explain why the forward force of the motor is not making the submarine accelerate. (1)

b) The forward force increases.

   i) What happens to the movement of the submarine?

   ii) Explain your answer. (2)

4 The diagram shows the forces acting on a car.

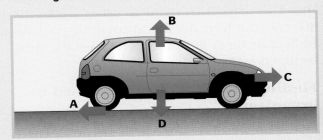

a) Choose the correct forces from the list to label the forces A to D. (4)

| friction   upward force of the ground |
| driving force of the motor   weight |

b) Copy and complete the following table, stating whether the car will speed up, slow down or stay the same speed. (3)

Force A is bigger than force C	
Force A is smaller than force C	
Force A is equal to force C	

5 A lorry has a leak and is losing oil. One drop of oil is lost every minute. The drops on the road are shown in the diagram as the lorry travels from A to C.

a) Between A and B, is the lorry stationary, travelling at a steady speed or accelerating? (1)

b) Between B and C, is the lorry stationary, travelling at a steady speed or accelerating? (1)

c) The forward force of the engine is constant as the lorry travels from A to C. Friction tries to slow the lorry down. What other force is increasing as the lorry travels from A to B? (1)

d) What is the name of the steady speed a vehicle reaches when its maximum driving force is equal to the forces trying to slow the vehicle down? (1)

6 a) Copy and complete the table, placing the conditions into the correct columns.

Increase thinking distance	Increase braking distance

Conditions:

driver who is drunk

ice on the road

worn brake pads

driver who is tired

rain (5)

b) Describe how an airbag can protect a driver or passenger during a crash. Use the following words in your answer: force, decelerate. (2)

7 A student has to lift a pile of books onto a table. Calculate the amount of work done lifting the books. Show your working. (2)

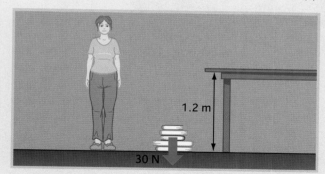

1.2 m

30 N

8

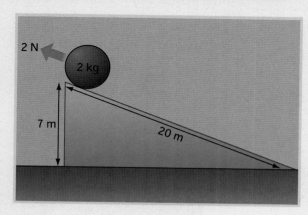

2 N

2 kg

7 m

20 m

a) Calculate the work done against friction as the ball rolls down the slope.

b) The ball is travelling at 4 m/s at the bottom of the slope. Use the equation to find the amount of kinetic energy the ball has.

kinetic energy = $\frac{1}{2}$ × mass × speed^2 (4)

9 a) Copy and complete the sentences:

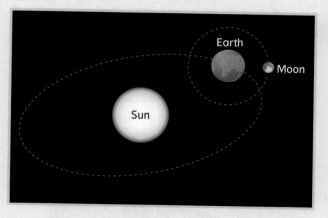

Earth

Moon

Sun

The Earth _____ the Sun in _____ days. The Earth spins on its axis once every 24 _____. (3)

b) i) At night, how can we see the stars in the sky?

ii) At night, how can we see the Moon and other planets in the sky? (2)

c) Stars and planets look similar in the night sky. Explain how we can tell which of the bright lights are stars and which are planets. (1)

10 a) Copy and complete the table:

Object mass (kg)	Planet gravitational field strength (N/kg)	Weight of the object on the planet (N)
2	10	
5	10	
10	1.6	
0.2	8	
6	16	

(5)

b) i) Explain why the weights of astronauts change when they go to the Moon.

ii) An astronaut has a mass of 80 kg on the Earth. What is the mass of the astronaut on the Moon? (2)

11 a) Choose the correct satellite, polar or geostationary, to fit each of the sentences.

i) Can observe the whole of the Earth in one day.

ii) Takes 24 hours to make one complete orbit.

iii) Used for communications and satellite television.

iv) Used to monitor the weather. (4)

b) How are scientists trying to gather evidence for extra-terrestrial life? (3)

Introducing waves

What are waves?

↑ Berkeley

A Earthquakes can cause a lot of damage, often killing people and animals, and destroying buildings. Earthquakes are shock waves travelling through the Earth and along its surface.

These waves are called **seismic waves** and carry a lot of **kinetic** (movement) energy from one place to another. A piece of equipment called a **seismograph** is used to detect seismic waves. Scientists can learn about the structure of the Earth by studying how the seismic waves pass through it.

B As the Earth's surface moves, the seismograph records the size of the shake and the time it arrives.

?

1 What does a seismograph detect?

2 An earthquake occurs in San Francisco. It is detected by a seismograph.

　a) What type of energy is carried by the seismic waves?

　b) Look at diagram C. How can you tell when the earthquake was detected?

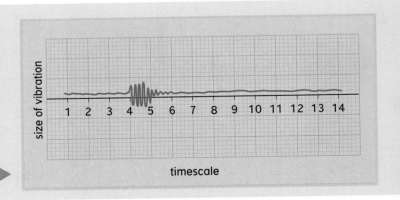

size of vibration

1 2 3 4 5 6 7 8 9 10 11 12 13 14

timescale

C

There are two main types of seismic waves: **transverse** waves and **longitudinal** waves. You can study both types of waves using a spring. Both types of waves have features in common:

● part of the spring is disturbed when the wave passes through
● regular patterns can be seen
● energy moves from one end of the spring to the other.

P How could you create your own seismograph trace?

D

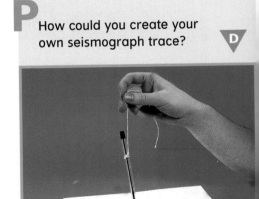

! In 1976, an earthquake in Tangshan, China killed 242 000 people.

Transverse waves

When the end of a spring is moved up and down, all parts of the spring move up and down repeatedly as energy passes from one end to the other. The spring is disturbed *at right angles* to the direction that the wave travels. This type of wave is called a transverse wave.

E

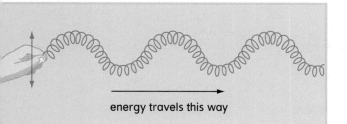

energy travels this way

Longitudinal waves

If the end of the spring is pushed forwards and backwards, sections of the spring are squashed or stretched as the energy passes from one end to the other. The spring is disturbed *in the same direction* that the wave travels. This type of wave is called a longitudinal wave.

F

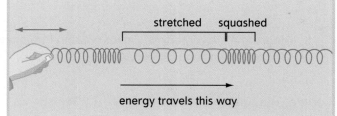

stretched   squashed

energy travels this way

3 Waves can be seen on the surface of bath water. Look at diagram G.

a) Are water waves transverse or longitudinal?

b) Which way does the cork move, up and down or left to right?

4 Transverse waves can also travel along ropes. Sketch what you would see as a transverse wave passes along a rope.

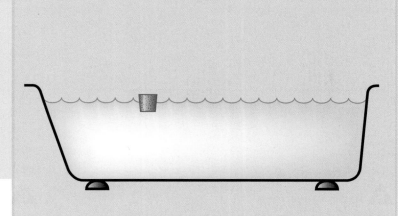

Summary

Waves transfer _____ from one place to another. They can be produced in ropes, springs, and _____. There are two different sorts of wave: longitudinal and _____. Both types of wave create regular disturbances. Seismic waves are shock waves from _____, which travel through the earth. They are detected using a _____.

earthquakes   energy
seismograph
transverse   water

5 Copy the table. Use ticks to compare transverse and longitudinal waves. The first line has been done for you.

Feature	Transverse waves	Longitudinal waves
these waves transfer energy	✓	✓
regular disturbances can be seen		
disturbances move from side to side		
disturbances move forward and back		

6 Why do seagulls sitting on the sea bob up and down as the waves pass, but not move in towards the beach with the waves?

Speed of waves

How fast do waves travel?

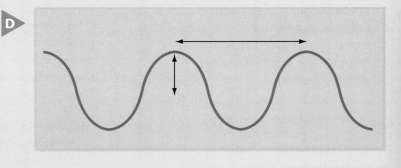

wave A

wave B

Often seismographs will show two vibrations caused by the same earthquake. The earthquake creates two different types of waves which travel at different speeds.

A

 1 Diagram A shows seismic waves passing through the Earth. Which wave is longitudinal, A or B?

Look at diagram B. The seismograph trace shows the shape of a seismic wave. Transverse and longitudinal waves are both shown as transverse waves on the trace. The main features of a transverse wave are shown in diagram C.

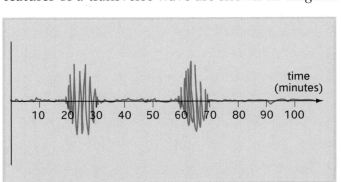

B A seismograph trace.

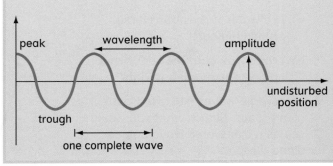

C A transverse wave.

The number of waves detected by the seismograph every second is the **frequency**. Frequency is measured in **hertz** (Hz). If three waves pass the seismograph in 1 second, then the frequency is 3 hertz.

 2 Jake is studying a seismograph trace.

    a) Four waves pass each second. What is the frequency?
    b) How many waves will pass in 2 seconds?

The length of one complete wave is called the **wavelength**. Wavelength is measured from any point on one wave to exactly the same point on the next wave. Wavelength is measured in **metres**.

3 Copy diagram D. Add these labels: amplitude, wavelength.

D

The height of a peak measured from the undisturbed position is the **amplitude**. The stronger the earthquake, the bigger the amplitude of the seismic waves.

E

You can work out the speed of a wave if you know:

- how many waves pass each second (the **frequency**)
- how long each wave is (the **wavelength**).

wave speed = **frequency** × **wavelength**
  (m/s)   **(Hz)**   **(m)**

Worked example

The frequency of a sound wave is 165 hertz. Its wavelength is 2 metres. What is its speed?

Frequency   = 165 Hz
Wavelength = 2 m
Speed   = frequency × wavelength
                = 165 × 2
                = 330 m/s.

4 A wave's frequency is 100 Hertz and its wavelength is 12 m. What is its speed?

Earthquakes at sea cause very fast waves, which slow down when they reach land. Their amplitude increases as they slow down. The amplitude can be up to 75 m, so these waves can be very destructive.

E

5 Look at diagram G. Both waves travel at the same speed.

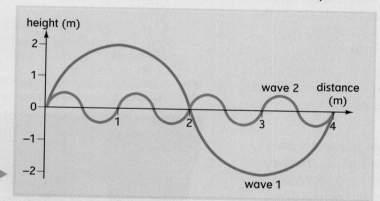

G

a) Which wave has the greatest amplitude?
b) Write down the wavelength of each wave.
c) If the frequency of wave 1 is 1 Hz, is the frequency of the other wave 4 Hz or 2 Hz?
d) What is the speed of each wave?

6 Three waves travel at the same speed. They have different frequencies and wavelengths. Copy and complete the table, filling in the gaps.

	Frequency (Hz)	Wavelength (m)	Speed (m/s)
1st wave		10	330
2nd wave	66		330
3rd wave		165	

P

How could you measure the speed of seismic waves in water?

F

Summary

The wavelength is the _____ of one wave. The amplitude is the _____ of the wave's peak from its undisturbed position. The number of waves passing a point each second is its _____. The speed of a wave is its frequency times its _____.

frequency   height
length   wavelength

Comparing waves

How do different waves compare?

Longitudinal seismic waves travel at about 2000 m/s near the surface of the Earth. They travel at about 14000 m/s deep inside the Earth. This is because the inside of the Earth is more **dense** than the surface. If scientists can work out the speed of a longitudinal seismic wave, they can work out what sort of rock it travelled through.

Speeds of longitudinal seismic waves in different sorts of rock.

granite - 5900 m/s

basalt - 6400 m/s

sandstone - 4300 m/s

1 a) Which rock do longitudinal seismic waves go through slowest?

b) Which rock is the most dense? Explain your answer.

Sound also travels as a longitudinal wave. Sound waves travel faster in solids (6000 m/s in steel), slower in liquids (1500 m/s in water) and slowest in gases (340 m/s in air). Sound waves do not travel at all in empty space (a **vacuum**).

Longitudinal seismic waves are produced by parts of the Earth vibrating. Sound waves are also produced from vibrating objects. If you feel your throat when you speak, you can feel your 'voice box' vibrating.

Light also travels as waves but light waves are transverse waves. Light waves are produced by glowing objects such as the Sun, a light bulb or a flame. These waves travel fastest in a vacuum, but more slowly through **transparent** materials such as glass, Perspex and water. Light will not travel through **opaque** materials (things which are not see-through).

2 Which material does sound travel fastest in?

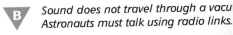
Sound does not travel through a vacu Astronauts must talk using radio links.

3 What sort of wave is light, transverse or longitudinal?

4 Are sound waves more like longitudinal seismic waves or more like light waves?

Table C compares light and sound waves.

	Light	Sound
cause of the energy	glowing object	vibrating object
travels quickest through:	empty space (vacuum)	solids
speed in air	300 000 000 m/s	340 m/s
type of wave	transverse	longitudinal

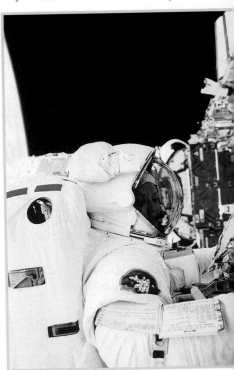

5 Copy and complete the table:

	Transverse wave	Longitudinal wave
a sketch of the wave		
example of each type of wave		
Will the wave travel through:		
● air		
● a vacuum		
● glass		
● wood		
● water		

! When things go faster than sound they are said to break the sound barrier. In certain weather conditions, you can see where the shock waves are produced as the sound barrier is broken. **E**

P How could you investigate what affects the sound that a vibrating object makes? **F**

Summary

Like all waves, light and _____ both transfer energy. Light waves come from _____ objects. Sound waves come from _____ objects. Light waves are _____ waves but sound waves are longitudinal. Sound waves need a substance to travel through but light can travel through a _____. Light travels _____ than sound.

faster   glowing   sound   transverse
vacuum   vibrating

6 You can see the Sun, but you cannot hear it. Explain why sound waves from the Sun do not reach Earth.

7 After an earthquake, people trapped under fallen buildings call for help but often can't be heard. People are advised to tap on metal pipes instead. Why?

8 If the Sun is 149 600 000 000 m from us and light takes 500 s to reach us, how fast does light travel?

Reflection

What is reflection and how is it useful?

Waves travel in straight lines. A straight arrow showing the direction that the wave travels in is called a **ray**. We can often see rays of light.

You can see the Moon at night because rays of sunlight bounce off it. Some of these rays go into our eyes. This effect is called **reflection**.

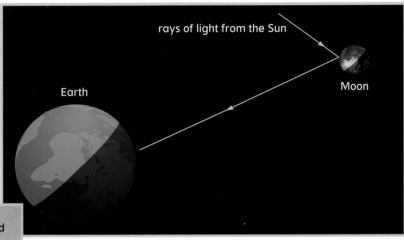

rays of light from the Sun

Earth

Moon

A

B *A ray of light being reflected.*

incoming ray

reflected ray

Many diagrams showing reflected light rays include an imaginary line called the **normal** drawn at right angles to the surface. All angles are measured using the normal.

?

1 What word describes a light ray bouncing off something?

2 Look at diagram D. Which line shows the normal?

D

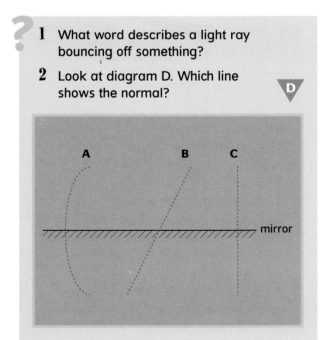

A   B   C

mirror

P

How could you investigate what angle light rays are reflected at?

C

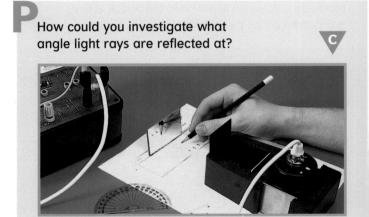

A plane surface is another name for a flat surface. When a light ray bounces off a flat, shiny surface, (a plane mirror) *the angle the ray arrives at equals the angle it leaves at.* This is the Law of Reflection.

The angle of the incoming ray (i^o)	=	The angle of the reflected ray (r^o)
or	i^o =	r^o

!

Reflected light from lasers is used to read the bar codes on items bought in shops.

Diagram E shows the important facts about reflection.

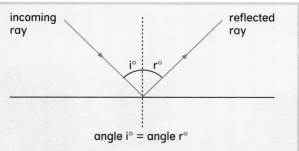

incoming ray

reflected ray

i° r°

angle i° = angle r°

E

3 What does the Law of Reflection state?

4 a) Are light waves longitudinal or transverse? (Hint: You might look back at page 210.)

b) Do they cause vibrations in the same direction as they travel or at right angles? (Hint: You might look back at page 207.)

5 A ray of light hits a plane mirror at an angle of 52°. What angle will the reflected ray leave the mirror at?

Different types of waves can be reflected:

- Sound waves reflecting off hard surfaces are heard as **echoes**.
- Light reflects from objects into our eyes, allowing us to see things.
- Waves travelling along ropes and springs can be reflected.
- Water waves reflect off river banks and harbour walls.

F

Sun

G

Summary

Waves can be drawn as _____ which travel in a straight line. Waves can bounce off some surfaces. This is called _____ . Light, sound and _____ waves can be reflected. _____ are reflected sound waves.

echoes   rays

reflection   water

6 What are reflected sound waves called?

7 Copy and complete diagram H. Show how the ray reflects from the mirror, so that Georgia can see her feet in the mirror.

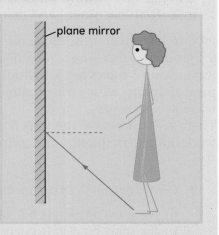

plane mirror

H

8 Some bats use sound waves to find their way in the dark. They listen to echoes from nearby obstacles.

a) Choose the correct answer. Sound waves return to the bats because the waves are:

A reflected   **B** absorbed
C curved   **D** absolved

b) How can a bat use both ears to tell if the obstacle is straight ahead or if it is slightly to one side?

Sound and ultrasound

How can we see sound waves?

We detect sound waves using our ears. However, some sound waves are too high pitched to hear. These waves are called **ultrasound**. Ultrasound can be produced by electrical vibrations. Hospitals use ultrasound to examine (scan) unborn babies. Ultrasound waves pass safely through the mother's skin and muscle, but **reflect** off the unborn baby, showing its bones, heart and other organs.

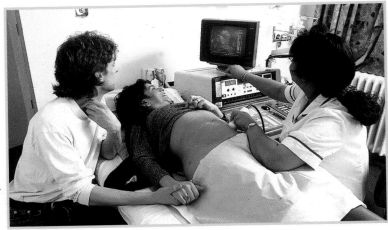

A

 1 What are ultrasound waves?

Ultrasound has other uses:

- **Quality control**: ultrasound reflects off cracks in metal structures like aeroplane wings so these defects can be found.
- **Cleaning**: the vibrations of ultrasound can dislodge dirt so ultrasound is used to clean industrial machinery and delicate jewellery.

Picture B shows an **oscilloscope** being used by a sound engineer. The screen displays a sound wave. Sound waves are longitudinal but to make measurements easier the oscilloscope displays the wave as a transverse wave. This is called a trace. There are squares on the screen to let the engineer work out the frequency and amplitude of the waves.

 Whales communicate underwater using ultrasound. Their messages can travel many kilometres through the water.

 2 Write down three uses of ultrasound waves.

B

Frequency is the number of complete waves produced each second. More waves can be seen on screen at high frequency.

Amplitude is the height of the wave's peak measured from its undisturbed position.

Frequency and pitch

- High-pitched notes have a high frequency and short wavelength.
- Low-pitched notes have a low frequency and long wavelength.

3 Copy diagram C. Draw another wave with:

a) twice the amplitude but the same wavelength
b) the same amplitude but half the wavelength

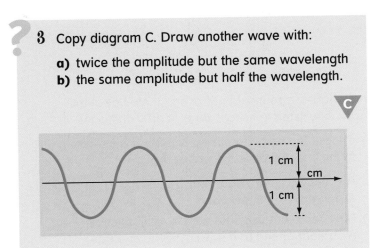

C

1 cm
cm
1 cm

und waves range from low rumbles (below 20 Hz) to very high-pitched sounds, above 20 000 Hz. We cannot hear sounds higher than 20 000 Hz.

Amplitude and loudness

Loud notes have large amplitudes. Quiet notes have small amplitudes.

4 Look at diagram G. Copy and label the drawing, showing where the sound is

a) quiet   b) loud
c) high pitched   d) low pitched.

D

E

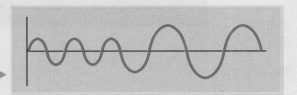

G

5 Copy and complete these sentences by choosing correct endings from the box:

a) High pitched notes have a . . . .
b) Low pitched notes have a . . . .
c) Loud sounds have a . . . .
d) Quiet sounds have a . . . .

| low frequency. | . . . low amplitude. |
| high frequency. | . . . high amplitude. |

6 Counter-tenors are men who can sing very high but they have normal speaking voices. Diagram H shows the trace of a counter-tenor speaking. Copy the trace and draw another one to show his trace when singing loudly at a concert.

H

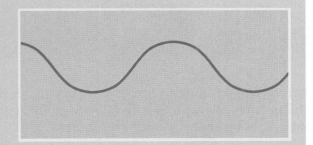

P How can you compare the pitch of different notes using an oscilloscope?

F

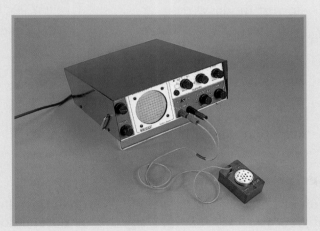

Summary

_____ is sound that is too high-pitched to hear. It is used for quality control, _____ and scanning unborn babies. Sound waves can be displayed on an _____. The frequency of a note controls its _____. High-pitched sounds have a _____ frequency. The _____ of a sound wave controls the volume of a note. Loud sounds have a _____ amplitude.

| amplitude | cleaning | high | large |
| oscilloscope | pitch | ultrasound | |

Refraction

What is refraction?

Archer fish squirt water at insects to knock them into the water. The fish does not look straight at its victim. This is because rays of light from the insect slow down and change direction when they go into water. This is called **refraction**. The fish sees these refracted rays as if they had travelled in a straight line and so the insect appears to be in a different place.

Waves change speed and direction when entering different substances (also called **media**):

- Light travels fastest in a vacuum, slower in air, slower, still, in water, and slowest in glass.
- Water waves travel fastest in deep water, slowing down and changing direction when they reach shallow water.
- Sound waves travel fastest in solids and slowest in gases.

 1 What happens to light rays when they go into water?

2 Copy and complete this table:

Type of wave	The waves travel fastest in:	The waves travel slowest in:
light waves		
sound waves	solids	
	deep water	shallow water

Seeing refraction

You can use a block of glass and a ray box to see refraction.

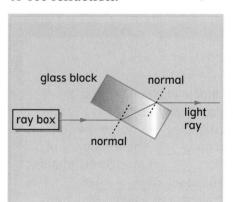

Waves travelling along the normal do not change direction.

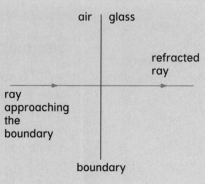

Waves arriving at any other angle do change direction.

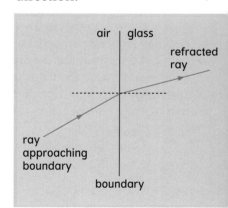

 3 When does a wave travel straight through a boundary?

Waves slow down as they go from air into glass. This makes them move *closer* to the normal. Waves speed up as they go from glass into air. This makes them move *away* from the normal.

4 Choose the correct diagram showing a refracted ray moving from water into air.

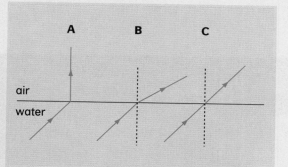

F

Mirages are caused when light is refracted as it travels between a layer of hot air rising from hot ground, and a layer of cooler air above.

K

5 Copy diagrams F and G. Draw in the missing light rays.

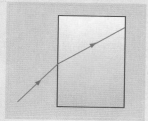

G

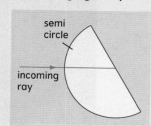

semi circle

incoming ray

H

P How could you find out if light refracts more in different materials?

L

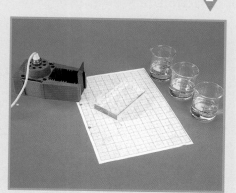

6 The straw in Jodi's drink looked crooked even though it was really straight. Copy and complete these sentences to explain why.

I

Light waves travel _____ in the drink and faster in air. The waves _____ direction at the boundary between the two substances but Jodi sees the light waves as if they carried on in a straight _____.

7 Choose the correct answer. Water in swimming pools often looks shallower than expected. This is because:

  A the floor is tiled
  B light refracts as it leaves the water
  C the chlorine affects your eyesight.

8 Copy and complete diagram I showing **a)** the light rays travelling from the floor to your eyes and **b)** the ray that makes the floor appear shallower.

J

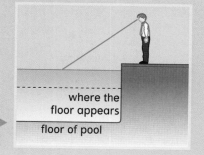

where the floor appears

floor of pool

Summary

Rays of light change _____ when they travel into a different material. This is because they change speed. This effect is called _____. The _____ is a line at right angles to a boundary. Light travelling along the normal does not _____ direction. Sound and _____ waves can also be refracted.

change   direction   normal
refraction   water

Total internal reflection

What is total internal reflection?

To examine the inside of a patient, doctors often use **endoscopes**. These tools use bundles of **optical fibres**. Light travels along the fibres into the patient. The reflected light travels back along other fibres to form a picture. Optical fibres use **total internal reflection** to do this.

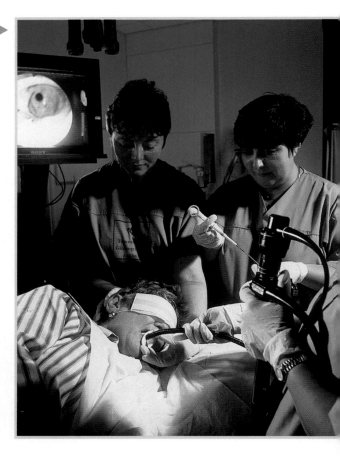

 1 What is an endoscope made from?

Light normally changes direction when it travels from glass, Perspex or water into the air, because of refraction.

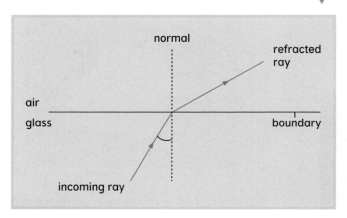

At a certain angle, the refracted light travels along the boundary. This angle is called the **critical angle**.

Above this angle, all the light reflects back from the inside surface and none passes through. The surface acts like a mirror. This is total internal reflection.

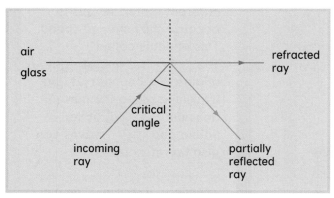

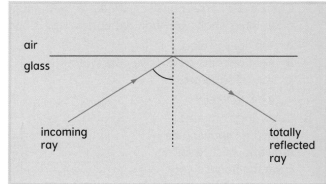

 2 What is the critical angle?

P How could you find the critical angle for glass?

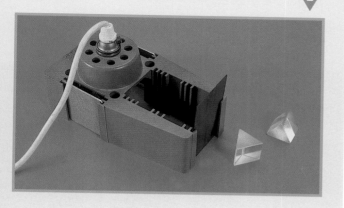

E

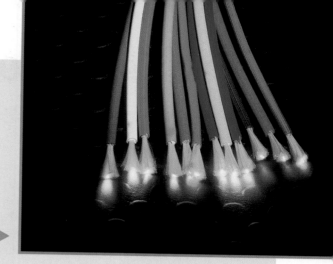

F

The thinnest optical fibres are a billionth of a metre wide and up to 10 km long.

Cat's eyes in the road reflect light from a driver's headlights back into the driver's eyes, lighting up the centre of the road. A prism in a cat's eye uses total internal reflection.

Diagram H shows how *repeated* total internal reflection occurs in optical fibres in endoscopes.

G

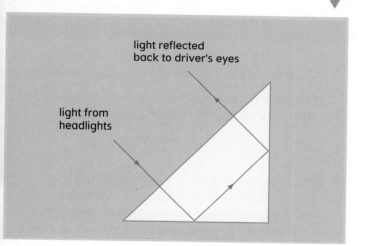

light reflected back to driver's eyes

light from headlights

H

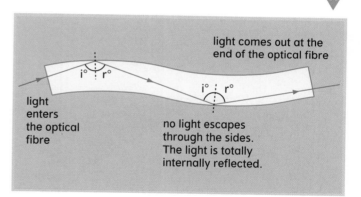

light comes out at the end of the optical fibre

light enters the optical fibre

$i°$ $r°$ $i°$ $r°$

no light escapes through the sides. The light is totally internally reflected.

3 What is the prism in a cat's eye for?

4 Where does light sent into an optical fibre come out? Choose the correct answer.

   A the sides of the optical fibre
   B the end of the optical fibre
   C it does not come out.

5 Why are two bundles of optical fibres needed in an endoscope?

6 Write a sentence explaining how an endoscope can be used to examine the inside of a footballer's damaged knee.

Summary

Light can be _____ from the inside surfaces of glass, Perspex, and water if it arrives above the _____ angle. Light travels down _____ _____ using total internal reflection. These are used in _____. Prisms in _____ _____ also use total internal reflection.

cat's eyes   critical   endoscopes
optical fibres   reflected

Dispersion

What is dispersion?

Sunlight is made up of different colours of light. These colours can be separated as the light rays shine through raindrops. The spread of colours is called the **visible spectrum**. You can also see a spectrum when white light shines through a prism. This separation of colours is called **dispersion**.

We see a spectrum because different colours of light travel at different speeds through a raindrop or prism. Each colour changes direction (refracts) by a different amount as it moves from air into water or glass, and back out again. Diagram B shows how dispersion occurs.

A

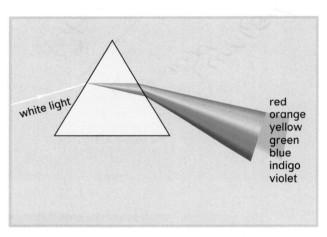

white light

red
orange
yellow
green
blue
indigo
violet

B *This is how a prism disperses white light into a spectrum. Red light changes direction least. Violet (purple) light changes direction most.*

C *The electromagnetic spectrum.*

1 What is the weather like when we see rainbows?

2 Put these colours in order with the one that changes direction most first:

red   blue   yellow

The light that we can see is called **visible light**. Light waves are members of a family of waves called **electromagnetic waves**. All electromagnetic waves can travel through empty space (**a vacuum**). When in a vacuum they all travel at the same speed (300 000 000 m/s). Electromagnetic waves form a spectrum of waves carrying energy. Visible light waves are in the middle of the **electromagnetic spectrum**.

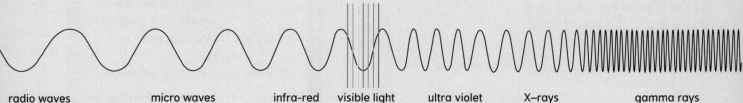

| radio waves | | micro waves | | infra-red | visible light | ultra violet | X–rays | gamma rays |
| 1000 m | 1 m | 1 mm | | 0.001 mm | | 0.000 001 mm | | 0.000 000 001 mm |

wavelength

3 Use diagram C to write down the name of the waves with the longest and the shortest wavelengths.

Sometimes, because of repeated total internal reflection in the rain drops, you get a double rainbow. Notice the order of colours in each one.

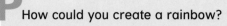

Because of dispersion, all the colours of the visible spectrum can be seen on bubbles and thin films of oil.

P How could you create a rainbow?

4 What is the speed of:

a) a light wave?
b) a radio wave?

5 Work out what these words are:

a) sp_ _ _: the same for all electromagnetic waves
b) d _ sp _ _ s _ _ _: when light is separated into its colours
c) l_ _ _ t: this is an example of an electromagnetic wave.

Summary

When sunlight passes through a _____, it splits into a _____ of different colours. This effect is called _____. Red light is refracted the _____ and _____ light is refracted the most. Visible light and other electromagnetic waves travel at the same _____ in a vacuum. Visible light is part of a series of waves called the _____ spectrum.

dispersion	electromagnetic	least
prism	spectrum	speed	violet

6 Write down the correct word in each case:

S_____: a rainbow is an example of one.

P_____: this can be used to disperse light.

E_____: this is carried by electromagnetic waves.

E _____-magnetic waves all travel at the same speed.

D_____: when light splits into its separate colours.

7 If electromagnetic radiation is shone through a prism, you can only see the visible spectrum. Using a diagram to help, explain where you could detect:

a) infra-red radiation
b) ultraviolet radiation.

Diffraction

What is diffraction and how is it useful?

When waves enter a harbour, they often spread into parts of the harbour that are not in front of the entrance. When waves spread through a gap or around objects it is called **diffraction**.

> **1** What effect allows the water waves to spread into the harbour?

When a wave is diffracted, its wavelength does not change. However, the size of its wavelength affects how much it is diffracted. Diagrams B and C show different water waves diffracting through a gap.

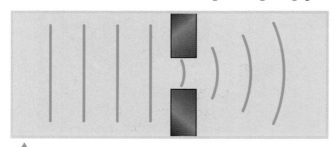

B *These waves are strongly diffracted.*

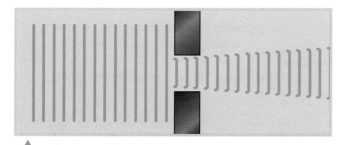

C *These waves are weakly diffracted.*

> **2** The wavelength of voices is about 1 m. Is the wave strongly or weakly diffracted through a doorway, 1 m wide?

Normally a hill will block radio waves. However, if the width of the hill is similar to the wavelength then the radio waves diffract strongly around the hill, improving radio reception. Waves used for TV do not diffract as much around hills because their wavelength is shorter than the waves used to transmit radio broadcasts.

A

If the wavelength is similar to the size of the gap, then the wave curves as it passes through the gap, and spreads out a lot on the far side. It is strongly diffracted.

If the wavelength is much smaller than the size of the gap, the wave does not curve or spread out much. It is weakly diffracted.

The same rule applies to all waves spreading around objects.

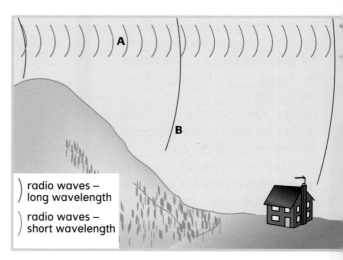

radio waves – long wavelength

radio waves – short wavelength

D *Long radio waves are received more clearly than short radio waves because they diffract strongly around the hill.*

3 Look at wave B on diagram D.

a) Is the hill much wider, much thinner or similar in width to the radio wavelength?

b) Will the radio waves diffract strongly or weakly around the hill?

c) Will the radio station be received clearly or badly on the other side of the hill?

P How would you find out whether high- or low- pitched notes are diffracted the most through a gap?

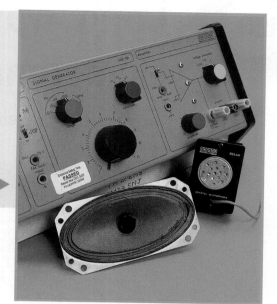

E ▶

4 If members of a class are chatting outside a room, what effect allows their voices to spread through the doorway and fill the room?

5 Which one of these waves cannot be diffracted? Choose the correct answer.

A water waves **B** sound waves **C** waves on a spring

6 What do diffracted waves do? Choose the correct answer.

A get louder **B** change pitch **C** spread out

7 What makes a wave diffract more strongly? Choose the correct answer.

A a longer wavelength **B** greater amplitude
C moving between different materials

Low-pitched sounds diffract easily around corners of buildings so that sounds are heard where you would expect silence.

All the different types of waves can be diffracted, but waves with longer wavelengths are diffracted most.

8 Diagram F shows sound waves passing a building. **F** ▼

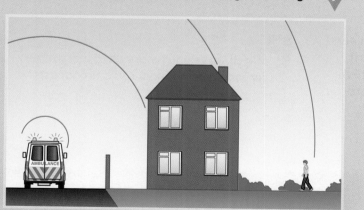

a) What effect makes the waves curve after passing the building?

b) Would the waves curve more or less if the building was much wider?

c) You cannot see sound waves. How could you tell that diffraction had happened?

Summary

A wave passing through a _____ or around an obstacle spreads around the edges. This is _____. The wavelength does not change. Electromagnetic waves, sound and _____ waves can be diffracted. Diffraction is strongest if the wavelength is _____ in size to the gap or obstacle. Diffraction helps the reception of _____ waves in hilly areas. It helps sounds to be heard in the _____ of buildings.

| diffraction | gap | radio |
| shadow | similar | water |

Long wavelength electromagnetic waves

How do long wavelength electromagnetic waves behave?

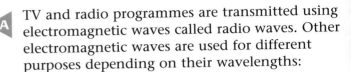

A TV and radio programmes are transmitted using electromagnetic waves called radio waves. Other electromagnetic waves are used for different purposes depending on their wavelengths:

- heating and cooking (3 cm)
- transmitting (sending) pictures and sounds round the world (1–2000 m)
- talking to astronauts in space (1 m)
- communicating underwater with submarines (100 km)
- tracking ships, and aeroplanes (1 cm).

The wavelengths of the different electromagnetic waves gives each type of wave its properties and uses. Electromagnetic waves are also called **electromagnetic radiation**.

Each type of radiation can be **absorbed** (taken in), **transmitted** (allowed through) or **reflected** by different substances. If radiation is absorbed by something it often heats up.

Sometimes the radiation that is absorbed creates an electric current in something. This current vibrates at the same frequency as the absorbed wave. This is how radio waves are turned into signals that you can hear in a radio.

? 1 What affects a wave's properties and uses?

2 What three things can happen to electromagnetic waves?

P Which wavelengths are used more often for local and national radio broadcasts?

Radio waves

- Typical wavelength: 200 m.
- Properties: They are reflected by an electrically charged layer in the Earth's upper atmosphere. This allows the waves to reach distant places despite the Earth's curved surface.
- Uses: They are used to transmit radio and TV broadcasts.

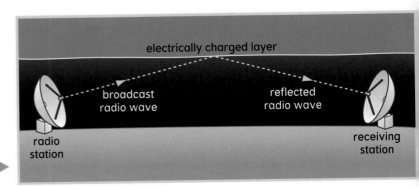

electrically charged layer

broadcast radio wave

reflected radio wave

radio station

receiving station

B

Microwaves

- Typical wavelength: 2.8 cm.
- Properties: They are absorbed by water molecules in food, passing on their energy so the food heats up. Microwaves are transmitted (pass through) the Earth's atmosphere easily.
- Uses: They are used to cook food using microwave ovens, for sending information to satellites and communicating within mobile phone networks.

Infra-red radiation

- Typical wavelength: 0.5 mm.
- Properties: All hot objects give out infra-red radiation. You can feel it as heat. Infra-red radiation passes through the Earth's atmosphere and can be sent as a narrow beam.
- Uses: Infra-red radiation is used in grills, toasters and electric fires. It is also sent as narrow beams from remote controls to operate electrical equipment. Infra-red radiation is also used to send information through optical fibre telephone cables.

It was first discovered that microwaves could cook things when pigeons near new microwave transmitters in World War Two were dying because they were cooked! Different wavelength microwaves are used in microwave ovens and mobile phones!

Summary

Electromagnetic waves have different properties because they have different _____. Infra-red radiation is used in toasters, electric fires, _____ and also in TV remote controls. Radio waves transmit radio and TV _____. Long radio waves are _____ by the atmosphere so can travel further. Microwaves cook food when _____ molecules in the food absorb their energy. They are used to send and receive messages from satellites because they pass through the Earth's _____ easily.

atmosphere   broadcasts   grills   reflected
water   wavelengths

3 a) Which types of radiation pass through the Earth's atmosphere?

b) Why can microwaves be used to communicate with satellites?

4 What type of radiation do each of these use?

a) a video remote control

b) a TV station

c) mobile phones.

5 A radio station in Moscow sends broadcasts to Siberia.

a) What type of electromagnetic wave is used?

b) Explain how the atmosphere helps the broadcast travel a long distance. Draw a diagram as part of your answer.

c) If a different station sends out microwaves, why don't they reach Siberia?

Analogue and digital signals

How are analogue and digital signals different?

In the past, smoke signals and yodelling allowed people to send messages across valleys in mountainous areas. Now we can talk on the phone to people on the other side of the world.

Speech and music can be changed into electrical signals, and sent along electrical cables. These signals can also be sent using radio waves, microwaves and infra-red waves. Speech and music can also be changed into light or infra-red waves, which are sent along optical fibres.

 1 What types of electromagnetic wave can be used to send signals to other people?

A

Analogue signals

When we speak, the frequency and amplitude of the soundwaves we make change continuously. Like sound waves, electromagnetic signals also change continuously. They are examples of **analogue signals**. Analogue signals are signals that can change frequency and amplitude continuously.

B

Digital signals

Morse code was used on ships to send messages as a series of long or short beeps. The signal was either on or off. Sound waves and electromagnetic signals can be changed into a series of beeps (**pulses**). Signals like this are called **digital signals**.

The light reflecting off this bar code is converted into a digital signal. C

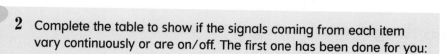

2 Complete the table to show if the signals coming from each item vary continuously or are on/off. The first one has been done for you:

	Can it vary continuously?	Is it only on or off?
the light from a lamp controlled by a dimmer switch	yes	no
the light from a torch		
the temperature of a drink		
the sound of a door bell		

Telephone companies can now send millions of calls at the same time using optical fibres. More information can be sent as digital signals through optical fibres compared with electrical analogue signals sent through cables of the same thickness. The information is more accurate because digital signals do not get distorted (altered) or weakened, even when they are sent over long distances.

! Digital recordings do not suffer from the hisses or crackles that can be heard on analogue recordings.

3 Give two reasons why many phone calls use digital signals now.

4 Which of the examples in diagram E are analogue signals?

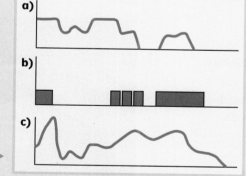

a)

b)

c)

E

5 Morse code uses dots and dashes to get a message over:

E = .   H = ...   L = . – . .   P = . – –   R = – .

Use the codes to spell out these words: HELP HERE

6 A digital camera contains millions of light detectors. When a photo is taken, light shines on these detectors and a picture is built up using information about the colour of light shining on each detector. Explain what a small part of a picture from a digital camera would look like if you looked very closely at it.

Summary

Speech and music can be sent as analogue or _____ signals. Signals are sent electrically along electric _____ or using electromagnetic waves. Infra-red and light waves can carry signals along _____ fibres. The amplitude and _____ of analogue signals vary continuously. Digital signals are coded as pulses, which are either on or _____. Compared with analogue signals, digital signals are less likely to be _____ and can be sent in greater numbers along any particular cable.

cables	digital	distorted
frequency	off	optical

Short wavelength electromagnetic waves

How do short wavelength electromagnetic waves behave?

A *This bank note has a fluorescent marker that shows up under ultraviolet light.*

Ultraviolet radiation

- Typical wavelength: 0.001 mm.
- Properties: Ultraviolet radiation is reflected as visible, purple light by special materials called **fluorescent materials**.
- Uses: Ultraviolet radiation is used to detect fraud. It is also used in fluorescent lights and sun-beds.

B *A special coating in a fluorescent light absorbs the ultraviolet radiation given out inside the light. The coating then gives out visible light.*

Some waves have wavelengths much shorter than visible light.

Banks and shops check bank notes using **ultraviolet** radiation. Ultraviolet radiation cannot be seen. However, if it shines on bank notes, ultraviolet radiation changes to purple light so the bank notes glow purple. This effect is called **fluorescence**. It does not happen with fake bank notes.

? 1 What type of radiation is used to detect the fake bank notes?

P Find out how fake objects can be detected.

! Aeroplanes that fly very high are exposed to strong ultraviolet rays from the Sun. The atmosphere gives people on the ground some protection from these rays.

X-radiation

- Typical wavelength: 0.000 001 mm.
- Properties: X-rays are absorbed by materials like bones and metals, but they pass through skin and cloth easily.
- Uses: X-rays are used to detect cracks in metals and breaks in bones by producing shadow pictures.

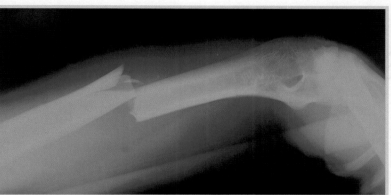

Gamma radiation

- Typical wavelength: 0.000 000 001 mm.
- Properties: Gamma rays can kill living cells. They have a high frequency and so gamma rays carry a lot of energy.
- Uses: Gamma radiation can be used to treat cancer by killing cancer cells. It can keep food fresh and **sterilise** surgical equipment by killing harmful bacteria.

2 Copy and complete the sentence:

As the wavelength of the waves increases, their frequency _____ and the energy they carry _____.

3 Choose the correct type of radiation in each case:
a) It is used to treat cancer.
b) It is used to look for cracks in metal aeroplane parts.
c) It is used in sunbeds.

4 When Usha bought a CD, the shopkeeper checked her £10 note using an ultraviolet lamp. Usha fell as she left the shop and hurt her arm badly. In the hospital, the doctor held up the X-ray picture. 'You've broken your arm', he said. Copy and complete the table from the story:

Type of radiation	Use

5 Invisible ink, which fluoresces (glows purple) when ultraviolet light shines on it, helps the police to trace stolen goods. Explain why it is a better choice than normal ink for marking items of property.

Summary

Ultraviolet radiation is absorbed by fluorescent materials, then emitted (given out) as visible light. This happens in fluorescent _____. This effect is also used to detect _____. Ultraviolet radiation is also used in sun-beds. X-rays do not pass through metal or _____. Aeroplanes and bones can be examined for cracks using _____. Gamma rays kill _____ cells. They are useful for _____ equipment, killing _____ cells and destroying harmful bacteria in food.

bones   cancer   fraud   lights   living
sterilising   X-rays

Radiation and living cells

How does radiation affect living cells?

When a patient is treated for cancer, gamma radiation is used to kill the cancer cells. In low doses, gamma rays cause cancer but high doses directed at cancer cells will kill them. They also kill bacteria which cause infections. Gamma rays are also used to **sterilise** (disinfect) the equipment used in operations. Some food we buy is treated with gamma rays to preserve it by killing the bacteria in it.

 1 List three uses of gamma rays.

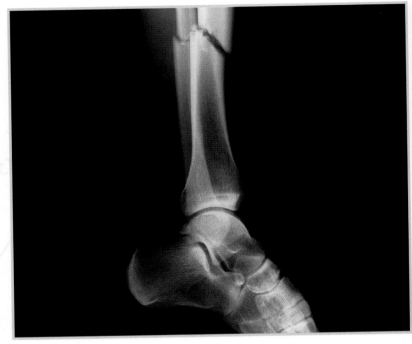

The bones show up because X-rays cannot pass through them. A

Other types of electromagnetic waves (radiation) can also affect living cells:

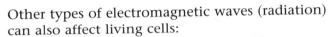B *The colour of your skin can protect you from skin cancer.*

- **X-rays** usually pass through the soft parts of the body but some cells absorb the rays. High doses kill cells but lower doses can cause cancer.

- **Ultraviolet radiation** (UV) in high doses kills cells. UV from the Sun can cause skin cancer. This is more common in fair-skinned people because light skin does not absorb UV as well as dark skin. More UV reaches deeper tissue where the cancer forms. Dark skin absorbs UV better so dark-skinned people have less risk of skin cancer.

> ! In Australia, skin cancer is a real danger. The slogan 'Slip Slap Slop' is used to advertise this danger. This stands for: slip on a top, slap on a hat, slop on sun protection cream.

- **Infra-red radiation** (IR) is absorbed by the skin and felt as heat.

C

- **Microwaves** are absorbed by the water in cells. The water heats up and can damage or kill the cells.

Too much of these types of electromagnetic radiation is dangerous. The longer you are exposed to the radiation, the more dangerous it is. Gamma rays are more harmful than X-rays, which are more harmful than UV. You can reduce the risks by reducing the time of exposure and wearing protective clothing.

D

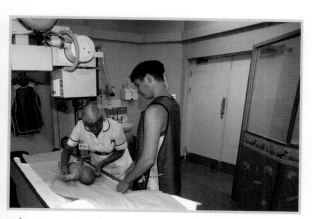

E *The father wears a lead apron to protect him from x-rays. The nurse will stand behind the shield on the right when the x-ray is taken.*

2 Which type or types of radiation:
  a) can cause cancer?
  b) comes from the Sun?
  c) is absorbed by water in cells?

3 What two factors can reduce the risk from radiation?

4 Choose the best method to protect yourself from skin cancer from this list:

  A staying in the sun for a long time
  B using sun cream
  C putting on eye shadow.

5 When cancer is treated, several gamma ray sources are carefully angled so the tumour receives a large dose but other cells get smaller doses. The rest of the body is shielded using lead sheets.
  a) Why is it important that only the tumour gets a high dose?
  b) How are other parts of the body protected?
  c) Why do the nurses leave the room when patients are being treated?

P How could you find out what sources of (safe) radiation there are in the room?

F

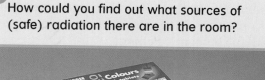

Summary

In large doses, gamma rays kill _____ cells, and _____ in food and on surgical instruments. In smaller doses, gamma rays, _____ and UV can cause cancer. Ultraviolet rays pass through the skin to cells deeper in the body. Darker skin _____ UV better, helping to protect the person against skin cancer. Microwaves are absorbed by the water in _____. The energy is released as heat which can damage or _____ living cells.

absorbs   bacteria   cancer
cells   heat   kill   X-rays

L14

Ionisation

What is ionisation?

Gamma rays are dangerous because they can alter atoms. An atom contains a central **nucleus** containing **protons** and **neutrons**. Around this are **electrons**.

Atoms normally have an equal number of positive and negative charges, so their overall charge is **neutral**. Protons have a positive charge, neutrons have no charge and electrons have a negative charge.

Atoms become positively charged if they lose an electron, and negatively charged if they gain an electron. Atoms which have become charged are called **ions**.

Gamma rays can knock electrons off atoms and turn them into ions. The atoms have been **ionised**. Gamma rays are an example of **ionising radiation**.

There are three main types of ionising radiation, **alpha** (α), **beta** (β) and **gamma** (γ).

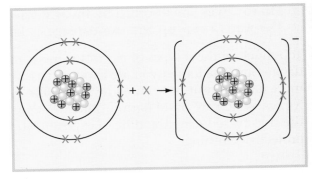

A *An ion is an atom that has gained an electron . . .*

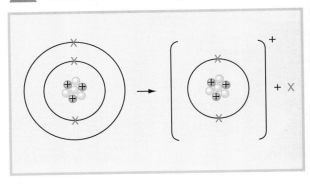

B *. . . or lost an electron.*

? 1 What can gamma radiation change atoms and molecules into?

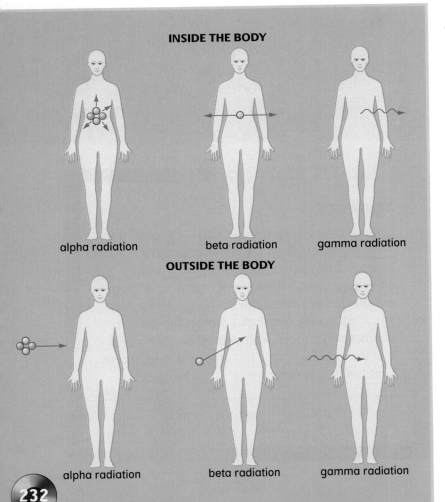

INSIDE THE BODY

alpha radiation   beta radiation   gamma radiation

OUTSIDE THE BODY

alpha radiation   beta radiation   gamma radiation

If atoms in the molecules of living cells are ionised, the cells are damaged. This upsets the processes in these cells, causing cancer and other illnesses. Damage to cells happens only if the cells absorb the radiation. The radiation is less dangerous if it cannot reach the cells or if it passes straight through them without being absorbed.

Alpha (α) radiation

The skin absorbs this type of ionising radiation. Alpha radiation cannot pass through into the cells inside the body and so it is the least dangerous type outside the body.

C *Alpha radiation cannot pass in or out of the body through skin. Beta and gamma radiation can enter and escape from the body through skin.*

However, if something containing alpha radiation gets inside you, it is strongly absorbed by cells inside the body, causing damage. This means that alpha radiation is the most dangerous type inside the body.

2 How does skin stop alpha radiation from entering our bodies?

Beta (β) and gamma (γ) radiation

Both of these types pass easily through skin and are absorbed by cells inside the body, causing damage. Beta and gamma radiation are most dangerous outside the body. However, if something giving out these types of radiation gets inside you, the radiation is more likely to escape from the body and not be absorbed by living cells. This means that beta and gamma radiation are less dangerous inside the body than alpha radiation.

D The hazard symbol for radiation.

The amount of damage caused depends on:

- the type of radiation
- whether the radiation is inside or outside the body
- the amount of radiation you are exposed to (large doses over a long time are most damaging).

3 Why is beta radiation less dangerous inside the body than alpha radiation?

4 Complete the words:
  a) When atoms become charged they have been i_____.
  b) Alpha radiation is not harmful o_____ the body
  c) Atoms and molecules are normally n_____.

! Radioactive metals give out ionising radiation but can be safely used in certain batteries. These batteries are used in heart pace-makers, saving millions of lives each year.

5 Copy and label diagram E to show how different types of radiation pass through the body.

E

Summary

An atom contains a central _____ containing _____ and neutrons. Around this are electrons. When radiation is absorbed, _____ cells are damaged. Atoms in the molecules inside the cells become ionised and these ions can cause cancer. Ionisation happens when _____ are knocked out of atoms and molecules. _____ atoms and molecules become charged. Alpha radiation is most damaging inside the body; beta and _____ radiation are most damaging outside the body. Larger doses of radiation are more _____ than small doses.

dangerous   electrons   gamma
living   neutral   nucleus   protons

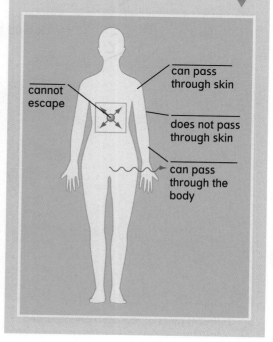

cannot escape

can pass through skin

does not pass through skin

can pass through the body

Ionising radiation

How do the different types of radiation behave?

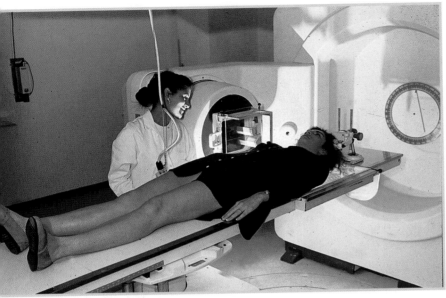

Radioactive substances emit (give out) ionising radiation from the nuclei of their atoms all the time. Different radioactive substances give out different types of ionising radiation – alpha, beta or gamma.

Radioactive materials come in different strengths. Some substances are very radioactive. They need to be carefully stored, for example inside lead containers.

A *Gamma radiation is used in hospitals to kill cancer cells.*

The three main types of ionising radiation are described in table B.

B

Name of radiation	Symbol	Passes through:	Is absorbed by:
alpha	α	very short distances in air	a few cm of air a thin sheet of paper skin
beta	β	air and paper	a thin sheet of metal
gamma	γ	most things except thick lead and concrete	a thick sheet of lead a very thick wall of concrete

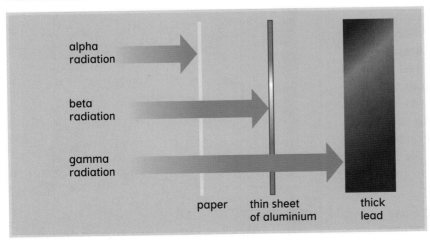

alpha radiation

beta radiation

gamma radiation

paper   thin sheet of aluminium   thick lead

C *Different types of radiation are absorbed by different amounts in different materials.*

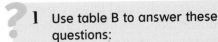

1 Use table B to answer these questions:

  a) How can concrete protect people from gamma radiation?

  b) Could this page absorb beta radiation?

  c) Could alpha radiation be safely stored in a strong, cardboard box?

2 What types of radiation are absorbed by lead?

Other materials contain very small amounts of radioactivity. They are found in the air, the ground, building materials and food. **Cosmic radiation** reaches us from space. The radiation surrounding us from all these sources is called **background radiation**. Background radiation cannot be altered; it is always around us. However strange it seems, background radiation is a part of normal life.

D Radioactive nuclear fuel is transported in steel flasks. Each flask has a mass of 50 tonnes.

3 Write down three sources of background radiation.

F A Geiger counter is used to measure the amount of radiation given off by something.

E Examples of items that give out background radiation.

! 200 million gamma waves pass through your body every hour from the soil and buildings.

Summary

Radioactive substances give out _____ all the time. Alpha radiation is absorbed easily in air, and by paper or _____. Thin sheets of metal absorb _____ radiation. Gamma radiation is very penetrating. It is only stopped by thick sheets of lead or metres of _____ . _____ radiation surrounds us. It comes from small amounts of radiation in the _____, building materials, the ground, food, and from _____.

air	background	beta	concrete
	radiation	skin	space

4 Copy and complete these sentences:
B_____ radiation surrounds us all the time.
Radioactive substances e_____ ionising radiation.
T_____ sheets of lead are needed to absorb gamma rays.
A_____ radiation is easily absorbed by skin.

5 Write a sentence explaining to a pupil in year 7 what is meant by background radiation.

6 What type of radiation do each of these sentences refer to?
a) It is used to kill cells in order to save lives.
b) It can't travel far without being absorbed.
c) It travels through air but can't pass though thin metal.

Half-lives

What happens to a radioactive material over time?

Before a leak can be mended in an underground pipe, you need to know where it is. A radioactive **tracer** is injected at one end of the pipe and a detector is used to discover where the radiation collects. From this, workers can tell where the problem is. The radiation is safe to use because the radioactivity dies away after a short time.

A

 1 Why is the radioactive substance used to find leaks safe to use?

Radioactive materials are **unstable**. They have atoms with nuclei whch constantly break up forming different atoms. This is called **radioactive decay**. The atoms of the original material are called **parent atoms**. The number of parent atoms that break apart in a second is called the **count-rate**.

Over time, the count-rate falls. The time taken for the count-rate to fall to half its value from when you started counting is the **half-life** of the material. Different materials have different half-lives ranging from millionths of a second to millions of years.

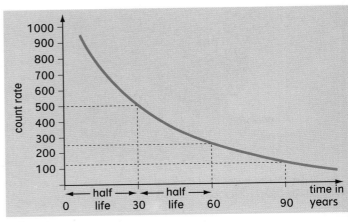

B *Every 30 years, the count rate in caesium halves.*

 2 What happens to the count-rate over time?

Worked example

What is the half life of this element?

Time (minutes)	Count-rate
0	100
2	70
4	50
6	40

- The original count-rate is 100.
- Half of the original count-rate is 50.
- The count-rate is 50 after 4 minutes.
- So the half-life is 4 minutes.

3 Table C shows the count-rate for a radioactive element.

C

Time (minutes)	Count-rate
0	60
10	45
20	37
30	30
40	23

a) What is the original count-rate?
b) What is half of the original count-rate?
c) After how many minutes is the count-rate 30?
d) What is the half-life for this sample?

You can calculate how many parent atoms are left in a sample. During one half-life, the number of parent atoms left in the material will halve.

Worked example

The half-life of radon gas is 4 days. There are 1000 atoms of radon to begin with. How many parent atoms will be left after 8 days?

- After 4 days there will be half the number of parent atoms (500 atoms).

- After another 4 days, there are half of 500 atoms (250).

- So after 8 days there will be 250 parent atoms left.

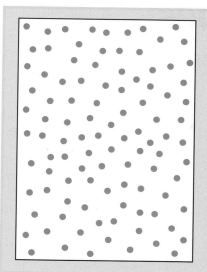 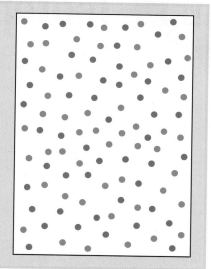

 D

In one half-life, half the parent atoms decay. You can never tell which atom will decay next.

! Uranium is used in nuclear power stations. Its half-life is 700 million years.

P You can make a model of radioactive decay using cubes like these. You drop them, remove some and drop them again. How would you decide which cubes to remove?

E

4 Use table F to answer these questions: **F**

Material	Half-life	Original count-rate	Number of parent atoms
X	10 minutes	100	1 000
Y	3 days	80	20 000
Z	7 years	200	500

Which material, X, Y, or Z:
a) Has the longest half-life?
b) Has a count-rate of 50 after 10 minutes?
c) Has 10 000 parent atoms after 3 days?

5 Carbon-14 has a half-life of 5600 years. There are 2000 atoms initially.
a) How long will it take for 1000 carbon atoms to decay?
b) If the sample is 11 200 years old, how many parent atoms remain?
c) Radium-226 has a half-life of 1600 years. There are 2000 atoms originally. How many radium atoms remain after 3200 years?
d) Explain which sample you expect to be the least radioactive after 3200 years.

Summary

Some _____ are unstable, and decay into other atoms. This is radioactive _____. The original atoms are called _____ atoms. The _____-_____ of a radioactive material is the time taken for the _____-_____ to fall to half its original value and the number of parent atoms to _____.

atoms	count-rate	decay
half-life	halve	parent

Isotopes

What are isotopes?

? **1** What is the difference between ordinary water and heavy water?

Many **elements** contain atoms of two types. Some of these types of atom are radioactive. The different types of atom are called **isotopes**.

One type of water has more mass than normal water because it contains an isotope of hydrogen called deuterium. 'Heavy water' looks like ordinary water, but molecules of heavy water have more mass than molecules of normal water. Molecules of ordinary water always contain atoms of two elements: hydrogen and oxygen. Table A compares the two elements.

A ▶

	Protons	Neutrons	Electrons
hydrogen	1	0	1
oxygen	8	8	8

Each different element has a different number of protons in the nucleus of its atoms, and different numbers of electrons circling the nucleus. This gives each element its particular chemical properties.

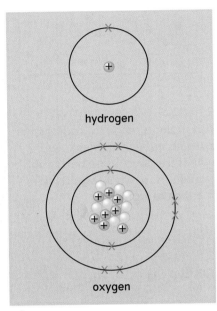

hydrogen

oxygen

B *Two different elements.*

All the atoms of the same element have the same number of protons in the nucleus and the same number of electrons circling around it.

Different isotopes of an element have a different number of neutrons, but the same number of protons and electrons, in their atoms.

Table D compares two isotopes of hydrogen.

? **2** What gives each element its chemical properties?

3 What does each atom of an element have the same number of?

4 What do atoms of different isotopes of an element have different numbers of?

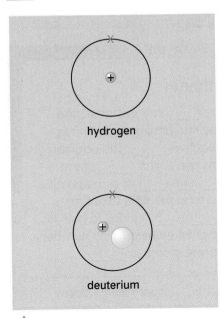

hydrogen

deuterium

C *Isotopes of hydrogen.*

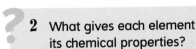 **D**

	Protons	Neutrons	Electrons
hydrogen	1	0	1
deuterium	1	1	1

Neutrons and protons are known as **nucleons**. The **mass** (or **nucleon**) **number** of an element is the total number of neutrons and protons in the nucleus.

- Hydrogen has one proton and no neutrons. Its mass number is 1
- Deuterium has one neutron and one proton. Its mass number is 2.

Element	Protons	Neutrons	Electrons	Mass number
carbon-12	6	6	6	12
carbon-14 (radioactive)	6	8	6	14
lithium-6	3	3	3	6
lithium-7	3	4	3	7
uranium-235	92	143	92	235
uranium-238	92	146	92	238

 5 What is the mass number of:
   a) helium, which has two neutrons and two protons?
   b) carbon, which has six neutrons and six protons?

A **radioactive isotope** (or **radioisotope** or **radionuclide**) is an atom with an unstable nucleus. As the nucleus splits up (disintegrates), it forms a different element by changing the number of protons it has and emitting (giving out) radiation.

 The isotope of uranium (uranium-235) used in power stations forms only 1% of the uranium on Earth.

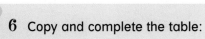 **6** Copy and complete the table:

	Protons	Neutrons	Electrons	Mass number
Carbon-12	6	6	6	
Carbon-13	6		6	13
Oxygen-16	8	8		16
Oxygen-17		9	8	17
Oxygen-18		10		

7 A radioisotope of hydrogen is tritium. Which of these can it not do?
   A emit radiation
   B receive broadcasts
   C behave like ordinary hydrogen in some ways.

8 Uranium-235 and uranium-238 are isotopes of uranium.
   a) State two ways that an atom of each is different.
   b) How could you tell that they are both the same element?

Summary

All atoms of an _____ have the same number of protons. Isotopes of an element have different numbers of _____. Neutrons and protons are called _____. The _____ (or nucleon) number is the number of protons plus the number of neutrons in the nucleus of an atom. Some isotopes emit _____, changing into another element with a different number of protons. The isotopes are radioactive, and are called _____ or radionuclides.

| element | mass | neutrons |
| nucleons | radiation | radioisotopes |

Using radioactive isotopes

How can we use radioactive isotopes?

Many people use aluminium foil when cooking. When the foil is made, its thickness can be closely controlled using radiation. When a beam of beta radiation is directed at the foil, the foil absorbs more or less beta radiation, depending on its thickness – thicker foil absorbs more radiation; thinner foil lets more radiation pass through.

A detector on the other side senses how much radiation passes through, warning workers if the thickness changes by too much.

Other things can be checked in the same way:

- the thickness of sheets of paper
- the quality of welded metal joints
- the level of powders in packets.

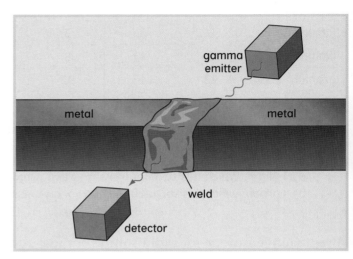

A Faults in the weld affect the radiation. This change is picked up by a detector.

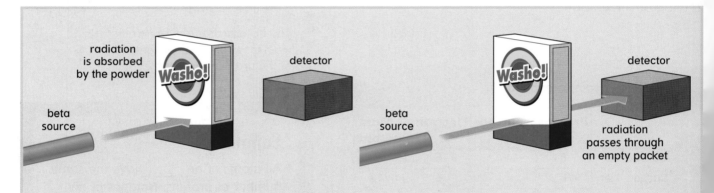

1 What is beta radiation used to control?

All living things contain a certain amount of radioactive carbon atoms. When these radioisotopes decay, they become nitrogen atoms that are no longer radioactive. Over time, the material becomes less radioactive. It is possible to discover how old an object is by measuring its radioactivity.

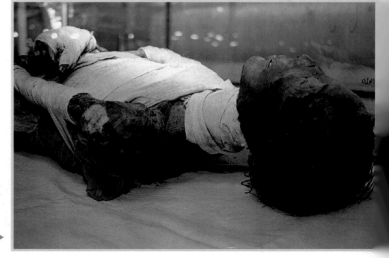

Measuring the amount of radioactive carbon in Egyptian mummies can accurately date them as thousands of years old. This photo is of Tuthmosis IV and he is over 3400 years old. **C**

Other radioactive materials behave in the same way, so, for example, rocks from the Moon can be dated too.

2 What can you measure to find out how old an object is?

! Living things can also be dated using radiation. This is Methuselah, the worlds oldest living thing. Its a bristle cone pine tree which is 4767 years old.

D

People who work with radiation need to know how much radiation they have been exposed to. To help monitor this, the person wears a radiation badge containing photographic film. After a period of time, the film is developed.

- a darker developed film means more radiation exposure.
- a lighter developed film means less radiation exposure.

A radiation badge. E

3 Choose the correct answer. The film in a badge worn by a radiation worker is used to:

A photograph the radiation equipment
B take holiday pictures
C measure the amount of radiation exposure.

P How could you discover how a film badge detects different types of radiation by making a model?

4 How could you use radiation to:
  a) decide which book contains more pages?
  b) discover how old a wooden carving is?
  c) control how much cereal is put into packets?

5 A radiation badge monitors how much radiation a person has received.
  a) Why is this important?
  b) Explain which is more important for the health of workers:
    i) that the workers are careful when they are using radiation
    ii) that the badges are tested often.
  b) Look at diagram F. Write down the workers in order, starting with the person exposed to most radiation.

Summary

Radiation is _____ more when it passes through thick materials. This way, the _____ of the material can be measured. Older radioactive materials emit less _____. This can be used to date materials, e.g. rocks. Radiation badges are worn to monitor a person's _____ to radiation. The film turns _____ if the person has been exposed more to radiation.

absorbed   darker   exposure
    radiation   thickness

F

Joe's film   Bakul's film   Tara's film

Atomic models

How was the structure of the atom discovered?

Imagine firing a bullet at a sheet of thin tissue paper. How amazing if it bounced back, returning the way it came! In 1907, two scientists called Ernest Rutherford and Ernest Marsden had such a startling result from their experiments, they felt as though this had happened. They were using alpha radiation to find out about the structure of the atom. Alpha radiation consists of positively charged particles made up of two protons and two neutrons.

 1 Choose the correct answer. Neutral means:

   A no charge
   B positive charge
   C negative charge.

Atoms are the building blocks of all matter. Rutherford and Marsden knew that atoms contained negatively charged electrons, which could be dislodged (removed) from the atom. They also knew that atoms have no overall charge (they are **neutral**) so must have some positive charge.

At the time, many scientists believed that the structure of an atom was a bit like a plum pudding or Christmas pudding.

To test the plum pudding model, Rutherford and Marsden fired positively charged alpha particles very quickly at a sheet of thin gold foil, a few atoms thick. They expected to see the alpha particles passing through because the positive charge was spread throughout the atoms of the gold foil like a cloud. However, the alpha particles scattered in different directions. A few even returned the way they came. This could only happen if the gold contained small, positively charged particles that could repel the alpha particles.

The **nuclear model** of the atom could explain their experiment.

● The centre of the sphere is a positively charged, heavy nucleus.

● Negatively charged electrons circle the nucleus, but are quite far from it.

● The atom is mostly empty space.

A *The plum pudding model.*

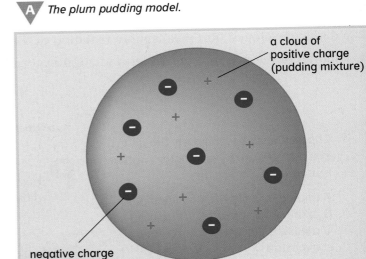

a cloud of positive charge (pudding mixture)

negative charge (plums or raisins)

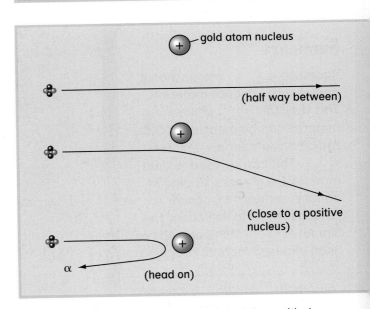

gold atom nucleus

(half way between)

(close to a positive nucleus)

α   (head on)

 2 How are the plum-pudding and nuclear models: **a)** similar **b)** different?

B *The Rutherford Scattering experiment: the positively charged nucleus repels positively charged particles.*

More research eventually discovered which particles make up the atom.

Particle	Mass	Charge	Where it is found
proton	1 unit	+1	nucleus
neutron	1 unit	0	nucleus
electron	negligible	−1	circling the nucleus

> The size of the nucleus compared to the rest of the atom is like a pea in the centre of a football pitch. At the size of a pea, the mass of the nucleus would be 230 tonnes.

 A boron atom has five protons and six neutrons in its nucleus. Five electrons circle around the nucleus.

P How could you use this apparatus to make a model of a scattering experiment?

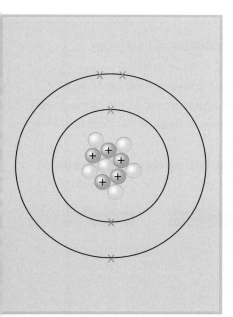

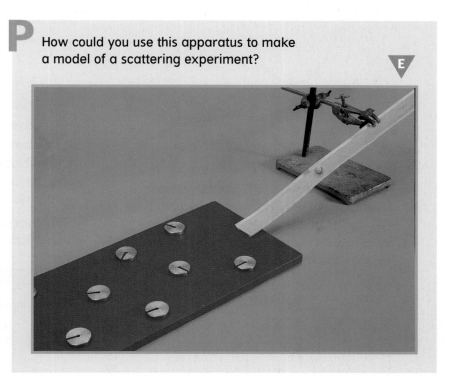

Summary

Atoms have a small central _____ made from protons (mass of 1 unit, charge +1) and _____ (mass of 1 unit, no charge). Electrons (tiny _____, charge −1) circle around the nucleus. There are _____ numbers of electrons and protons, so the atom has no electrical charge overall. Positively charged particles fired by Rutherford at a thin _____ sheet were scattered by the nucleus, providing evidence for this model of the atom.

equal   gold   mass   neutrons   nucleus

3 Choose the answer which is proof of the nuclear model:

    A electrons are negatively charged
    B positively charged particles are reflected by the nucleus
    C tissue paper can reflect bullets.

4 True or false?

    a) Atoms are similar to a plum pudding.
    b) The nuclear model replaced the plum-pudding model.
    c) Protons have a negative charge.

5 **a)** What charge do neutrons have?
    b) Why wouldn't neutrons fired at an atom be reflected by the nucleus?

Further questions

1 Copy the wave shown in the diagram.

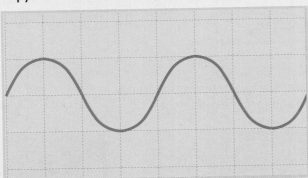

a) Label the amplitude. (1)

b) How many complete waves are shown? (1)

c) Add another wave which has the same frequency but which produces a sound twice as loud as the original wave. (2)

d) What name is given to sound waves that are too high for us to hear? (1)

2 The diagram shows the electromagnetic spectrum.

| radio waves | micro-waves | infra-red | visible light | ultra-violet | X–rays | gamma waves |

a) State two things that all electromagnetic waves have in common. (2)

b) Which types of waves have the most energy? (1)

c) Which type of waves

   i) are felt as heat?

   ii) are used in mobile-phone networks?

   iii) can create shadow pictures to detect cracks in bones? (3)

3 a) What type of waves are created during earthquakes? (1)

b) How are these waves detected? (1)

4 Here is some information about three waves in the sea.

Wave	Wavelength (m)	Frequency (Hz)	Speed (m/s)
X	2	0.2	
Y	8	0.5	4
Z	1	0.4	

a) Copy and complete this equation:

wave speed = wavelength × _____. (1)

b) What are the speeds of waves X and Z? (2)

c) Which two waves travel at the same speed? (1)

d) Which wave is in deep water and travelling faster? (1)

5 The diagram shows waves in deep water approaching a gap.

a) Copy the diagram and draw the next three waves. (3)

b) What name is given to this effect? (1)

c) The diagram below shows the same gap when the water is shallow (low tide).
Copy the diagram and draw the next six wave fronts. (3)

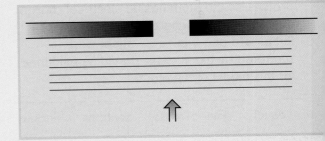

6 a) Draw a rough copy of this diagram and complete it to show what happens to the radio waves as they reflect off part of the Earth's atmosphere. (2)

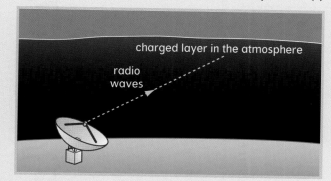

charged layer in the atmosphere

radio waves

b) Why can the atmosphere allow radio waves to be broadcast over long distances? (1)

c) Name one type of electromagnetic wave that can pass through the Earth's atmosphere? (1)

d) State two uses of microwaves. (2)

e) Which have longer wavelengths, microwaves or radio waves? (1)

7 The diagram shows what happens to sunlight as it passes from air into a raindrop.

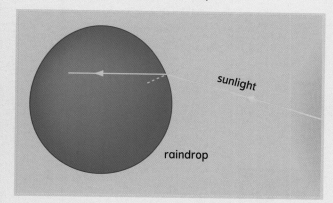

sunlight

raindrop

a) What happens to the speed of light as it enters the raindrop? (1)

b) What is this effect called? (1)

c) Total internal reflection occurs at the back of the raindrop, reflecting the light. State one other use of total internal reflection. (1)

d) What effect causes the sunlight to separate into different colours? (1)

e) What is a rainbow an example of? (1)

f) When dispersion occurs:

i) which colour changes direction least?

ii) Which colour changes direction most? (2)

8 Sunbathing is thought to contribute to skin cancer. Explain why these measures protect people from the Sun's radiation:

a) staying out of the Sun in the middle of the day (1)

b) staying in the Sun for short periods of time only (1)

c) wearing clothing to cover your skin. (1)

9 a) Write a sentence explaining how large amounts of gamma radiation affect living cells. (1)

b) How does the effect change with a small dose of radiation? (1)

c) To treat cancer, gamma radiation is directed at the patient. Why is alpha radiation not used? (1)

d) Describe two other uses of radiation. (2)

10 a) What happens to the count rate of a radioactive source over time? (1)

b) The half-life of a substance is 2 years. If its count rate is 1000 counts per second in 2001, what is its count rate 4 years later? (2)

11 a) Write down two safety precautions that should be taken when using a gamma source in the school laboratory. (2)

b) Explain why alpha radiation is least dangerous outside the body. (1)

12 Choose from these words to complete these sentences. You may need to use some words twice.

electrons	neutrons	nucleon
	nucleus	protons

Atoms have a small central _____ made up from _____ and _____, surrounded by negatively charged _____.

The total number of protons and neutrons in an atom is its _____ number.

Atoms of the same element have the same number of _____.

Isotopes are atoms of the same element with different numbers of _____. (7)

Periodic Table

Group numbers

Key:

Mass number A	
Atomic number (proton number) Z	1 **H** hydrogen 1

1	2												3	4	5	6	7	0 or 8
																		4 **He** helium 2
7 **Li** lithium 3	9 **Be** beryllium 4												11 **B** boron 5	12 **C** carbon 6	14 **N** nitrogen 7	16 **O** oxygen 8	19 **F** fluorine 9	20 **Ne** neon 10
23 **Na** sodium 11	24 **Mg** magnesium 12												27 **Al** aluminium 13	28 **Si** silicon 14	31 **P** phosphorus 15	32 **S** sulphur 16	35 **Cl** chlorine 17	40 **Ar** argon 18
39 **K** potassium 19	40 **Ca** calcium 20	45 **Sc** scandium 21	48 **Ti** titanium 22	51 **V** vanadium 23	52 **Cr** chromium 24	55 **Mn** manganese 25	56 **Fe** iron 26	59 **Co** cobalt 27	59 **Ni** nickel 28	64 **Cu** copper 29	65 **Zn** zinc 30		70 **Ga** gallium 31	73 **Ge** germanium 32	75 **As** arsenic 33	79 **Se** selenium 34	80 **Br** bromine 35	84 **Kr** krypton 36
85 **Rb** rubidium 37	88 **Sr** strontium 38	89 **Y** yttrium 39	91 **Zr** zirconium 40	93 **Nb** niobium 41	96 **Mo** molybdenum 42	98 **Tc** technetium 43	101 **Ru** ruthenium 44	103 **Rh** rhodium 45	106 **Pd** palladium 46	108 **Ag** silver 47	112 **Cd** cadmium 48		115 **In** indium 49	119 **Sn** tin 50	122 **Sb** antimony 51	128 **Te** tellurium 52	127 **I** iodine 53	131 **Xe** xenon 54
133 **Cs** caesium 55	137 **Ba** barium 56	139 **La** lanthanum 57	178 **Hf** hafnium 72	181 **Ta** tantalum 73	184 **W** tungsten 74	186 **Re** rhenium 75	190 **Os** osmium 76	192 **Ir** iridium 77	195 **Pt** platinum 78	197 **Au** gold 79	201 **Hg** mercury 80		204 **Tl** thallium 81	207 **Pb** lead 82	209 **Bi** bismuth 83	209 **Po** polonium 84	210 **At** astatine 85	222 **Rn** radon 86
223 **Fr** francium 87	226 **Ra** radium 88	227 **Ac** actinium 89																

Glossary

absorbed (in Biology) Digested food is taken into the blood from the small intestine.

absorbed (in Physics) When energy is taken up by a substance and none is reflected.

acceleration How quickly the velocity, or speed, of an object changes. acceleration (m/s^2) = change in speed (m/s) / time (s)

acid gas scrubber Removes acidic gases, e.g. sulphur dioxide, from industrial smoke, before they are released into the atmosphere.

acid rain Rain containing sulphuric acid and nitric acid. Acid rain has a pH of less than 5.6

acidic gases Gases which dissolve in water to produce an acid, e.g. sulphur dioxide, carbon dioxide and nitrogen oxides.

activation energy The minimum amount of energy that particles need in order to react.

adaptation / adapted A feature of an organism or cell that allows it to do something successfully. These organisms or cells are said to be 'adapted' to their job or function.

air resistance A force that acts on any object moving through air. The faster the object the bigger the air resistance in the opposite direction.

alcohol E.g. ethanol. A chemical produced by the fermentation of sugars using yeast.

alkali metals Elements listed in Group I of the Periodic Table. They are all are very reactive and react with water to produce a metal hydroxide and hydrogen.

alleles Different forms of a gene for the same characteristic, e.g. alleles for blue eyes and brown eyes.

alpha radiation Radioactive particles given out by the nucleus of an unstable atom. Alpha particles are fast moving helium nuclei that carry a 2+ charge. They do not travel far through air and are stopped by paper.

ammonium nitrate A salt used in fertilisers. It is made by neutralising ammonium hydroxide with nitric acid

amplitude The maximum vertical distance that a wave moves from its rest position during a vibration. The bigger the amplitude of a sound wave, the louder the sound and the more energy being carried.

anaemia A disease caused by a shortage of iron in the diet. The person cannot make enough red blood cells.

analogue signal A signal which varies continuously in amplitude and frequency, like music.

anode Positive electrode in electrolysis.

Ar The symbol for the relative atomic mass or RAM of an element.

artificial selection The selection and breeding of plants or animals by man to produce offspring which have useful characteristics, e.g. plants that are resistant to disease. Also called selective breeding.

asexual reproduction Reproduction involving one parent that produces genetically identical offspring.

atmosphere A mixture of gases that surrounds the Earth.

atomic number The number of protons in an element's atoms.

atom The smallest particle of an element. It has no overall electric charge.

background radiation Radioactivity that we are exposed to all the time.

bacteria Very small single-celled organisms with no nucleus.

balanced When things are balanced there is no change in the movement of the object.

balanced equation When the number of different atoms on either side of a chemical equation are the same. An equation which is not balanced is not correct.

beta radiation Radioactive particles given out by the nucleus of an unstable atom. Beta particles are high energy electrons that carry a 1- charge. They are stopped by thin sheets of metal.

biomass The total dry mass of an organism or organisms.

body cell Any cell of an organism, other than its sex cells.

boiling point When a liquid is at its boiling point it is as hot as it can get. It is evaporating as fast as it can.

bond A chemical link between atoms. All chemical bonds are very strong.

braking distance The distance a vehicle travels from when the brakes are applied to when it stops.

braking force The force needed to stop a vehicle.

breed A group of organisms within a species that have various characteristics in common, e.g. a Poodle is a breed of dog. (Usually refers to animals.)

brine A solution of sodium chloride in water

carbon A non-metallic element which exists in two forms: diamond and graphite. Graphite is the only non-metal that can conduct electricity.

carbon cycle How carbon is cycled between living organisms and the air.

carbon dioxide A colourless gas. It is produced by respiration and used up in photosynthesis.

carnivore An animal that eats meat.

carrier An organism that carries one allele for a disease, but does not have the disease itself. They can pass the faulty gene on to their offspring.

catalyst Something that speeds up a chemical reaction without being changed at the end of it.

catalytic converter A device fitted to car exhaust systems that reduces the amount of toxic gases released into the atmosphere. It contains catalysts.

cathode Negative electrode in electrolysis.

cell division When a cell divides to form new cells.

CFCs Chemicals that were used in fridges and aerosol cans and damage the ozone layer, which protects us from harmful U-V rays.

characteristics Features that an organisms has, e.g. freckles.

chloride A salt of hydrochloric acid, containing the chloride ion.

chromosomes Thread-like strands found in the nucleus of a cell. Chromosomes are made of DNA and contain the 'instructions' for a living thing.

clones Organisms produced by asexual reproduction or genetic engineering, which all have identical genes.

collision theory The theory which explains how different factors affect the rate of a chemical reaction.

combustion A chemical reaction that involves a substance reacting with oxygen and releasing a lot of heat. Sometimes called burning.

comet An object made of frozen gases and dust that orbits the Sun.

common salt The chemical sodium chloride.

community All the organisms living in a particular habitat.

compete / competition When organisms need the same resource they 'compete' with each other for it, e.g. plants compete for light, water and mineral salts.

compost Dead material which has been broken down by decomposers. It will release mineral salts into the soil.

compound A substance which is made up of two or more different elements, chemically bonded together.

concentrated A solution that contains a lot of the solute.

concentration The amount of solute that is dissolved in a litre of solvent.

constellation A group, or pattern, of stars in the sky, e.g. The Plough

consumer An organism that eats other organisms.

contraception Birth control to prevent a baby being conceived.

contract Muscle cells contract by getting shorter and fatter.

cosmic radiation Rays of high energy particles that reach Earth from outer space.

count-rate A measure of the radioactive decay of a substance.

covalent bonding When atoms join together by sharing electrons in order to gain a full outer shell of electrons.

critical angle The angle of incidence at which a ray of light travelling from glass, water or air is refracted so that it runs along the edge of the material.

crossed Fertilisation between two selected individuals.

cutting A side stem taken off a plant. It is allowed to sprout roots to make a new plant.

decay When microbes feed on the remains of a dead organism and it rots away.

deceleration How quickly the velocity, or speed, of an object slows down. The opposite of acceleration.

decompose (in Chemistry) Splitting up a substance by a chemical reaction.

decomposers Organisms that break down dead organisms, e.g. bacteria and fungi.

deforestation When large areas of forests are cleared, for farming or construction.

dense Made up of very closely packed particles.

diatomic gases Gases which exist as molecules made up of two atoms, e.g. hydrogen, H_2; oxygen, O_2

diffraction The spreading out of waves as they pass through a gap or past the edge of an obstacle.

digestion Breaking down food into smaller units that the body can use. (Proteins are broken down into amino acids, carbohydrates are broken down into glucose and fats are broken down into fatty acids and glycerol.)

digital signal An electrical signal that is made up of a series of pulses.

disease resistance When an organism has protection against a disease.

dispersion The splitting of white light into the seven colours of the visible spectrum.

displacement reaction Competition reaction between elements. A more reactive element displaces a less reactive one from it's compound.

distance-time graph A graph showing the distance something has travelled against the time taken.

dominant A dominant allele always shows itself in the offspring.

drag The force of friction that works in air or in a liquid.

driving force The force that makes a vehicle move.

echo The reflection of a sound wave.

egg cell The sex cell produced by a female.

elastic potential energy The kind of energy stored in something that has been stretched or squashed and which can bounce back to its original shape.

electric charge Positive or negative electricity.

electrical discharge tube A device that conducts electricity through a gas by forming electrons and ions.

electrolysis Splitting up a substance by electricity.

electromagnetic radiation When electromagnetic waves are given out by an object.

electromagnetic waves Transverse waves that travel at 300,000,000 m/s. They include radio waves, microwaves, infra-red, visible light, ultra-violet, X-rays and gamma rays.

electron structure The arrangement of electrons in shells around the nucleus of an atom.

electrons Tiny negatively charged particles.

element A pure substance made up of one type of atom.

ellipse An oval shape.

embryo splitting / transplanting When the cells of a very young embryo are separated from each other so that each can develop into an organism. They are put into a uterus to develop.

emitted Something given out by an object is said to be the emitter.

endoscope A long, narrow medical instrument used to look inside the body.

energy level Position where electrons are in an atom, sometimes called an electron shell.

energy transferred The amount of energy changed from one type into another.

environment The surroundings where an organism lives, including all the living and non-living factors.

environmental variation Features of an organism which are due to environmental factors e.g. having a scar

enzymes A substance that speeds up a chemical reaction in the body (a biological catalyst). Each enzyme works best at a particular temperature and pH.

evaporation When a liquid changes into a gas

evolution How the organisms living on Earth have changed.

exothermic A chemical reaction which gives out heat energy to the surroundings e.g. burning

expand When the size of a substance increases due to being heated. The particles gain energy and move further apart.

extinction / extinct The process by which all the members of a species die out and become extinct.

fair test An experiment in which only one variable is changed at a time to allow a fair comparison.

fats Food substances needed as a store of energy and for insulation.

fermentation When yeast respires without oxygen and converts glucose into ethanol and carbon dioxide.

fertilisation The joining together of male and female sex cells.

fertilised egg cell Produced when the nuclei of a sperm and an egg join together.

fertiliser A chemical put onto soil to replace lost mineral salts and so make plants grow more healthily.

fertility drugs Hormones given to women to help eggs be released from the ovaries.

fertility treatment Medical treatment to help a woman become pregnant.

fluids Substances which can flow (a gas or a liquid).

fluorescence / fluorescent When light or other radiation is given off from atoms or molecules. Something that does this is said to be 'fluorescent'.

food chain Shows what eats what in a habitat. (It also shows the direction that energy flows from organism to organism.)

food web Shows how several food chains are linked together

force A push or a pull. Force is measured in units called newtons (N).

formula (in Chemistry) The symbol for a compound showing the types and number of atoms present e.g. H_2O is the formula of water.

formula (in Physics) A mathematical equation e.g. speed = distance/time

frequency The number of waves per second. It is measured in Hertz (Hz).

friction A force which works in the opposite direction to something which is moving.

fungi Simple organisms which do not have chlorophyll e.g. moulds, yeasts.

fuse A thin wire that melts and breaks if the current in a circuit gets too big.

galaxy A group of millions of stars held together by gravity, e.g. the Milky Way.

gamete A sex cell, e.g. a sperm cell or an egg cell.

gamma wave A high energy form of electromagnetic radiation that has a very short wavelength.

gas A state of matter in which the particles move rapidly and are very spread out.

gene Part of a chromosome. It contains the 'instructions' for a particular feature (e.g. eye colour).

genetic engineering Altering the genetic makeup (DNA) of an organism.

genetically identical Having exactly the same genes, e.g. clones

giant structure A substance made up of many atoms or ions bonded together to form a large 3-D structure e.g. diamond, sodium chloride. A substance with a giant structure will have high melting and boiling points because of its large number of bonds.

global warming The gradual heating of the Earth's atmosphere. It is caused by the 'greenhouse effect'.

glowing objects Objects that give out light.

gravitational field strength The gravitational force on a 1 kg mass in a gravitational field. On the Earth's surface it is approximately 10 N/kg.

gravity The force of attraction between any two bodies. It increases with increasing mass of the bodies and decreases if they are further apart.

greenhouse gas A gas that traps heat in the Earth's atmosphere (e.g. carbon dioxide).

group Column of elements with similar properties in the Periodic Table.

Haber process An industrial process that produces ammonia gas from the raw materials of air, water and methane.

habitat The place where an organism lives.

half-life The time it takes for half of the atoms in a radioactive substance to decay.

halide A salt containing halogen atoms e.g. a fluoride, chloride, bromide or iodide.

halogen A non-metallic element found in Group VII of the Periodic Table.

herbicide A chemical used to kill unwanted plants (weeds).

herbivore An animal that eats only plants.

hertz The unit of frequency of vibrations 1Hz = 1 vibration per second.

hormones Chemical 'messengers' that make a body process happen. Hormones are secreted by glands and are carried around the body in the blood plasma.

Huntington's disease An inherited disease of the nervous system caused by a dominant allele. Symptoms include involuntary movements and mental deterioration.

infra-red radiation Another term for heat radiation.

inherit Receive from your parents.

inherited disease A disease passed from parents to offspring in the form of a defective allele.

inherited variation Features of an organism controlled by alleles inherited from their parents, e.g. eye colour.

ion An atom or group of atoms with an electrical charge.

ionic bond A strong force of attraction between oppositely charged ions.

ionic lattice A giant crystal structure made up of many oppositely charged ions held together by ionic bonds.

ionised When an atom has lost or gained electrons to form an ion.

ionising radiation Radiation that causes atoms to gain or lose electrons and form ions.

isotopes Atoms of the same element that have different numbers of neutrons in their nuclei.

joule (J) Unit for measuring energy or work.

kilometres per hour (km/h) A unit of speed.

kinetic energy The kind of energy in moving things.

lactic acid The waste product of anaerobic respiration in humans.

lactose A type of sugar found in milk.

landfill site An area of land where waste materials are buried.

lichen A mutualistic relationship between a fungus and an alga (simple plant). They often occur as crusty patches on tree trunks and walls.

lipase An enzyme that digests fats to fatty acids and glycerol.

liquid A state of matter in which the particles are close together but randomly arranged. The particles can move over each other.

longitudinal A wave motion where the vibrations are parallel to the direction in which the wave is moving, e.g. a sound wave.

lubricant A substance used to reduce friction, e.g. oil.

m/s^2 The unit of acceleration.

malaria A disease caused by a microbe which lives in the blood. It is transmitted by mosquito bites and causes fevers and headaches.

mark To place a mark on an animal to show that it has been caught.

mass The amount of material that makes up an object. It is usually measured in units called kilograms (kg) or grams (g).

mass (or nucleon) number The total number of protons and neutrons in the nucleus of an atom.

matter The material that something is made up of.

melt To change from a solid to a liquid by heating.

melting point The temperature at which a solid changes to a liquid.

metals Strong shiny elements that can be hammered into shape. Metals are good conductors of heat and electricity.

metre (m) A unit of length.

metres per second (m/s) A unit of speed.

metres per second squared (m/s^2) The unit of acceleration.

microbe A tiny organism that can only be seen with a microscope. Microbes can cause disease.

microwaves Short wavelength radio waves in the electromagnetic spectrum.

miles per hour (mph) A unit of speed.

Milky Way The spiral galaxy of stars which the Earth is part of.

molecule A pair or group of atoms bonded together.

monitoring Observing and recording changes.

Mr Symbol that represents the relative formula mass of a compound.

mutation A sudden change in a gene.

natural satellite A small object that orbits a larger one that was not put into space by man, e.g. the Moon is the natural satellite of the Earth.

natural selection The survival of those organisms best adapted to live in a habitat. It is the basis of the Theory of Evolution.

negative The pole of a cell or battery that repels negative charges and attracts positive ones.

negligible Something so small that it is not worth considering.

neutral (in Chemistry) Substance that is not an acid or an alkali. Has a pH of 7.

neutral (in Physics) i) One of the wire that carries electricity in an appliance. ii) Something with equal amounts of positive and negative charge.

neutron star A very dense star that has collapsed due to its own gravity.

neutron An uncharged particle found in the nucleus of an atom. Its mas is similar to that of a proton.

newton (N) The unit of force.

newtons per kilogram (N/kg) The unit of gravitational field strength.

nitrates The salts of nitric acid. Nitrates are needed by plants to make proteins.

nitrogen oxides Pollutants in vehicle exhaust fumes and from power stations. These are acidic gases which can form acid rain.

noble gas An element in Group 0 (Group VIII) of the Periodic Table. All are very unreactive gases.

non-metals Elements which are not metals. They are poor conductors of heat and electricity.

normal A line drawn at right angles to a surface.

nuclear model The theory or model used to explain the properties of the atom.

nucleon A particle found in the nucleus of an atom, i.e. a proton or a neutron.

nucleus (in Biology) The control centre of a cell containing chromosomes made of DNA.

nucleus (in Physics) The centre of an atom, made up of protons and neutrons.

offspring The immediate descendant(s) of an organism.

opaque Does not allow light through.

optical fibre Thin strand of glass that light travels through by total internal reflection. Used in telecommunications and by surgeons to see inside the body.

oral contraception The use of hormones, taken in the form of a pill, to prevent pregnancy.

orbit The curved path taken by an object that moves round another object, e.g. a planet around the Sun.

oscilloscope (CRO) An instrument used to display waves on a screen.

ovary The female sex organ that produces the female sex cells (egg cells).

ozone A form of oxygen found in the upper atmosphere that protects us from UV radiation by absorbing it.

parallel (in Physics) When the current in an electrical circuit can flow along different routes.

parent atoms Atoms from which new atoms of different elements are formed.

parents Organisms from which offspring are produced.

particle An extremely small piece of matter.

percentage mass percentage mass of an element in a compound = mass of element in the formula x 100 / relative formula mass of the compound.

pesticide A chemical used to kill organisms that eat crops as they grow.

photochemical smog A chemical fog caused by the action of sunlight on vehicle exhaust fumes.

photosynthesis Process that plants use to make their own food. It needs light to work. carbon dioxide + water = glucose + oxygen

pituitary gland A gland attached to the brain that produces hormones. One of these hormones controls the release of eggs from the ovaries.

polar orbit An object in polar orbit will pass over the North and South poles once in each orbit.

population The number of organisms of one particular species living in the same habitat.

positive The pole of a cell or battery that repels positive charges and attracts negative ones.

predator An animal which hunts and kills other animals for food.

prey An animal which is hunted and eaten by a predator.

probe A device which can be linked to a computer to measure changes e.g. temperature probe, pH probe.

producer An organism that makes food from simple raw materials. Green plants are producers.

products Substances formed by a chemical reaction.

properties Describes how a substance behaves.

proportion The size of a variable compared to the whole.

protease An enzyme that digests protein into amino acids.

proteins Important substances used for growth and repair in living things.

proton number The number of protons in an atom. Also called the atomic number.

protons Tiny positively charged particles in an atom's nucleus.

pyramid of biomass A diagram that represents the total biomass of the organisms at each level in a food chain.

quality control The sampling and checking of a manufactured product in order to maintain quality.

R.A.M (Relative Atomic Mass) Relative atomic mass, symbol Ar. The mass of an atom compared to the mass of a carbon atom.

R.F.M (Relative Formula Mass) Relative formula mass is the sum of the RAMs of all the atoms in a compound.

radio telescope An instrument used in astronomy to detect radio waves produced by objects in space.

radio wave A type of electromagnetic radiation that has a long wavelength. Used to carry radio and TV programmes.

radioactive Atoms that have unstable nuclei and give off one or more types of radioactivity (alpha, beta or gamma).

radioactive decay When an atom emits one or more types of radioactivity as its nucleus disintegrates.

radioactive isotope / radioisotope An atom that is radioactive. The atoms have unstable nuclei that can break apart to give off one or more types of radioactivity (alpha, beta or gamma).

radionuclide An atomic nucleus that gives off radioactivity.

rate of reaction How fast or slow a chemical reaction occurs.

ratio A comparison of the size of two factors.

raw material A basic starting material from which a useful substance is produced.

ray A narrow beam of light.

react When chemicals combine together to form something new.

reactants Substances used up in a chemical reaction.

reaction (in Biology) The change in behaviour of an organism as it responds to a stimulus.

recapture When an organism in the wild that has been caught before, is caught again.

recessive A recessive allele only works when present on both chromosomes in a pair.

recycled When something is used again in a system.

red giant A star that has used up its hydrogen, swollen in size and cooled.

reflect Bouncing something back from a surface.

reflected / reflection The image formed when light from an object is reflected from a surface.

refraction When a wave passes from one medium into another (e.g. from water into air) its speed is altered. A change in the direction of the wave also occurs if it is not travelling along a normal.

release Put an organism back into the wild.

resistant When an organism has protection against a disease.

respiration Chemical reaction inside cells to release energy from glucose. glucose + oxygen $\longrightarrow$ carbon dioxide + water

resultant The final, single force acting on an object.

reversible reaction A chemical reaction that can go forwards or backwards depending on the conditions, e.g. nitrogen + hydrogen $\rightleftharpoons$ ammonia

salts Compounds formed when an acid reacts with a base.

satellite An object that orbits a planet or a star. The moon is the Earth's natural satellite.

satellite dish A curved dish which has an aerial at its centre to receive signals from a communications satellite.

seismic waves Shock waves sent out by earthquakes.

seismograph A machine that can produce a picture showing the vibrations produced by seismic waves.

selective breeding The selection and breeding of plants or animals by man to produce offspring which have useful characteristics, e.g. plants that are resistant to disease. Also called artificial selection.

sewage Waste matter from homes, farms and industry that is carried in drains and sewers.

sex chromosome Either of the X or Y chromosomes that determine the sex of an organism. In humans a female has XX sex chromosomes and a male has XY sex chromosomes.

sexual reproduction Reproduction that involves two parents, a male and a female. Sex cells from each parent join together at fertilisation.

shells Energy levels around the nucleus of an atom in which electrons orbit.

sickle-cell anaemia An inherited disease in which the red blood cells can become sickle shaped and cannot carry as much oxygen as normal.

silver halides Silver salts which contain halogen atoms e.g. silver chloride, silver bromide.

smog A mixture of smoke, fog and chemical fumes.

smoke A cloud of small particles produced when something is burnt.

solar system The Sun and all the planets (and asteroids) that orbit it.

solid A state of matter in which the particles are tightly packed in a regular pattern. The particles can only vibrate about a fixed position.

sound waves Longitudinal waves produced when something vibrates.

species A group of organisms with similar characteristics that can breed with each other and produce fertile offspring.

speed How fast an object travels. Speed = distance/time

speed of light How fast light and all other types of electromagnetic waves travel; 300 000 000 m/s

sperm cell The male sex cell.

stable An unreactive substance that is unlikely to change suddenly.

state symbols Letters written in chemical equations in brackets after each formula to indicate the state of the chemical. (s) represents a solid, (l) represents a liquid, (g) represents a gas and (aq) represents a substance dissolved in water.

states of matter The three states of matter are solid, liquid and gas.

sterile i) Unable to produce offspring. ii) Free from any living micro-organisms.

streamlining Making the shape of something smoother so there is less resistance to drag.

sulphur dioxide A pollutant gas produced by burning fossil fuels. It causes acid rain.

supernova An exploding star.

surface area The total area of all the surfaces of a shape.

symbol Letter, or letters, used to represent an element. e.g. Na is the symbol for sodium.

thinking distance The distance a car travels, from when a driver realises that he needs to break until the break pedal is pressed.

tilted axis The Earth spins about its axis. The axis is not vertical, it is tilted by 23.5°. This tilt causes the different seasons.

tissue culture Technique used to grow plant cells into new plants.

tolerant When an organism can withstand the effects of a toxic substance.

total internal reflection When a ray of light travelling towards the edge of a transparent block is completely reflected and stays inside the block. (This happens when the angel of incidence is greater than the critical angle.)

transferred When energy is changed from one type into another.

transmitted i) sent out radio waves ii) particles or energy have passed through something.

transparent Allows light to pass through easily.

transverse A wave motion in which the vibrations are at right angles to the direction the wave is travelling in, e.g. all electromagnetic waves.

ultra violet rays / radiation Electromagnetic radiation that causes a sun tan. Over exposure can cause skin cancer.

ultrasound Sound waves with a frequency above 20 000 Hz that cannot be heard by the human ear. Used to scan body tissues and for echo-sounding.

unbalanced When things are unbalanced there is a change in the movement of an object.

unbalanced force When the forces acting on an object are not equal and opposite, causing the movement of the object to change.

unreactive A chemical which is unlikely to change, it has a stable structure.

unstable A substance that easily breaks down or emits radioactivity.

vacuum An empty region of space.

variation The differences between organisms of the same species.

variety A group of individuals within a species that have particular features in common. Usually refers to plants.

velocity Speed in a particular direction.

velocity-time graph A graph to show how the velocity of an object changes with time.

vibrating object An object that is moving to and fro.

visible light / spectrum The part of the electromagnetic spectrum that can be detected by the eye. Made up of red, orange, yellow, blue, indigo and violet light.

wavelength The length of one complete cycle of a wave.

weight A force due to gravity acting on an object.

white dwarf A small, dense star formed when a red giant collapses.

word equation Way of showing what happens in a chemical reaction using words.

work done Work is done when a force causes movement. Work done (J) = Force (N) x Distance moved in direction of force (m)

X-rays Very penetrating, short wavelength electromagnetic waves. Used to detect broken bones.

yield The amount of a product formed in a chemical reaction.

Index

253

Pearson Education
Edinburgh Gate
Harlow
Essex

www.foundationscience.co.uk

Fourth impression 2005
ISBN 0582 43699 0

Designed and produced by Pentacor Plc, High Wycombe

Printed in China
GCC/04

The publisher's policy is to use paper manufactured from sustainable forests.

Acknowledgments

The publisher would like to thank many people for their help, support and encouragement in the production of this book. In particular: Graham Barney; Dr Peter Borrows; Edward Carroll; Andrea Coates; David Fagg; Anne Forbes; Andrew Ireland; Dr Penny Marshall; Michael O'Neill; Eleanor Owen; Andy Piggott; Alastair Sandiforth; John Tranter.

The Publishers are grateful to the following for their permission to reproduce copyright photographs:

AKG Photo page 143 *t*; Andes Press Agency page 6 l *b* and 138 *l*; Heather Angel pages 6 *rm*, 6 *rb*, 9, 19 *t*, 22, 24 *m*, 35 *l*, 43 *b*, 47 *b*, 57 *tl*, 58 *l*, 70 *tr* and 83 *r*; Alvey & Towers page 157; Ardea page 20, 79 and 82 *m*; Art Directors & TRIP pages 36 *tl*, 36 *tr*, 37, 46 *tr*, 46 *ml*, 56 *tr*, 78 *b*, 82 *t*, 86 *b*, 91 *br*, 91 *tr*, 95, 105 *r*, 110 *b*, 107 *b*, 128 *t*, 132, 144 *t*, 146 *rt*, 148, 153 *b*, 156, 159 *tl*, 162 *b*, 170 *r*, 171 *tr*, 198 *t*, 198 *m*, 203, 210 *tl*, 210 *t m*, 220, 221 *tr* and 225 *l*, Anthony Blake Picture Library page 98 *t* and 98 *tr*; Neill Bruce 184 *m*; Trevor Clifford pages 7 *b*, 29, 33 *b*, 67 *tr*, 87, 88, 90, 91 *bl*, 93, 96 *b*, 99, 100 *b*, 101 (*all*), 103 *t*, 103 *b*, 106 *t*, 107 *t*, 108, 111, 113, 119 *t*, 119 *b*, 128 *b*, 130, 131, 133, 136, 141 *l*, 141 *r*, 144 *b*, 149, 151, 152 *tl*, 152 *b*, 159 *tm bl*, 163, 171 *tl*, 173, 175, 179, 180 *b*, 185, 206 *b*, 209 *b*, 211 *r*, 212, 215, 217 *br*, 219 *l*, 221 *br*, 223, 227, 228 *r*, 235 *bl* and 243; Bruce Coleman 16 *bl*, 18 *ml*, 46 *br*, 108 and 231 *br*; Corbis page 80 *b*, 116 *b*, 145 *r* and 226 *t*, DK Picture Library pages 57 *tr* and 64 *tr*; Paul Deakin page 158 *t*; Environmental Images 23, 27 *l* and 73 *r*; Environmental Picture Library 30 *tl*; Greg Evans 30 *tr*, 52 *br* and 105 *l*; Mary Evans Picture Library pages 36 *m*, 42, 80 *t*, 116 *t*, 134, 135 *r* and 202 *m*; Flight Collection page 182; Galaxy Picture Library pages 200 *t*, 201 *ml* and 202 *b*; Geoscience Features Picture Library 24 *tl* and 67 *tl*; Ronald Grant Archive page 192; Holt Studios pages 6 *rt*, 7 *t*, 16 *tr*. 21 *b*, 26, 32 *b*, 33 *t*, 47 *t*, 67 *bl*, 72 *t*, 72 *lt*, 72 *lb*, 114 and 159 *tr*; C Hoseason page 31 *rt*; ICCE pages 16 *tl* (Jacolyn Waked), 21 *t* (Daisy Blow), 30 *bl* (Glyn Davies), 34 (Carol Shayle), 46 *mr* (Joe Blossom) and 107 *m* (Jacolyn Waked); Landm Slides 210 *tr*; Frank Lane Picture Agency page 56 *tl*; Mark Levesley pages 37, 39 *r*, 56 *ml* and *r*, 56 *bl* and *r*, 74 *m*, 75 *r*, 91 *mr*, 96 *t*, 104 *t*, 104 *b*, 146 *rb*, 159 *trb*, 159 *tmt*, 159 *br*, 184 *b*, 214 *b*, 217 *l*, 225 *r*, 226 *m*, 228 *b*, 230 *b* and 231 *tr*, Bridget Mackay page 190; Johnson Mathey page 100 *t*; Medi Pics page 69 *l*; Moviestore Collection page 50 *t* and 202 *t*; NASA/Galaxy 186; Natural History Museum page 70 *tl*; NHPA pages 18 *l*, 73 *lt*, 73 *lb*, 166 *b*, 169 and 216; National Medical Slide Bank page 76 *b*; Natural Visions/Brian Rogers pages 43 *t*; New Media page 152 *tr*; Oxd Scientific Films pages 8 *t* and *b*, 16 *br*, 18 *tr*, 18 *b*, 19 *b*, 24 *tr*, 25 *r*, 30 *br*, 38 *b*, 39 *l*, 41 *b l*, 46 *b l*, 50 *br*, 52 *t*, 61 *l*, 71 *tl*, 71 *tm*, 71 *tr*, 74 *t*, 74 *bl*, 74 *bm*, 74 *br*, 75 *l*, 94, 183 *r*, 189 and 221 *l*; Popperfoto pages 31 *l*, 83 *m*, 102 *b*, 168, 171 *b*, 206 *tr* and 240; Rex Features 25 *l* and 35 *r*; Peter Roberts Collection 184 *t*; Coral Rogers 191 *b*; Science Photo Library pages 6 *tl*, 24 *b*, 27 *r*, 31 *rb*, 32 *t*, 36 *b*, 38 *t*, 41 *t*, 41 *br*, 48 *t*, 48 *m*, 48 *b*, 50 *bl*, 52 *bl*, 53, 54, 55, 58 *t*, 59 *t*, 59 *m*, 59 *b*, 61*r*, 62, 63, 64 *t r*, 64 *l*, 65, 69 *r*, 76 *t*, 77 *t*, 77 *b*, 78 *m*, 82 *b*, 83 *l*, 86 *tl*, 86 *tr*, 91 *ml*, 102 *t*, 105 *m*, 106 *b*, 110 *t*, 118, 135 *l*, 143 *b*, 145 *l*, 146 *l*, 150, 153 *t*, 159 *bm*, 160, 162 *t*, 166 *t*, 170 *l*, 172 *r*, 176, 178, 180 *t*, 181 *t*, 200 *b l*, 200 *br*, 201 *b*, 206 *tl*, 209 *t*, 201 *ml*, 210 *b*, 211 *l*, 213, 214 *t*, 217 *t*, 218, 219 *r*, 226 *b*, 229 *t*, 229 *b*, 230 *t*, 234, 235 *t*, 235 *br*, 239, 241 *t* and 241 *b*; Shout Picture Library pages 231 *l* and 236; Skyscan page 222; Sporting Pictures Library pages 174, 181 *b*; Paul Sutherland page 197; Terra Nitrogen UK LTD pages 117 and 118; John Walmsley page 138 *r*, 172 *l*, 183 *l*, 191 *t*, 193 and 230 *m*; Simon Watts page 122; Wellcome Picture Library page 78 *t*; Wellcome Trust page 49; Janine Wiedel page 46 *tl*.

t=top, b=bottom, m=middle, l=left, r=right

Cover Photos: Climber – Telegraph Colour Library (John Terence Turner)
            Seedling – BSIP Marlaud/ Science Photo Library
            Wind Farm – Russell D. Curtis/ Science Photo Library

Contents Photos: Photodisc

Every effort has been made to trace and acknowledge ownership of copyright. If any have been overlooked, the publisher will be pleased to make the necessary changes at the earliest opportunity.
Freelance Picture Research by Jacqui Rivers.